WONDERFUL
WEEDS

WONDERFUL
WEEDS

AN EXTENSIVE & FULLY ILLUSTRATED
GUIDE FROM SEEDLINGS TO FRUIT

Who would therefore looke dangerously up at Planets, that might safely looke downe at Plants?

– John Gerard, the herbalist, in his dedication "to the courteous and well willing readers" of his newly published *Herball* (1597)

First published in Great Britain in 2016 by Papadakis Publisher

An imprint of Academy Editions Limited

Kimber Studio, Winterbourne, Berkshire, RG20 8AN, UK
info@papadakis.net | www.papadakis.net

 @papadakisbooks PapadakisPublisher

Publishing Director: Alexandra Papadakis
Design Director: Aldo Sampieri
Editor: Peter Liddle
Production: Dr Caroline Kuhtz

ISBN 978 1 906506 60 5

Cover: Spear Thistle (*Cirsium vulgare*)
Page 1: Marsh Thistle (*Cirsium palustre*)
Page 2: Indian Balsam (*Impatiens glandulifera*)
Pages 6–7: Cow Parsley (*Anthriscus sylvestris*)
Page 8: A Peacock Butterfly (*Inachis io*) on a Common Nettle (*Urtica dioica*)
Page 11: Insect vistors on Hogweed flowers (*Heracleum sphondylium*)

CONTENTS

EXPLANATORY NOTES

GENERAL INFORMATION

WEED CONTROL

The aim of this book is to provide a comprehensive and clearly illustrated guide to enable recognition of the most widespread weeds in the British Isles. Although some guidance on weeding practice is included, it is beyond the remit of this book to offer detailed advice on the eradication, organically or otherwise, of serious weed invasions that may affect farms, market gardens or large estates. There are more qualified sources of information for current best practice in treating major weed problems, including local agricultural suppliers. A good starting point for comprehensive and up to date advice is the website of the Department for Environment, Farming & Rural Affairs (DEFRA). Other valuable websites, especially for organic weed management, include Garden Organic and their associated Organic Weeds website, The Soil Association farming section, and Organic Farmers. Website addresses for all these organisations are listed in the bibliography.

SELECTION OF SPECIES INCLUDED

The Garden Organic website lists, illustrates and describes 130 weed species, and includes all the weeds described in the eleven books on British weeds published between 1910 and 2013. From this basic starting point, other currently widespread weed species have been added, while species no longer widely considered to be a nuisance have been omitted. A total of 182 species are described and illustrated, although two species, *Hyacinthoides hispanica* and *Hyacinthoides non-scripta*, are not weeds, but are included to show the parentage of *Hyacinthoides* x *massartiana*, the widespread Hybrid Bluebell. In addition, two further species, *Cochlearia danica* and *Phacelia tanacetifolia*, are also described. The former provides a remarkable example of how human needs have resulted in the escalating migration of a small coastal native, salt-loving species, to the margins of winter-salted roads throughout much of Britain. The latter species, *Phacelia tanacetifolia*, is an introduced casual seed alien. It seeds and thrives vigorously, and has been cultivated by some farmers and horticulturalists for many years as an aid to the control of insect pests, and as a nutrient rich food plant for honey bees to encourage crop pollination. The old plants are then used as green mulch. A number of recent studies by respected biologists have expressed concerns about whether its benefits outweigh its negative impact. It has been demonstrated that the numbers of unwelcome insects expand where it is grown and, furthermore, its rapid expansion often has a detrimental effect on the equilibrium of local flora and vegetation.

Grasses are notoriously difficult to identify without good background knowledge of the Grass family. Therefore, of the main weedy species (probably less than twenty), only the species that are reasonably easy for amateurs to identify have been included. Water-weeds are not included among the plants described. However, it is noted that five introduced species of aquatic plants were recently identified by the Non-native Species Organisation as highly invasive, and subsequently banned from sale in the UK by DEFRA in April 2014: Australian Swamp Stone Crop/New Zealand Pygmy Weed (*Crassula helmsii*), Water Fern (*Azolla filicules*), Parrot's Feather (*Myriophyllum aquaticum*), Floating Pennywort (*Hydrocotyle ranunculoides*) and Water Primrose (*Ludwigia grandiflora*).

NAMES OF PLANTS

BOTANICAL TERMINOLOGY

For simplicity, every species is listed alphabetically by its most widely used common name, followed by the botanical binomial name in parentheses. In the index, a species can be found by either name. For example, to find Dandelion, simply look up either Dandelion or *Taraxacum officinale*. This will also lead to the pages where there are other weed species with shared family level characteristics; in this example, Asteraceae: Daisy family. For consistency with other recent wild flower accounts and websites, if a species has more than one common name, the first listed common name follows *Interactive Flora of the British Isles* (Stace *et al.* 2004).

Every effort has been made to ensure that any unfamiliar botanical terminology used is clarified by illustration, or in the accompanying descriptions, and a glossary is provided at the end of the book for further explanation.

BOTANICAL NAMES

Although essential to botanists and other natural scientists, scientific names of species can be daunting to others. A botanical name is essential because it is unique to a particular plant species. It must conform to the strict standards of the International Code of Botanical Nomenclature (ICBN), which are accepted and used by botanists worldwide for all formally published plant species names, thus facilitating international scientific communication between botanists. Similar practice is followed for the naming of organisms in other branches of biology. The names of the plant families to which the species are assigned follow recent recommendations of the Angiosperm Phylogeny Group (APG, 2015).

ORGANISATION OF WEED SPECIES

The 40 plant families (groups of species sharing similar characteristics) are arranged primarily into non-flowering and flowering species: the horsetails, followed by the ferns, and then the flowering plants: dicotyledons and monocotyledons. The dicotyledons are so named because the seeds produce two juvenile leaves (cotyledons) on germination; here they are placed before the monocotyledons, species with seeds that produce only one juvenile leaf on germination. The family names of the two flowering plant groups are presented in alphabetical order using their botanical family name, followed by the common name of a well-known species within the family, e.g. Asteraceae: Daisy family.

ORGANISATION OF THE BOOK

With few exceptions, photographs of key stages in the life cycle are provided for each species: seedlings and/or young plants, adult habit, flowers, fruits and seeds plus, selectively, other relevant features such as roots, tubers, or bulbs. Characteristics that cannot be illustrated, for example: flowering period, height, means of propagation and odour, are also included in the descriptions. As a hands-on reference book with non-botanists in mind, the individual descriptions have purposefully been kept simple. However, the Bibliography offers a comprehensive starting point of specialist information where weeds, weed management and the native British flora can be further explored.

REFERENCE SOURCES FOR THE IDENTIFICATION OF BRITISH WILD FLOWERS

The best starting point for the identification of any unknown plant is by making careful observations, notes, sketches and/or photographs, including date, place and the habitat where it was found. The range of such noteworthy details is exemplified within the descriptions of species included in the book.

WILDFLOWER WEBSITES

The web is probably the most immediate source of information for many of us. There are a number of websites for British wildflowers, and the best provide clear descriptions with a range of images showing the key characteristics of each species. Most of the websites can be searched using either the common or botanical name of the plant, if this is known. If the name is not known and an identification is sought there are also websites with the facility to enter key characteristics of the plant to produce a likely answer – for example, the Botanical Society of Britain & Ireland website. However, such websites may prove frustratingly difficult to use effectively without any botanical experience. Other possibilities for unidentified species include websites with less technical search options, and the possibility of submitting photographs for identification.

WILD FLOWER GUIDES

Wild flower guides have the widest appeal to the layperson, and many are a visual delight. They are consulted by the general public and professional botanists alike, because they provide a very accessible introduction to the flora of particular regions or countries. The descriptions vary in length and detail, but they are written with amateur botanists in mind. In many of these guides a problem for non-botanists often still exists: these publications tend to group species within the families to which they belong, assuming basic knowledge of family characteristics. For example, if the flowers are daisy-like a plant is *highly* likely to belong within family Asteraceae. If it is four-petalled and yellow it is probably a member of the Cabbage family (Brassicaceae) but it could be Greater Celandine, a member of the Poppy family (Papaveraceae). In this example, count the number of stamens: four to six and it will be Brassicaceae, more numerous and it is likely to be Greater Celandine. Buttercups and Potentillas are also yellow-petalled, but with ten or more stamens, and five petals! It is detective work, and fun, once the basics are mastered. Where better to practice than with the weeds described in this book?

Another potential problem is that families are often arranged in systematic order, not alphabetically (as they are in the present book). In biology,

systematic implies the closeness of the genetic relationship between one group of organisms and another. As genetic research moves forward and more DNA data become available within a given group of organisms, the genetic relationships between the recognised species within the group may need to be realigned. Some species may even have been moved to a different family, because DNA analysis has indicated a much closer family link than previously suspected from visual characteristics. For example, in the present book Fumariaceae, previously a family in its own right, is now included in family Papaveraceae, because recent DNA data have provided conclusive genetic evidence of a family level relationship between the two groups of species. Thus, most wild flower guides, whatever their date, will reflect the current state of family level relationships between species at the time the book was published. Scientifically fascinating as the above may be, it is daunting for the relaxed amateur, simply enjoying the delights of the countryside and trying to identify wild flowers for the pleasure of the moment. One alternative method is to sort by colour, as employed by *The Oxford Book of Wildflowers*, first published in 1960 and still popular. To suggest that a wildflower guide is not much use if the plant isn't flowering is unimportant – it was the flower that attracted the observer and made them want to know its name: attraction is what flowers do best!

WEED GUIDES – A CENTURY OF WEEDING

Since the early 1900s twelve books have been published that describe and illustrate British weeds. The first three were published prior to WWII, and specifically address weeds of arable land and pasture. All were produced in collaboration with the then prevailing Agricultural Board, in order to help farmers manage their land more effectively and advise on effective weed control.

Later books either embrace both farm and garden weeds, or simply focus on the latter. Modern farming methods tend to rely on services within the farming industry for up to date advice on the identification and management of current problem weeds. In agriculture, the five worst weeds cited in the Weeds Act 1959 remain the same today: Ragwort (*Senecio jacobaea*), Spear Thistle (*Cirsium vulgare*), Creeping Thistle (*Cirsium arvense*), Broad-leafed Dock (*Rumex obtusifolius*) and Curled Dock (*Rumex crispus*).

After WWII, the first published guide to widespread British weeds is that of R.J. Chancellor (1966), and it focuses on the identification of weed seedlings, as does the later publication of John Williams & John Morrison (1987). Other weed guides (see Bibliography) are more obviously directed towards horticulturalists and gardeners: Mea Allan (1978), Roger Phillips (1986), Sally Roth (2001), John Walker (2003), David Hessayon (2009), Ken Thompson (2009) and William Edmonds (2013).

OPTICAL & RECORDING EQUIPMENT USED (FIELD & STUDIO)

Hand lenses: x10 and x20
A Nikon Coolpix 7900 fitted with a macro lens
A notebook and pencil for field notes and sketches

DISCLAIMER

In the pages that follow the species described represent only the most nationally widespread weeds. If the plant invading your patch does not appear to be described in the pages of this book, further sources of information are listed in the Bibliography.

PREFACE

Most native wild flower species are not troublesome, and some are quite rare or special. However, a significant minority, including many species we class as weeds, are naturally programmed to reproduce efficiently when favourable conditions prevail. This causes problems ranging from minor annoyance in small gardens, to major contamination of arable crops. Without doubt there are a fair number of wild plants that represent a serious challenge to farmers, horticulturalists and gardeners, but even these, regarded with an unbiased eye, are beautiful. In early spring, who has not felt uplifted by a myriad of Dandelions spilling across a roadside bank, or showing a small child how to "tell the time" by blowing on the soft orbs of its parachute-equipped seeds? Weeds are among the most common of our wild flowers; the most readily recognisable of them all. In gardens, these are the species which first fall victim to hoe, fork or herbicide – a reminder of the most popular definition of a weed being "a wildflower in the wrong place." A number of guides to British weed species have been published since 1900, aiming to help farmers, horticulturalists and gardeners identify weeds accurately, so that they might seek advice and implement countermeasures to control these invasive species on their land. Until quite recently it has been almost impossible to provide sufficiently detailed images to enable amateurs to make confident identifications, particularly of young pre-flowering plants. This is exacerbated by our rapidly changing and more urbanised environment, where fewer people have the privilege of learning about local wild flowers first hand, from parents, grandparents, friends and/or teachers.

In this book, ease of identification has been a key goal. Digital photography is now so widely used and inexpensive that it is possible to produce detailed images for every weed species in a way that would have been impossible in the past. Highly skilled botanical artists and botanists have traditionally interpreted, delineated and described some of the exquisite detail that can now be clearly revealed to anyone with access to a digital camera. Digital imaging does not negate the educated eye of the botanical artist, but it does provide a more immediate view of the subject, and helps our understanding and interpretation. Today almost anyone in the developed world has the means to photograph plants, and to compare and identify them more easily against previously published descriptions and images, either online or in guide books. Digital photography complements good field observations, using hand lens, notebook and pencil.

With few exceptions, every weed species included in the present book is represented by life stage images. The images are accompanied by additional information, for example: plant height, dimensions of flowers, leaves, fruits and seeds, flowering period, odour, pollinators, weed management, uses

and folklore. Older published accounts of weeds had to be much more economic with illustrations. This has meant that, in the past, superficially similar species such as speedwells and willowherbs have been difficult for non-botanists to distinguish between, leaving them unable to decide which ones are invading. One might argue, "so what, if the plan was to remove them anyway?" However, it is hoped that more comprehensive images might lead to correct identification, and might save non-weedy species from unnecessary destruction.

Weeds are part of our natural ecology, and whilst they might be considered a nuisance in relation to some human activities, it is important not to underestimate their natural role in the ecology of the countryside. Almost without exception, they play host directly or indirectly to insect visitors, for example: bees, butterflies, moths and flies (as a source of nectar and/or pollen and as hosts for eggs/larvae) and leaf cutter bees (as a nesting material). They also provide fruits and seeds for birds and animals. Furthermore, weeds have less apparent but equally important roles as nitrate indicators (nettles), nitrogen fixers and forage (clovers) and soil stabilisers (weeds with extensive roots or root mats). It is worth bearing in mind that approximately half of our annoying weeds are annuals, and are quite easy to weed out or eradicate if we are able to recognise the young plants, and are vigilant with regard to seeding time, weeding ahead of this stage.

A high percentage of currently widespread weedy species have been well known to farmers and horticulturalists for a long time. Most weed guides prior to WWII were prepared only with agriculture in mind. Weeds that had escaped into the wild from horticulture and private gardens were not generally a problem to farmers. Few people with gardens, however, from cottagers to the gardeners of the great estates, would have been without a good knowledge of the weeds and cultivated plants in the gardens they tended.

Prior to the 1960s the British gardening public bought their plants from specialist nurseries. These nurseries often specialised in particular types of plants, for example shrubs, fruit trees, roses, hardy plants, and alpines. Most shrubs, roses and fruit trees were usually bare-rooted and dug up to order, with the bare roots swathed in compost and sacking for transportation. Few plants were container-grown – an idea that would be introduced from the USA during the 1960s.

The rise of the garden centre in Britain was meteoric. From tentative experimentation by a few pioneering nurseries in the mid-1950s, Britain witnessed an explosion of such establishments during the 1960s and 1970s. After post-war austerity, people with greater spending power could take away trays of bedding plants and potted perennials without the previous delay. Early garden centres were fairly modest, but an increasing demand for on-site cafes and later, for items not necessarily directly relevant to gardening soon arose. A 'pensioner's day out' was born, and garden centres have become highly successful business ventures.

The phenomenal rise in the popularity of garden centres and, more recently, the abundance of television gardening programmes, has inevitably had an impact on the wider distribution of previously less well-known cultivars. Some of these may become a major challenge, especially in smaller gardens: for example, the lovely but rampant *Clematis armandii*, and some of our glorious rambling roses (including *Rosa banksii*, and *Rosa* cv. 'Rambling Rector') or ivy cultivars, initially planted to disguise unsightly features and subsequently taking over. Nevertheless, it is a happy thought that many cottage garden plants, even those prolific, difficult to curb species, are still firm favourites: Snow-in-summer (*Cerastium tomentosum*), Love-in-a-mist (*Nigella damascena*), Lily of the Valley (*Convallaria majalis*), Lady's Mantle (*Alchemilla mollis*) and Granny's Bonnet (*Aquilegia vulgaris*) to name just a few. Some of the weeds described in this book are also among frequently grown garden flowers, including Musk Mallow (*Malva moschata*), Canadian Goldenrod (*Solidago canadensis*), Purple Toadflax (*Linaria purpurea*), Foxglove (*Digitalis purpurea*) and Evening Pimrose (*Oenothera biennis*).

Perhaps because our native flora is not vast, and certainly not exotic, the British have always had a penchant for showy, non-native species. These include the crown-forming, sword-leaved New Zealand Flax (*Phormium*): a genus of two species from which many cultivars have been bred. The graceful yellow, orange, red or black-stemmed bamboos, some of which have vigorous runners sending up sharp shoots through lawns and borders, often spread much further than planned (it is always wise to check on eventual height, over-ground spread and underground spread *before* purchase when choosing unfamiliar perennial plants). A few well known non-native species have remained popular in our gardens for some centuries, including the stiffly sword-leaved, clump-forming Yucca; the earliest to arrive, was *Yucca gloriosa*, introduced from the Americas as early as 1596. Pampas Grasses (*Cortaderia*), a genus of about 23 clump-forming grass species, have also been a British favourite since the mid-19th Century, and have been particularly beloved in the 20th Century for small front gardens, despite viciously sharp-edged leaves.

Currently, there is nothing to surpass the scourge of Japanese Knotweed (*Fallopia japonica*), which seems to have the unfettered ability to crack brickwork, tarmac and

concrete, and cause mayhem wherever it drops anchor. Suffice to remind ourselves that Japanese Knotweed was the darling of the must-have plants in fashionable gardens of the mid-19th Century. It seems unbelievable now – be warned! So bad is its spread in the UK that it is classed as controlled waste and requires a licence for disposal. The International Union for Conservation of Nature (IUCN) 'Invasive Species Specialist Group' (ISSG) lists it among the "world's worst weeds". However, in Japan, where it has natural predators, it grows in harmony with the environment, and is not considered to be an environmental problem. In the 1960s Russian-vine (*Fallopia baldschuanica*), a relative of Japanese Knotweed, became incredibly popular for covering unsightly sheds and other outbuildings. Now out of favour and ignored (but still available from plant catalogues) it happily romps its way through neglected hedgerows, fortunately without the destructive vigour of its seriously malignant cousin from Japan.

If this book proves to be a really useful guide for identification of our most frequently encountered weeds it will be doing its job. However, it is hoped that its readers might also consider weeds a little more thoughtfully. They may invade our well-groomed outside spaces with the utmost temerity, but weeds ought to be respected for their tenacity – some of these species are among Britain's most widespread and longest surviving wild flowers, pre-dating even agriculture in Europe, let alone gardening and horticulture. Remember too, that weeding thoughtlessly might lead to another British native species becoming scarce, or lost forever. There are many examples of over-zealous weeding, often agricultural, resulting in species once classed as weeds now being revered as rare wild flowers, including Corncockle (*Agrostemma githago*), Corn Buttercup (*Ranunculus arvensis*) and Pheasant's Eye (*Adonis annua*). Other beloved British wild flowers once included in arable weed guides include the Cowslip (*Primula veris*), Wood Anemone (*Anemone nemorosa*), Pasque Flower (*Anemone pulsatilla*) and Meadow Saffron (*Colchicum autumnale*).

Whenever possible, dispose of weeds thoughtfully by green manuring, composting or using local garden waste recycling, even if this results in an aching back at the end of an arduous day in the garden. Perhaps this weed-filled book will become valued among other garden-related books to be thumbed through during winter, or on rainy days, and the images might inspire a closer look at our currently expendable plants before they are composted. Whilst weeding, it is also fun to think about the posher relatives of the weed being pulled out, for example: Chickweed is in the same plant family as carnations, and Herb Robert is a less revered relative of our horticultural geraniums and pelargoniums.

Page 12: Pheasant's Eye (*Adonis annua* – family Ranunculaceae), flower and foliage

Opposite: Pasque Flower (*Anemone pulsatilla* – family Ranunculaceae), flowers. Both species were almost lost through over-weeding and are now treasured as wild flowers

14

INTRODUCTION

THE DEFINITION OF A WEED

In the native and non-native flora of any country there are usually a significant number of species that are considered to be a nuisance, mainly to agriculture and horticulture. These are the species that thrive and multiply in areas of human settlement, where they can benefit from the resulting nutrient enriched soils of field, garden, roadside, rubbish tip and other human interventions with the land. A weed might be a species that has long been cultivated because it was, or is, considered useful or pretty, for example: the native Foxglove (*Digitalis purpurea*) or non-native Evening Primrose (*Oenothera biennis*). Both species produce copious seed and spread very easily. The size of adult weeds varies. Many, such as Chickweed and Groundsel, are quite small and would go unremarked in the wild. Some weeds, however, are tall and quite showy: Ragwort, with its masses of bright yellow flowers, cannot be overlooked when it takes over in pastureland, and Rose-bay Willowherb clothes railway sidings and roadsides with glorious spikes of deep pink flowers, and reddish seeding stems with fluffy seeds in late summer.

WILD FLOWER OR WEED?

In any region, local weedy species considered to be the most troublesome may vary or change over time. Some species may become less of a problem, usually because of a change in the conditions that enabled them to flourish, or because good weed management controlled or prevented their spread. Subsequently, other species might move in to take advantage of the change of conditions, and proliferate. If the lost weed is a non-native species, its disappearance is generally considered to be a good thing, as would be the case if we could find a way of eradicating Japanese Knotweed. However, when a native species becomes very rare, or is lost to the nation forever by over-zealous weeding, this is truly a tragedy. Not all weeds have the resilience of our now revered native Field Poppy (*Papaver rhoeas*), with seeds that may remain in the ground undisturbed, and germinate after as long as 100 years if the conditions are right.

If challenged to define a weed, most of us would probably resort to some form of the well-known description, "Any plant growing where it is not wanted by man." The American philosopher and poet, Ralph Waldo Emerson, proposed a slightly more subtle (and mildly cynical) definition in *Fortune of the Republic* (1878): "What is a weed? A plant whose virtues have not been discovered." Both definitions reflect a very human, utilitarian attitude towards plants and animals, implying that they are there to be exploited for the benefit of mankind. We don't want them hanging around and getting in the way if they provide "neither use nor ornament". This attitude is reflected in the terminology used for local wild plants: 'wild flowers', whether insignificant or pretty, are not considered to be a nuisance (some are rare, or restricted in their distribution), 'herbs' are useful for eating, flavouring or medicinal purposes, and 'weeds' are a tiresome, rapidly spreading annoyance, particularly in land prepared for growing crops. Thus, all wild plants are defined by their relationship to humans.

The word *weed* derives from the Old English *weod*, meaning wild flower or herb. There are other uses for the modern word *weed*. Two of the best known are: 'widow's weeds' which originates from Old English *waed* or *wóde* meaning clothing – thus a widow's mourning clothes – and the other, more unkindly use: a 'weedy' man, by which we infer a man of little vigour; a curious application bearing in mind the exasperating resilience and success of weedy plants.

In the Bible, nuisance weeds are referred to as *tares* – a word once used in Britain, but now considered archaic or biblical. Definitions of the word are varied, but one common use is in reference to darnel (*Lolium tenulentum*), a species of grass which had a reputation for being poisonous to animals and humans. The grasses are a huge family worldwide (more than 10,500 species), and for a long time botanists were puzzled that only one species was considered poisonous. Modern science has shown that symptoms following ingestion of darnel seed clearly point to infection by fungi – notably Ergot, the alkaloids of which are toxic to humans and animals. Furthermore, poisoning by Ergot-infected rye bread was prevalent in the Middle Ages.

USES OF WEEDS

The concept of weeds and herbs (Old English *erbs*) as distinct from wild flowers has its beginnings in the gradual development of settled man, crop growing and animal husbandry. We can comfortably assume that cave dwellers and subsequent early civilisations were not too disturbed by local plants, especially as many of them were found to have practical applications such as eating or brewing primitive medicines or drugs. Woad (*Isatis tinctoria*) was used for pigment, and Bracken provided bedding and draught exclusion, whilst other weeds were used as animal fodder. In human settlement areas high nitrate levels are usually recorded, mainly from human and animal urine. By comparing pollen counts from archaeological sites, palaeo-palynologists have recorded relatively high pollen counts for nitrate-loving species, such as nettles. Another wild plant associated with high nitrate levels, survival or opportunism is Rose-bay Willowherb (*Chamerion angustifolium*) also known as Fireweed. In recent history it was to become a very common

Field Poppies and Wild Chamomile in a wheat field

and heart-warming sight on bombed out areas of London and other big cities in the UK, during and after WWII.

As an example of nitrate lovers, Stinging Nettles are particularly interesting: from the earliest human settlements, there is evidence of their assimilation into the local economy, due in part to their highly fibrous stems. Nettles were frequently used to make rope and cloth (hemp), and there are many records from the European Bronze Age and from North America, of cloth and/or rope manufacture from nettle fibre. Much more recently, it is recorded that due to a severe shortage of cloth in Germany during WWI, the Kaiser's soldiers marched in nettle shirts. Similarly, the war ministries of Britain used cultivated nettle fibres at this time (at an estimated 60% lower cost than imported cotton), for the manufacture of wagon covers, tents, sacking and clothing, including military underwear. Although the thought makes us feel itchy, nettle fibre can be spun as fine as cotton or linen, and it is currently enjoying a revival among the eco-friendly fashion conscious.

Until comparatively recently in Britain, the word 'herb' (Latin: *herba*) would have been used to describe any wild (uncultivated) non-woody plant. Today, however, most people think of herbs as plants with pleasantly smelling or tasting leaves, stems, seeds or roots used to flavour food, or in the manufacture of aromatic oils, soaps and perfumes. Some may also think of the plants traditionally used by herbalists for treating wounds and curing the sick, or by witches or wizards to cast spells, brew healing potions, or to extract poisons (see Socrates' Hemlock among the weeds described and illustrated).

VERNACULAR NAMES AND PLANT LORE

Local (common, folk, vernacular) names are often *very* local, varying even between neighbouring counties, and for very common species there may be dozens of names countrywide. For example, Hogweed or Cow-parsnip are the two most widely used common names for *Heracleum sphondylium* (not to be confused with the introduced Giant Hogweed, *Heracleum mantegazzianum*), and are the names used in the weed descriptions in this book. However, Hogweed enjoys a great number of local names. In *Weeds of Farm Land*, Winifred Brenchley lists 53 local variants: Bear's Breech, Bear-skeiters, Beggar-weed, Bilders, Billers, Broad-leaved Keck, Broad Kelk, Bunnel, Bunnerts, Bunnun, Bunwand, Caddell, Cadweed, Camlicks, Clogweed, Cow-cakes, Cow-clogweed, Cow-keeks, Cow-keep, Cow-mumble, **Cow-parsnip**, Cushia, Dry Kesh, Dryland, Scout, Eltrot, Ha-ho, Hardhead, Heltrot, **Hogweed**, Keck, Kedlock, Kex, Keglus, Kelk-kecksy, Kesh, Kesk, Kewsies, Limperscrimp, Lumper-scrump, Madnep, Meadow Parsnep, Old-rot, Pig's Bubbles, Pig's Cole, Pig's Parsnip, Pigweed, Piskies, Rabbit-meat, Sweet Biller, Swine Weed and Skytes. Geoffrey Grigson lists even more names (69) for the same species, and doesn't include every name on Brenchley's list, making a total of over 80 local names for this very familiar, previously economically important weed.

Further confusion may be caused by the fact that not all local names are *very* local. Some names occur in a number of regions but may be used for different species, sometimes not even in the same plant family. For example, the name 'sorrel' appears in two very different plant families: in Oxalidaceae, Wood-sorrel (*Oxalis acetosella* L.) and Yellow-sorrel (*Oxalis corniculata* L.) and, in the unrelated family Polygonaceae, Sorrel (*Rumex acetosa* L.) and Sheep's Sorrel (*Rumex acetosella* – both *acetosa* and *acetosella* meaning sour-tasting). Similarly, the common name Batchelor's Buttons is widely, though not exclusively, used for various species in unrelated plant families (including a few of the weeds described in the book, though not as a best-known common name): *Vinca minor* (family Apocynaceae); *Arctium minus*, *Bellis perennis*, *Centaurea cyanus*, *C. nigra*, and *C. scabiosa*, *Chrysanthemum parthenium*, *Tanacetum vulgare* (family Asteraceae); *Silene dioica*, *S. latifolia* subsp. *alba*, *Lychnis flos-cuculi*, *Agrostemma githago*, *Silene dioica*, *S. latifolia* subsp. *alba*, *Lychnis flos-cuculi* and *Stellaria holostea* (family Caryophyllaceae); *Umbilicus rupestris* (family Crassulaceae); *Knautia arvensis* and *Succisa pratensis* (family Dipsacaceae); *Geranium lucidum* and *G. robertianum* (family Geraniaceae) and *Caltha palustris*, *Ranunculus acris*, *R. bulbosus* and *R. repens* (family Ranunculaceae). Clearly, this situation could create some confusion in our modern, cosmopolitan society, if an exclusive botanical name for each species did not exist.

International travel is now commonplace, and the potential for confusion caused by local plant names also extends beyond national borders, particularly in north-western Europe where many of Britain's native wild flowers are also native. For example: Dandelion in France is *Pis-en-lit* (Piss-in–the-bed), in Spain: *Diente de León* (Lion's Teeth) and in The Netherlands: *Gewone Paardenbloem* (Horse Flower). Suddenly, the botanical name *Taraxacum officinale* seems beautifully simple. Imagine an international botanical (agricultural or horticultural) conference where every species the delegates wished to discuss was referred to by the common name used in their own country – a Tower of Babel would result. Vernacular or common plant names are, nevertheless, very important, because they are more familiar to most people than botanical names. Common names are also more established – many old names for wild plants pre-date the Linnaean system of binomial naming (1753) by centuries. For this reason the present book gives priority to the *most widely encountered* common names over botanical names. Furthermore, common names often have a story to tell, especially in the case of weeds which are among the most common of our wild flowers. The richness of their differing local names is testament to their importance in local culture: the most familiar of all our wild plants. Wild flowers and their common names is a fascinating subject. In *Flora Britannica*, Richard Mabey describes the local importance and folklore of many well-loved British wild species. For anyone wishing to explore their common names further, Geoffrey Grigson in *An Englishman's Flora* offers a fascinating and scholarly account.

Corncockle (*Agrostemma githago* – family Caryophyllaceae), habit and flower

SURVIVAL STRATEGIES

Larger animals, human or otherwise, are more directly dependent on plants than plants are on animals. This is because plant evolution (earliest land plants c. 480mya – million years ago) and early insect evolution, around the same time, long precede the evolution of seed-bearing plants (c. 400mya), reptiles (c. 300mya), small mammals (c. 200mya), and birds (c. 150mya). Flowering plants came even later (c. 130mya) and the mutually beneficial plant-insect interactions that we know today had their beginnings around 90mya ago. First records of mammals (small rodent-like animals) are recorded from 180mya, and the Cretaceous-Palaeogene 'KT extinction event' (c. 65 mya) provided a niche, left by the demise of dinosaurs, for the evolution of larger mammals. The earliest mammalian creatures showing some humanoid characteristics (early hominids) are recorded by about 4mya. From these early ape-like creatures 'nest-making' and cave dwelling hominids (*Homo habilis*) evolved by about 2.5mya, followed by tool-making hominids (c. 2mya), and later upright man (*Homo erectus*) c. 5,000ya (years ago); lastly, modern humans (*Homo sapiens*) are recorded from around 250,000ya.

Evolutionary development and change is driven by 'adapt-and-survive' strategies, exemplified by the extinction of dinosaurs and the gradual rise of mammals. Any biological organism, from microscopic bacteria to an elephant, represents a food source, directly or indirectly, for other organisms. Plants are masters at absorbing nutrients from the dead or discarded biomass that surrounds them. They convert it to suit their needs and, subsequently, the needs of herbivores, who, in turn, make good eating for omnivores and carnivores. All plant species living today, including the weedy ones, have evolved numerous ways of surviving and adapting. Critical to plant evolution, in the summary timeline above, is the later co-evolution (from c. 90mya) of mutually beneficial strategies between insects and flowering plants. We struggle to imagine thousands of years, let alone millions, but the early *foundations* of the exquisite and mutually beneficial relationships, between many of the insects and flowering plants that we observe today, evolved many millions of years after primitive plants and insects first evolved on dry land.

Among the vast, and infinitely varied array of plant species that clothe the planet, many extraordinary strategies for survival and procreation have evolved, as well as a breath-taking range of size and form. Current estimates of the number of plant species worldwide suggest at least 352,000 and probably closer to 400,000. The British Isles plays host to around 3000 native species, including trees and shrubs, of which less than 200 are considered to be fairly widespread, mostly herbaceous, weeds.

SEXUAL AND ASEXUAL REPRODUCTION

Flowering plants generally favour sexual reproduction over asexual reproduction. The reproductive parts of flowers are: the *stamens* which carry the male genetic material, *pollen*, and the female *pistil* which has a receptive upper surface – the *stigma* on which the pollen is deposited to effect fertilisation of the ovaries at the base of the pistil.

For most species of plants, like animals, it is important to cross-fertilise (i.e. pollinate) to maintain the health and vigour of the species. The individual plants of many species are self-incompatible and cannot achieve self-fertilisation, even if the pollen of one flower falls onto the pistil surface of another flower on the same plant. Given that plants are usually rooted to the spot, and cannot move about to seek a mate, most plants (c. 85%) have evolved to use external carriers (*vectors*) to achieve cross-fertilisation. Although this may seem a complicated arrangement, it is a highly successful strategy.

Flowering plants and insects have co-evolved to share a mutually beneficial system: lured by colour, scent, nectar and pollen, a wide variety of insects, including various social bees (e.g. honey bees) and solitary bees, flies, beetles, butterflies and moths have evolved to take floral rewards (nectar and/or pollen) while getting dusted with pollen to transfer to other flowers of the same species.

Wind is the other main pollination vector, although here the evolutionary adaptations are completely one-sided. The plants have evolved flower structures to take advantage of wind currents, for example: stamens with long filaments (plantains and grasses), masses of stamens (sedges) and flowers in long thin tassels (stinging nettles).

SELF-FERTILISATION

Most flowers have an open *chasmogamous* ('open marriage') fertilisation system to achieve cross-fertilisation, but a minority of species are able to self-fertilise. It is unusual, and often represents a 'switch' triggered by climate conditions. Only a minority of plants are able to self-fertilise habitually. There are two main types of self-fertilisation: *autogamy* and *cleistogamy*. Autogamy is more frequent than cleistogamy. It is particularly associated with the Cabbage family (Brassicaceae) where a number of species, especially the smaller-flowered ones, have the ability to cross-fertilise flowers on the same plant. It is also common in Caryophyllaceae, the Campion family.

Cleistogamy ('closed marriage') is unusual. The plant achieves pollination by producing flowers that don't open to expose the sexual organs (male stamens and female pistil), and fertilisation has to occur within the closed flower. The Peanut (*Arachis hypogaea*) is probably the most widely known species where this is the normal condition. Most species that produce cleistogamous flowers usually produce normal flowers too. Among the weedy species described there are only a few species that sometimes produce cleistogamous flowers: Field Pansy (*Viola arvensis*), Henbit (*Lamium amplexicaule*), Pale Persicaria (*Persicaria lapathifolia*) and Redshanks (*Persicaria maculosa*). Notably, *Viola* is a large temperate genus of about 400 species, many of which

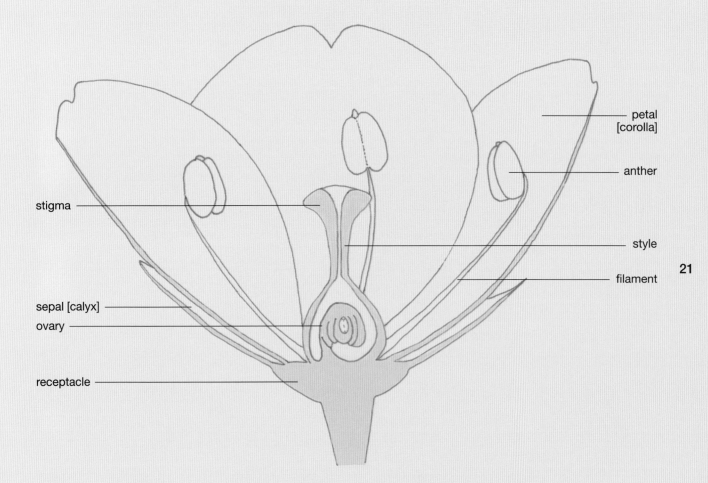

petal
[corolla]

anther

stigma

style

filament

21

sepal [calyx]

ovary

receptacle

Structural diagram of a simple five-petalled flower to
show main parts (longitudinal section)
Note: stigma plus style = 'pistil',
filament plus anther = 'stamen'

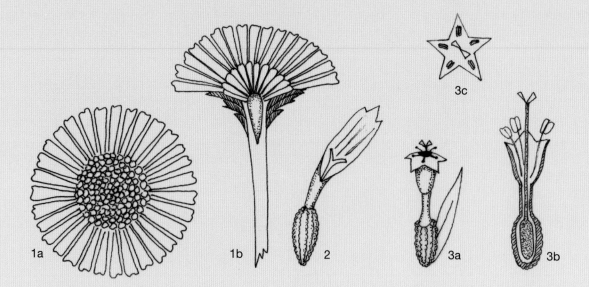

The structure of a typical daisy 'flower'.

The 'flower' is actually a condensed inflorescence (group of flowers). The outer 'petals' are individual 'ray florets', while the inner circle of tiny 'bobble-like' structures are the 'disc florets'. Ray florets are bisymmetric and may, in different species, be either hermaphrodite, female or sterile, while disc florets are radially symmetric and usually hermaphrodite. (Note that not all members of the Daisy family have both ray and disc florets.)

1a) A radially symmetric whole inflorescence from above;
1b) vertical section through inflorescence (exaggerated 'view' to show radial florets as well);
2) a female only ray floret: note branched pistil and seed below;
3a) hermaphrodite, radially symmetric disc floret with seed below and a 'receptacular scale' (which is present in some species);
3b) section through disc floret, showing central pistil connected to ovary below;
3c) disc flower from above – five petals, five stamens and a central branched pistil

22

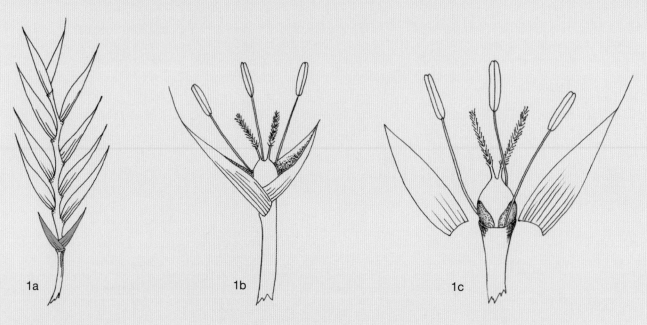

Structure of a typical grass flower.

1a) An inflorescence which, depending on species, may comprise one to many florets on a rhachis (flower-bearing axis/stalk), the base of the rhachis subtended by a lower and an upper glume (shaded)

1b) an individual flower comprising paired bracts (or 'palea'), outer and inner; an ovoid ovary with a (usually) two-branched feathery pistil and (usually) three stamens
1c) a flower with paired bracts removed to show the paired lodicules at the base of the ovary, these are generally thought to be vestigial petals or sepals

are able to produce cleistogamous flowers. In the pages that follow, the images of flowers for these species show normal (chasmogamous) flowers with the exception of Henbit where an inflorescence of cleistogamous flowers is also shown.

Gynodioecy is another interesting example of divergence from the widespread hermaphroditic condition. Gynodioecious flowers are either hermaphrodite or have only female organs (pistils). The female only flowers are smaller than the hermaphrodite flowers. Among the weed species described it occurs in the flowers of Ground-ivy (*Glechoma hederacea*).

MONOECY AND DIOECY

About 20% of plant species have evolved to have separate male and female flowers. The most common types are *monoecious* or *dioecious*.

Monoecious species (from the Greek meaning one house) have separate male flowers (stamens only) and female flowers (pistil only) occurring on the same plant. Examples among the weeds include the spurges (euphorbias), the Small Nettle (*Urtica urens*) and Pendulous Sedge (*Carex pendula*). Annual Mercury (*Mercurialis annua*), also in family Euphorbiaceae, occasionally has monoecious plants.

Dioecious species (from the Greek meaning two houses) have plants with male only flowers, and other plants with female only flowers. Among the species described there are a number of examples including Hops (*Humulus lupulus*), Mind-your-own-business (*Soleiria soleirolii*), Stinging Nettle (*Urtica dioica*), campions (*Silene dioica* and *S. latifolia* subsp. *alba*) and White Bryony (*Bryonia dioica*). Annual Mercury (*Mercurialis annua*) is usually dioecious, occasionally monoecious, while Dog's Mercury (*M. perennis* – not among the weed species) is consistently dioecious.

ASEXUAL REPRODUCTION

Many plants, notably perennials, are also able to reproduce without producing seed (asexually or vegetatively) by runners, bulbs, corms, stem cuttings, budding and so on. This has proved very valuable in horticulture, as well as agriculture. However, these processes are forms of cloning (producing exact replicas) and in nature, few species would depend primarily on this method of procreation as it is not the healthiest option.

HOW WEEDS SURVIVE AND THRIVE

WEED LIFE SPAN

Annual species, because of their short life span, rely on good seed set and seed dispersal systems. Biennials are not so dissimilar, but regeneration is over a two year interval. During the first year the young plants rarely flower and set seed. Instead, the first year's growth is a vegetative phase during which the plant grows and accumulates

sufficient food reserves for flowering and seed production the following year. After seed set a biennial plant normally dies, however, the vegetative phase might last more than one year in unfavourable conditions or, conversely, flowering may occur in the first season if conditions are favourable. Weed management methods follow those used to control annual broad-leaved weeds (i.e. most weeds except annual grasses). Among the best known weedy biennial species are: Evening Primrose (*Oenothera biennis*), Foxglove (*Digitalis purpurea*), Caper Spurge (*Euphorbia lathyris*), Marsh Thistle (*Cirsium palustre*), Spear Thistle (*Cirsium vulgare*), Common Burdock (*Arctium minus*), Hemlock (*Conium maculatum*), Hogweed (*Heracleum sphondylium*), Giant Hogweed (*Heracleum mantegazzianum*) and Goat's-beard (*Tragopogon pratensis* subsp. *minor*).

WEED HABITAT

Weeds are highly opportunistic with regard to habitat. In general they are not 'fussy eaters', or oversensitive to who their neighbours might be. Nevertheless, not all weeds have cosmopolitan habits, and if the conditions don't suit, the weed will not establish and thrive. Unfortunately from farming and horticultural perspectives, they often respond well to the conditions provided for cultivated plants.

Particular soil types are important to some weeds: alkaline conditions (pH >7) are notably attractive to Bulbous Buttercup (*Ranunculus bulbosus*), while acidic conditions (pH < 7) are perfect for *Rhododendron ponticum* to flourish. Sandy soils are favoured by a number of other calcifuge weeds (plants favouring non-chalky or limestone soils) including Corn Spurrey (*Spergula arvensis*), Gorse (*Ulex europaeus*) and Treacle Mustard (*Erysimum cheiranthoides*). Habitat is very important to some weeds, for example Bracken, which thrives in humic woodland conditions. Other weed species prefer more open moist/damp conditions, for example Great Hairy Willowherb (*Epilobium hirsutum*). Helxine (*Soleirolia soleirolii*) is most at home with light shade and damp 'feet', while Enchanter's Nightshade (*Circaea lutetiana*) enjoys a damp shady bank, but it is an opportunist and not averse to spreading its runners through the herbaceous border, given the chance.

WEED SURVIVAL TACTICS

Plants have evolved an incredible range of tactics to ensure survival of species. Even across the species described in this book, a remarkable range of strategies are represented, including the following examples:

• *Seed dispersal via animal ingestion/defecation:* Wild Arum – bright orange fruits encasing the seeds (mainly dispersed by birds), Blackberries – temptingly delicious to a number of predators (including humans).

• *High production of tiny windborne seeds:* Buddleia, Rhododendron.

• *Pepper pot fruits:* Poppies.

• *Projectile seeds:* Spurges, yellow-sorrels, Himalayan Balsam, the bitter-cresses.

• *Fruits with hooked hairs:* Cleavers (Goosegrass), Enchanter's Nightshade.

• *Persistent hooked bracts enclosing the fruits (seeds):* Common Burdock.

• *Persistent calyx with hooked hairs enclosing the fruits (seeds):* Forget-me-not.

• *Feathery parachute seeds:* Willowherbs and many species of the Daisy family, including Dandelions, thistles and milk-thistles, hawkweeds, Canadian Fleabane, Canadian Goldenrod, ragworts, Groundsel, Jack-go-to-bed-at-noon and Coltsfoot.

• *Seed longevity:* Chickweed up to 25 years, knotgrasses up to 60 years, and poppies, an extreme example, can survive in the ground for as much as 80-100 years.

• *Vines with tendrils:* White Bryony.

• *Prostrate spreading (rooting) stems:* Butterbur, a dioecious species, but with a predominantly male distribution, White Clover, the resourceful perennial Slender (Creeping) Speedwell, which rarely sets seed, but still pops up in the lawn from stem cuttings.

24

• *Runners (above ground):* Bindweeds.

• *Trailing stems that root at nodes or tips:* Creeping Cinquefoil, Silverweed, Blackberry.

• *Creeping rootstocks (underground root runners):* Rose-bay Willowherb, Great Hairy Willowherb, Couch Grass, Ground-elder, Stinging Nettle, Enchanter's Nightshade, Coltsfoot, Butterbur, Convolvulus and Bindweed, Creeping Thistle, Field Milk-thistle.

• *Adhesive roots:* Ivy.

• *Deep tap roots:* Dandelions, Prickly Lettuce, Cow Parsley.

• *Bulbs or corms:* Wild Arum, Ramsons, Crow Garlic – a species that favours this method over the energy resources required for flower production, the flower heads of this species are often restricted to tiny bulbs and flowers are not formed.

• *Rapid reproductive cycle (more than one generation annually):* Groundsel, bitter-cresses, Thale Cress, Chickweed, speedwells.

• *'Bonsai' weeds:* A number of weeds, notably those that grow in grassland, are able to survive our penchant for close mowing by temporary 'dwarfing' – strengthening their leaf bases and roots, so that their life cycle can still be achieved (e.g. Common Daisy, Dove's-foot Crane's-bill, Cat's Ear).

NURTURING NATURE

The importance of wild flowers to other forms of wildlife should not be overlooked. However widespread or weedy, they are likely to provide food, and shelter for nesting, resting or concealment. Because *weedy* wild flowers are plentiful, many species are frequently visited by insects, birds or small mammals, especially for dropped fruits and seeds. The most obvious example of insect visiting is provided in June and July by Hogweed (Cow-parsnip); a benign landlord with its large plates of tiny white flowers, inviting a remarkably cosmopolitan assemblage of insect visitors to stop and rest and take nectar. These visitors include many species of tiny beetles and small flies, as well as butterflies and bees. Among the great variety of insect flower visitors, many species of flowers have evolved to take advantage of particular insects for cross-pollination: for example Wild Arum, Foxglove, Bugloss, and Red or White Campions. Many bee species are important flower visitors, not just the Honey Bee (*Apis mellifera*), which represents only one of about 250 species of bee in the UK, including 25 species of bumblebee and 225 species of solitary bee.

INSECTS, BIRDS AND SMALL ANIMALS

Animals (including humans) can carry seed burs (for example Burdock, Cleavers and Enchanter's Nightshade); on feet, fur or clothing. Birds and small animals eat the fruits of blackberries and later excrete the seeds, providing a richly manured start for seed germination. Many resident birds and small animals feed on fruits and seeds to fatten up before the winter sets in. Some native British birds are habitual seed-feeders, for example, Goldfinches feed on thistle and Dandelion seed, Bullfinches eat the seeds of docks and nettles, Blue Tits will take pollen and nectar, while the Lesser Whitethroat eats elderberries and blackberries. Turtle Doves feed almost entirely on fruits and seeds of wild flowers including Buttercups and Chickweed.

Garden bird tables are fascinating and provide a welcome extra food source for birds, as well as a great deal of pleasure for us. However, nature's bird table is best: many seeds in bird seed mix are not seeds that our native birds would find in the wild. Niger seed, for example, is from a West African species of daisy (*Guizotia abyssinica*) cultivated in Africa for its seed oil. Finches love it, but they won't find it in Britain anywhere but in a garden (or a cage!).

A Bumblebee, (probably *Bombus lucorum*) visiting a Scabious cultivar (family Dipsacaceae)

SOWING WILD FLOWER SEEDS

To some extent, seeds of any wild species will only thrive if sown in the right environment. For example, seeds of an acid-loving plant will probably not develop and thrive if sown on chalky soil; seedlings of shade-loving species will struggle if they are overexposed on a sunny site, and so on. However tempting the packet might look, do the homework first, especially if the plan is to scatter seed beyond garden boundaries. Check which species are represented by the seeds in the packet. It should say on the packet, but if doesn't, it would be wiser not to sow them at all (or at least only in a private garden). Assuming the species are listed on the packet, do they represent locally common and/or compatible wild species? Or, does the packet include seeds of frequently cultivated species (for example, Marigolds, Aquilegias, Opium Poppies, Love-in-a-mist etc.), or other non-native species? If any uncertainty remains, seek advice from local ecologists before sowing anywhere except a garden.

THE CONCEPT OF WEEDS AND WEEDING

CROP WEEDING

Cultivation of land for food goes hand in hand with removing weeds to allow the seeded crop space to grow and mature, and being able to harvest that crop without too much weed contamination. Until well into the 20th Century, weeding was hard work, especially on farms, but eradication methods were respectful of the environment, though labour intensive. The farming communities knew their weeds, could recognise the seedlings of annual and biennial weedy species and hoe them out before they became a serious nuisance. Perennial weeds, if not hoed out as seedlings, were dug out by their roots and the roots burned. Women as well as men were often employed to do the arduous hoeing between rows of seedling corn and root crops.

WEED WARFARE – BARE KNUCKLE STYLE

With vast areas of land available for clearance and cultivation, one might assume the Americans were ahead of Britain and the rest of Europe in terms of weed control, but perhaps not: An 1895 United States Department of Agriculture (USDA) publication by L.H. Dewey, with the rather menacing title *Weeds; and How to Kill Them*, was re-issued in March 1905 with this Letter of Transmission printed on the inside cover:

"Sir: I have the honour to transmit herewith copy for a second edition of Farmers' Bulletin no. 28, entitled "Weeds; and How to Kill Them," prepared under the direction of the botanist, Mr. Frederick V. Coville, by Mr. Lister H. Dewey, Assistant Botanist. The lessening of crops, the damage to machinery and stock, and the decrease in value of land due to weeds involve a large loss, which is sustained almost entirely by the farmers. This bulletin contains descriptions of many of the worst weeds, with simple directions for their extirpation, and, while no method of

destroying weeds is proposed which obviates the necessity of patient effort it is believed that the suggestions made will prove helpful to thoughtful farmers. (Respectfully etc.)".

CHEMICAL WARFARE

It is comparatively recently, since WWII, that farmers and gardeners started to seriously embrace chemicals for weed control. That is not to say that pre-WWII there was no chemical weed control going on, but most of it was experimental, and not without considerable hazard and error. The pre-WWII farm or garden shed would have had an assortment of fairly basic chemical remedies on the shelf for insect and weed control. By 1910, chemicals in agricultural use (either in solution for use in sprays, or in powder form) were ammonium sulphate, common salt, carbolic acid, sodium arsenite (a very poisonous, highly caustic chemical, also being used in Hawaiian rubber plantations and Australian sugar cane plantations), and sulphates of iron and of copper. Ammonium sulphate, with its high nitrogen content, was also popular as a fertiliser. Weed eradication by hand, or with machinery such as harrows, was still strongly advised in 1920, but spraying with chemicals and manuring were also being used. Nevertheless, farmers were still far from finding a good selective method that would kill the weeds and keep the crop. By 1938 *lawn sand* (ammonium sulphate and iron sulphate mixed with sand for easier application) had been an established weed eradication treatment for lawns for about 25 years. The British chemical armoury had expanded to include sulphuric acid (used against Bracken). Calcium cyanamide (nitro-lime) was used as a fertiliser because it is converted by water into ammonia, and kainite – a valuable source of potassium.

Other chemicals in use remained much the same as those introduced earlier in the century, with a few additions such as carbolic acid for use against wild onion (probably *Allium vineale*) and sodium chlorate for Ragwort. The golden rule of sowing clean (uncontaminated) seed was still paramount. Little progress, or change in weed management, would occur for the next decade: war raged in Europe, and the Women's Land Army moved in to work the farms and keep the country fed while the younger men were away fighting.

COMPULSORY DESTRUCTION OF WEEDS

Then, as now, there was the problem of 'the neighbour's weeds' – as if one's own were not enough. The Corn Production Acts (Repeal) Act of 1921 deemed that, *"It is desirable that all occupiers of land should cut down and destroy injurious weeds growing on their land, especially those weeds that may readily spread to adjoining lands."* The Minister of Agriculture and Fisheries' powers, under this act, were delegated to agricultural committees during the same year. The most injurious weeds subject to this recommendation were five: Spear Thistle (*Cirsium vulgare*), Creeping (Field) Thistle (*Cirsium arvense*), Curled Dock (*Rumex crispus*), Broad-leaved Dock (*Rumex obtusifolius*) and

26

Ragwort (*Senecio jacobaea*). This is particularly noteworthy as the current DEFRA list of 'most injurious agricultural weeds' has not changed (and dates back to the Weeds Act of 1959). Today, most of these can usually be controlled by the use of phenoxyacetic acid herbicide, however, the control of Ragwort is further subject to the more rigorous provisions of the Ragwort Control Act 2003. It is not simply a major nuisance because of weed spread but, more seriously, because it contains toxins injurious to animals, especially to horses, and even to humans. Balanced against the negative effects of this species are its benefits. As a native plant, it is very important to other forms of wildlife in the UK. It supports a wide variety of insects, including the highly recognisable black and yellow striped larvae of the beautiful Cinnabar Moth (the larvae will also eat other species of Ragwort). It is also a major nectar source for many insects. In many situations Ragwort poses no threat to horses and other livestock; it is a natural component of many types of unimproved grassland and is important to a number of invertebrate species that are in need of protection.

CHANGES TO FARMING PRACTICE

Post-WWII changes to farming practice and weed management are well-documented elsewhere, and are beyond the scope of this book. In summary, the years of post-war austerity continued into the late 1960s and early 1970s, with farmland still being worked in a fairly traditional manner and small changes gradually filtering through. The crunch came when, in 1973, Britain joined the Common Market (the year after Britain adopted the decimal system), and the price of corn shot up. Small fields, along with hedges, meadows and ditches disappeared almost overnight to make way for vast fields more akin to American prairies. All Britain's agricultural resources were sacrificed on the altar of higher food production, with scant attention to its natural heritage. Wildlife was severely threatened and depleted by loss of habitats and biochemists were having a field day with the development of new agrochemical weed killers, including *Round Up* which contains glyphosate, a broad spectrum herbicide chemical once deemed safe but currently being reassessed for potential toxicity to humans and other animals.

Increasingly these 'exciting' new policies resulted in insufficient markets for the vastly inflated corn yields being produced within the Common Market. Many of the novel, enthusiastically embraced agricultural practices were to prove seriously detrimental to the countryside and to wildlife, while causing lasting damage by the destruction of much of our traditional meadowland. Many other natural habitats for particular species were also lost in a dramatically short space of time; notably hedgerows and the imponderable, quiet rhythm and balance of more traditional farming methods. Since that very destructive period, much has been done to try and redress the damage caused by the worst effects of those imaginative but short-sighted policies which seemed not to care for the natural rhythm of the countryside. In 1988 the *Set-aside Policy* was introduced

to encourage the reduction of arable crops. Participating farmers would set aside 20% of their arable land in return for government compensation. The land was to be left fallow to encourage the return of native species. The scheme remained in place until 2008. Since then, a potentially more workable policy has been in place, encouraging farmers to exercise greater awareness of the countryside they farm through initiatives such as reinstigating and maintaining traditional wide headlands at the margins of their fields, where native flora and fauna have a chance to survive. More understated than its predecessors, perhaps this common sense approach stands a better chance of succeeding and enduring.

WISE WEEDING

Surprising reappearances may occur for wild flowers that have previously fallen prey to harrow and plough. This is often due in part to improved methods of agricultural practice, and to working with botanists and conservationists to ensure a fairer deal for wild places and the flora and fauna they support.

WEED OR WILD FLOWER?

For some common wild flowers, weed status comes or goes over time. A number of species included in one or more of the early 20th Century weed guides are back among our most treasured wild flowers. Notably, Wood Anemone (*Anemone nemorosa*), Pasque Flower (*Anemone pulsatilla*), Corncockle (*Agrostemma githago*), Corn Buttercup (*Ranunculus arvensis*) and Cowslip (*Primula veris*).

Another reason for the reappearance of species that have been designated weeds, and almost disappeared, is that some wild species have seeds that can spend remarkably long periods of dormancy buried within the soil, and then germinate when the conditions are right. There are a number of weedy species with unusually long seed dormancy, including Chickweed and the knotweeds. However, the most celebrated example is that of our beloved Field Poppy (*Papaver rhoeas*). Until the 1970s, poppies were a very common sight among ripening corn – heart-lifting to the casual onlooker, but a serious nuisance in arable crops for farmers until its targeted eradication with aggressive weed killers during the Common Market years. Miraculously, this poppy has made a comeback in the last few years, thanks to its remarkably long seed longevity (at least 80 years, possibly as long as a century). Its extraordinary appearance in the battlefields of the Somme region during WWI, as a result of digging out entrenchments for warfare, is well-documented, and its widely-held symbolism is a very poignant reminder of the horrors of war.

INTRODUCED WEEDS

About one sixth of the widespread weed species included in this book are introduced plants (see species descriptions for detail). There are four categories of wild flower species in the

27

UK that relate to the length of time they have been part of the British Flora: *native* species are those already in the UK prior to human settlement. In wild flower accounts these are the species that are fully described. Introduced species are referred to as *archaeophytes* if they arrived and became naturalised in the British Isles before 1500AD. Later arrivals, the *neophytes*, arrived and have become naturalised since 1500AD. The future of the newest arrivals, *casuals*, cannot be predicted. Like all travellers, some will no doubt settle, while others will disappear.

Of the introduced species described, archeophytes are rare. The following are considered to be very early introductions, or of uncertain origin (the latter marked with *): Thorn-apple (*Datura stramonium*), Treacle Mustard (*Erysimum cheiranthoides*), Swine-cress (*Coronopus squamatus*), Greater Celandine* (*Chelidonium majus*), and Caper Spurge* (*Euphorbia lathyris*). Most of our introduced weeds, about 30 species, are neophytes (see individual descriptions for details), including the greatest menace of all, Japanese Knotweed (*Fallopia japonica*). Like many of our introduced weeds, Japanese Knotweed arrived as a horticultural novelty: the entire UK population of *Fallopia japonica* has spread throughout the country from a single female clone, introduced into Britain in 1850 from the Leiden nursery of Philipp von Siebold.

The British fascination, and fashion, for growing non-native species provides back stories for a few of our serious nuisance weeds including *Rhododendron ponticum*, the wild Rhododendron (all other Rhododendrons grown in the UK are in cultivation, and mostly cultivars), and Himalayan Balsam (*Impatiens glandulifera*).

RHODODENDRON PONTICUM

This species was first introduced into Britain in 1763 by Conrad Loddiges, a German émigré, while he was working as a gardener in Hackney. Later he would set up his own seed and nursery business. At this time, young Rhododendron plants were supplied to the Marquis of Rockingham, and it was his interest in the plant that led to its popularity among fashionable gardeners. Although not a problem in its native south-west European soil, it has become a rampant menace in many otherwise unspoiled areas of Britain, notably in the west.

Historically, there is a link between the rapid spread of *Rhododendron ponticum* and a renewed interest in the Indian or Common Pheasant during the early 18th Century. Originally introduced as a game bird, probably by the Romans, the Indian Pheasant population had seriously dwindled by the beginning of the 18th Century. However, the now thriving populations of *Rhododendron* were seen, by the gentry and their estate workers, as perfect ground cover for a game bird with limited ability to remain airborne for long. In a fairly short space of time almost every country estate owner was growing *Rhododendron ponticum* in their acres. Evergreen, and rapidly spreading by suckering,

layering and copious seed production, it wasn't long before the scene was set for country weekend shooting parties to become a fashionable pastime. Then, as now, the estate employees would earn extra money acting as beaters when a shoot was held. A beater's job is to flush the pheasants out of the undergrowth, so that they may be shot with a 'sporting chance' on the wing; a practice that survives to this day. In his historical novel *Lavengro*, George Borrow, clearly *au fait* with the fashions of the age, includes a character who remarks (in 1825): "Today, when I took up the newspaper, I saw in a speech of the *Duke of Rhododendron*, at an agricultural dinner ..."

HIMALAYAN BALSAM

Another seriously troublesome weed, Himalayan Balsam, was first introduced to Kew Gardens from the Himalayas in 1839 by Dr. Royle, a British botanist working in Kashmir. It was already a serious problem for farmers in the Kashmir region. The first records in the wild (1855) are from Middlesex (where Kew Gardens are located, on the River Thames) and Hertfordshire; however, its seriously widespread distribution is thought to have been the result of humans passing seed to others. It has long been a favourite cottage garden plant, but the fascination of its violently projectile seeds to both children and adults undoubtedly sped up the establishment of an increasing number of wild populations. By the end of the 19th Century it was being described as "another terrible weed". Himalayan Balsam is a major menace in canals and other waterways, and parties of volunteers help halt its spread during the early summer before it starts flowering and producing its seed-firing fruits.

FOREIGN TRAVEL

A number of troublesome introduced plants have arrived by various routes from foreign climes, often directly, or in association with imported goods such as birdseed. The immense affordability and popularity of foreign travel is a great way for seed to hitch a lift. So far, airports do not request arriving or departing passengers to take full showers, or to sterilise clothing and luggage before leaving the terminal in order to reduce potential weedy invaders. Nevertheless, there are strict rules (and laws) controlling the import and export of plant material between countries, including the UK. Even *within* the UK (or any other country) seeds can travel far and wide with great facility. Rivers, canals, roads and railways, feet and shoes, bicycles, cars and lorries are great ways for seeds to spread. However, not all seeds are from invasive species, and there has to be a degree of tolerance because, however vigilant, it is almost impossible to prevent seed-hoppers with no respect of borders.

RECOGNISING WEEDS AT SEEDLING STAGE

The best place to start is usually at the beginning. If a weed can be recognised at seedling stage, the problem can often be solved before it gets out of hand. Plant growers are becoming increasingly conscious of overuse of herbicides and pesticides, and are often keen to follow best practice and avoid their use wherever possible. Previous generations of gardeners, small holders and farmers were used to wielding the hoe on seedling weeds, and conscientious gardeners still do. It is tiring but healthy work, and has the reward of being far better for the environment than overuse of chemicals. Young, pre-flowering plants of non-pernicious weeds can also be dug, or ploughed in, as green manure. This is particularly worthwhile if there are young perennial cultivated plants among the seedling weeds. Perennial weeds tend to be much more challenging if left, because their longer lifespan allows them to build up strength and resilience. They can develop stronger, longer stolons, for example in Great Hairy Willowherb, or stronger, deeper tap roots (Dandelions), or woodiness (Elder). This calls for careful digging out of roots or stolons and burning, and possibly application of a suitable herbicide. One thing is certain – the longer the plants are left, the worse the removal job.

WEED CONTROL WITHOUT CHEMICALS

Take care only to put weeds into the domestic compost system before flowering stage – unless the compost heap is very large, it is unlikely to gather sufficient heat to destroy seeds. Smaller garden weeds that might be setting seed, and cannot be domestically composted without risk of their survival, can be put into the local council garden waste collection. Even

if this means paying an annual fee, it will be worth it – local authority composting systems are vast and, like any large compost heap, big enough to generate the heat needed to destroy most seeds. Bonfires are a traditional and legal option, but neighbourly consideration is always advisable if there are nearby properties. A flame gun (or flame thrower) is a useful way of keeping weeds at bay on drives and pathways where there are no plants to damage. In large gardens or allotments where appearance doesn't matter, weeds can be covered with old newspapers, carpet or cardboard to cut out air and light from offensive spreading weeds such as Ground-elder. However, remember that this is not a quick fix solution, and it will be unsightly until the problem goes away.

It is not impossible for the average garden owner to be considerate about whether it is necessary to use a chemical remedy for a weed problem: there may be a practical, more environmentally friendly alternative. If weed killer does seem to be the only way forward, check that whatever is used is the safest and most up to date chemical product available. Plan the application of weed killer to avoid the possibility of children or pets having any contact with the chemicals, and store any unused chemical out of reach of young children. Don't be tempted to use ancient cans of weed killer at the back of the garden shed, now superseded by a more up to date, less poisonous, remedy. The ancient containers at the back of the shed can be disposed of thoughtfully in consultation with the staff at the local recycling facility.

29

Overleaf: Rhododendron (*Rhododendron ponticum* – family Ericaceae), spreading, invasive, often almost horizontal branches

NON-FLOWERING PLANTS

EQUISETACEAE *(Horsetail Family)*

Field Horsetail, Common Horsetail *(Equisetum arvense)*

Native. Perennial. Extensive hairy-blackish underground stems that spread below the soil to a depth of several feet, these produce ovoid tubers that detach easily to establish new plants. Non-flowering. Creamy-beige fertile stems, c. 10-25 cm high, precede sterile frond-like green stems which are much taller (20-80 cm high); the stems and fronds are segmented and can be pulled apart. Among the horsetails *Equisetum arvense* is unusual in having separate stems for the spore-bearing heads, in most other species of *Equisetum* the spore heads are borne at the tip of the green non-fertile stems. Annual life cycle: fertile fronds are produced and ripen between March-June, while non-fertile fronds appear and gain height between May-June. Common and widespread throughout the British Isles, natural habitats include riverbanks, fixed dune grassland, sea cliffs and montane flushes; however, it has become closely associated with human activity, and is strongly resistant to herbicides. It now occurs frequently on roadsides, railway embankments, waste places and gardens. May grow up to 1000 m above sea level.

34

Regeneration strategies The spores which are shed locally are contained in the little mushroom-shaped sporophylls that comprise the heads of the fertile stems. They ripen in April and, initially, are all alike. The sex of the young plants (*prothalli*) that develop from the spores is decided by local conditions: poor nutrition tends to produce male plants, while rich nutrition usually results in female plants. Established plants can spread rapidly via the extensive underground rhizomes.

Weed control Deep-digging and removal of rhizomes, or follow current best, preferably organic, practice for large invasions (see Bibliography and internet).

Herbal, culinary, cultural and folklore It has enjoyed considerable economic value because it is rich in silica which has made it highly effective in the polishing of hardwoods, ivory and brass. It was used by hurdy-gurdy players to remove resin build-up from the wheels of their instruments, and is still used by woodwind players to shape and scrape reeds. For the finest finish, it is still considered superior to sandpaper. Apparently among children, because the stems and fronds are easily pulled apart, it has gained the modern folk-name of 'Lego plant'.

Toxicity All horsetails are toxic to livestock.

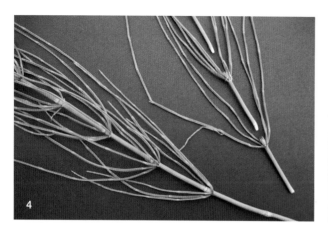 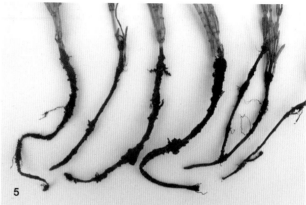

1) Fertile cone stems 2) young sterile stems 3) adult sterile stems 4) jointed sterile stems 5) young plants – roots

DENNSTAEDTIACEAE *(Bracken Family)*

Bracken, Brake *(Pteridium aquilinum)*

Native. Perennial. Non-flowering, deciduous in winter. Rhizome far-creeping, hairy but not scaly, with short, ascending branches. The young leaf fronds (*croziers*) emerge in early to mid-May, the adult fronds 30-180 cm long, but can be as small as 15 or as large as 400 cm, tend to lean towards horizontal; leaf stems up to 2 m long, c. 1 cm diameter, erect, dark and hairy at base. The *sori*, tiny spore containing structures, form a continuous ridge around the underside of fertile leaf frond margins; spores ripen July-August. Bracken has a worldwide distribution, and is troublesome in many localities. It is common throughout the British Isles, from sea level to 3000 m, especially in woods, on heaths and moorland, and light acidic soils, where it often dominates.

Regeneration strategies Most frequently by far-creeping rhizomes, which will grow to a depth of 50 cm, occasionally to 100 cm; less often spores, given the right conditions, develop on the underside of the older fronds and subsequently germinate to produce young fern plants.

Weed control Dig out and burn rhizomes and root stocks, or follow current best, preferably organic, practice for large invasions (see Bibliography and internet).

Herbal, culinary, cultural and folklore Bracken attracts wood ants, beetles, wasps and sawflies. Traditionally the dried fronds were cut and gathered to use as winter animal bedding, and as mattress stuffing. It was also used as thatch. Bracken ash was used as a source of potash in the soap and glass industries until about 1860 and the rhizomes were used in tanning leather and to dye wool yellow. It is historically of interest to cite the significantly named Norfolk village of Braconash, which also has a track leading to the neighbouring village of Hethel, called Potash Lane. The spores were reputed to confer invisibility, but only if gathered on St. John's Eve (23 June) at the precise moment of his birth!

Toxicity The plant contains the carcinogenic compound ptacquiloside and some communities, mainly in Japan where the young stems are used as a vegetable, have some of the highest stomach cancer rates in the world.

35

1) Young fronds 2) young fronds unfurling 3) young adult stems 4) adult green fronds 5) old fronds in autumn

FLOWERING PLANTS
Dicotyledons

ADOXACEAE *(Viburnum Family)*

Elder, Bourtree *(Sambucus nigra)*

Native. Deciduous, short-lived perennial shrub. Height up to 10 m. Leaves comprise usually five to seven leaflets, each c. 3-9 cm long. A broad flattish head (10-20 cm across) of massed tiny creamy-white, sweetly-scented, hermaphrodite flowers. Flowering June-July. Widespread through the British Isles, especially in woodland, scrub, roadsides, waste ground and hedges.

Pollination Small flies and other insects.

Regeneration strategy By seed: vigorous new shoots can reach 2-2.5 m in one growing season. Juicy seed-containing berries provide attractive food for birds and animals, thus ensuring seed spread.

Weed control Weed out and compost young growth. Cut back and dig out larger growth and roots, which can then be burned.

Herbal, culinary, cultural and folklore Flowers used to make cordial and wine. Berries also used for wine. There is a long-held rural superstition that Judas Iscariot hanged himself on Elder. In the UK it is one of the herbs gathered for St. John's Eve. The berries produce a mauve dye. In 18th Century Germany, before the advent of laundry blue-ing agents for whitening linen, dye from the berries, combined with copper, was used for this purpose. Although insect-pollinated, pollen of this species is also carried by wind currents and may occur in significant amounts in seasonal pollen counts.

1) Young plant 2) flowering habit 3) flower heads 4) ripe fruits

AMARANTHACEAE *(Goose-foot Family)*

Common Amaranth, Red-root Amaranth, Pig Weed *(Amaranthus retroflexus)*

Introduced neophyte. First UK record 1759. Possibly earlier from southern USA. Annual, rarely perennial. Height up to c. 90 cm. Stems hairy. Leaves mid-to-deep green, large, ovate. Flowers monoecious, in closely packed finger-like inflorescences at top of the stem. Fruits very small, one-seeded. Flowering August-October. Sporadic invader of cultivated or waste ground.

Pollination Wind. Also self-fertile.

Regeneration strategy An opportunistic and rapid coloniser of disturbed ground; large numbers of seeds from single seeded capsules, with high germination rate (c. 70%) but only in warmer months. Seed dormancy c. six years.

Weed control Green manuring, or hand-weed before flowering stage and compost.

Herbal, culinary, cultural and folklore Iron-rich, used as a spinach-like vegetable; young leaves used as salad. Seed considered to be very nutritious in various parts of the world. Yellow and green dyes are obtained from this species.

Toxicity It is a nitrogen-accumulator, and nitrates are implicated in various serious health problems. It is inadvisable to consume any parts of the plant unless it has been organically grown.

1) Habit 2) flower heads

Common Orache *(Atriplex patula)*

Native. Annual. Height 30-90 cm. Lower leaves elongate but with broad, upward angled basal projections. Flowers monoecious, in groups on mealy stems, without petals or sepals: male flowers with conspicuous yellow anthers. The emergent style of each female flower is enclosed within a pair of tiny pointed bracts within which the seed develops. A somewhat variable species. Flowers August-October. Occurs on cultivated ground and waste places, inland and coastal. Widespread except for north-west Scotland and parts of northern Ireland. Avoids highly acidic ground.

Pollination Wind and sometimes insects, although often self-pollinated.

Regeneration strategy Only by seed. Of the many seeds shed, about half will not germinate until subsequent years and can remain viable for up to 30 years.

Weed control Green manuring, or hand-weed before flowering stage and compost.

Herbal, culinary, cultural and folklore A spinach relative and 'poor-man's pot herb', it was traditionally cooked and eaten in the same way. A British weed introduced to North America.

40

1) Flowering spikes 2) typical leaf form 3) male flowers 4) female flowers and fruits (pin scale 22 mm long)

Prostrate Orache, Spear-leaved Orache *(Atriplex prostrata)*

Native. Annual. Height 30-90 cm. Leaves smooth or mealy on underside only. Main leaves large, more or less broadly triangular, leaf margins sparsely toothed. Flowers monoecious, densely grouped on stems, without petals or sepals: male flowers with small yellow-red stamens, female flowers enclosed in tiny pointed bracts within which the seed develops. Flowering June-October. Common both inland and around the coast, south of the Mersey-Humber line. Above this line it is only frequent in coastal areas, growing in brackish to salty habitats and on shingle.

Pollination Primarily wind, but also visited by insects.

Regeneration strategy Only by seed which can remain dormant in the soil for at least five years.

Weed control Green manuring, or hand-weed before flowering stage and compost.

Herbal, culinary, cultural and folklore A spinach relative and 'poor-man's pot herb', it was traditionally cooked and eaten in the same way.

41

1) Young plant 2) habit 3) flowers 4) fruits

Fat Hen *(Chenopodium album)*

Native. Annual. Height up to 130 cm. A variable species, plant habit and leaf shape may differ between populations. The ribbed green stems may be striped white or red. Leaves more or less mealy, especially on underside; main leaves variable in shape, mostly triangular-rhomboid with upward angled basal margins. Flowers tiny, hermaphrodite, light yellow stamens conspicuous; sepals mealy, clustered densely on stems. Fruits very small and in clusters, each fruit a rounded five-segmented star, each segment containing a seed. Flowering June-October. Occurs throughout the whole of the British Isles, becoming less frequent in western and northern Scotland. An abundant annual weed of arable crops, waste ground, gardens, manure heaps and roadsides, growing best on rich, fertile clays and loams. Less common on calcareous soils and peat. A troublesome weed of root crops and Barley.

Pollination Wind, although some insect-pollination has been suggested.

Regeneration strategy By seed only. An average plant will produce about 3000 seeds, however, seeds from the same plant do not all germinate at the same time but at intervals over some weeks. Some may remain dormant for years until stimulated by light.

Weed control Green manuring, hand-weed before seed set, or follow current best practice for large invasions (see Bibliography and internet).

Herbal, culinary, cultural and folklore A spinach relative, and another 'poor-man's pot herb', it was traditionally cooked and eaten in the same way. A British weed introduced to North America. Remains of plants have been recovered from geographically wide-ranging UK archaeological sites from the Bronze Age and later. Seeds of this species (and also Corn Spurrey and Black-bindweed) are recorded from the stomach contents of Tollund Man (Denmark, early Celtic Iron Age – c. 400BC-200AD).

1) Seedling 2) young adult plant 3) stripy stems 4) flowering stem 5) fruits and seeds

Fig-leaved Goosefoot *(Chenopodium ficifolium)*

Native. Annual. Height 30-90 cm. Leaves notably elongated, widely flanged and upwardly angled at the basal leaf margins; overall greener and less mealy than *Chenopodium album*. Flowers tiny, hermaphrodite, light yellow stamens conspicuous; sepals mealy, clustered densely on stems. Fruits very small and in clusters, each fruit a rounded five-segmented star, each segment containing a seed. Flowering July-October. Occurs on waste ground and arable land. Especially common in southern England.

Pollination Wind.

Regeneration strategy By seed only. A large plant can produce over 130,000 seeds.

Weed control Green manuring, or hand-weed before flowering stage, and compost.

Herbal, culinary, cultural and folklore A spinach relative and 'poor-man's pot herb', it was traditionally cooked and eaten in same way.

43

1) Young plant 2) habit 3) typical leaf shape (upper and lower faces) 4) hermaphrodite flowers 5) flower heads 6) fruits

APIACEAE *(Carrot Family)*

Ground-elder, Goutweed, Bishop's Weed *(Aegopodium podagraria)*

Native. Rhizomatous perennial. Main leaves divided into three or six leaflets, each leaflet up to 40 mm long and 20 mm wide. Height of flowering stems 40-100 cm. Flower heads (*umbels*) 2-6 cm across. The main umbel comprises many smaller umbels, each bearing tiny white hermaphrodite flowers. Paired fruits ovoid. Flowering May-July. Occurs in waste places, a persistent weed in gardens and on roadsides and riverbanks.

Pollination A wide variety of small insects.

Regeneration strategies Seed; but more seriously, far-creeping rhizomes.

Weed control Remove and re-pot any plants to be retained from site first, making sure no pieces of Ground-elder root are included in the plant clump. Clear invaded area by digging out the rhizomatous roots – which are not deep-rooted – to the last scrap, repeating the procedure every two to three weeks during the growing season. All rhizomes should be destroyed. *Beware* – garden centres offer a variegated form of Ground-elder, which is likely to be just as invasive.

Herbal, culinary, cultural and folklore Formerly grown as a pot-herb, and used medicinally to treat gout. Boiled leaves reputedly make rather spicy and tolerable eating.

1) Young plants and root system 2) habit 3) flowers 4) ripe seed head

44

Fool's Parsley *(Aethusa cynapium)*

Native. Annual. Height 5-120 cm. Leaves mid-green, smooth, fern-like. Flower heads (*umbels*) 2-6 cm across: each small flower head within the main umbel has three to four downward pointing, longish leafy bracteoles. Individual flowers within head hermaphrodite, tiny, white. Paired fruits ovoid, ribbed. Flowering June-September, though can be as early as May or as late as December. Common and widely distributed throughout England; rarer in Scotland. Occurs on arable land and waste ground.

Pollination Self-pollination is probably the main strategy, small insects may also visit the flowers.

Regeneration strategy By seed alone. Produces many fruits/seeds which, when dry, are easily transported by wind or water.

Weed control Green manuring, hand-weed, or dig out before seed set and compost.

Herbal, culinary, cultural and folklore A British weed introduced to North America. The common name of Fool's Parsley refers to the hazard of misidentifying the foliage of this species for culinary parsley.

Toxicity All parts toxic. Animals seem instinctively to avoid eating it, probably because of its fetid odour, especially pressed or rubbed. The toxins are the alkaloids coniine and cynapine.

45

1) Seedling 2) habit 3) flowers, seed head and leaves 4) underside of green seed head 5) mature seed head and seeds

Cow Parsley *(Anthriscus sylvestris)*

Native. Usually biennial or short-lived perennial. Height 60-150 cm. Variably downy compound fern-like leaves, mid-green. Flower heads (*umbels*) 6-10 cm across, individual flowers very small, hermaphrodite, white. Paired fruits oblong, ovoid. Flowering April-June. Widespread and common throughout the British Isles, with the exception of parts of north-west Scotland. A common feature of road verges, field margins and hedgerows. It is the earliest flowering of the common and widespread members of this family, and one of the great joys of the English countryside.

46

Pollination Visited by a wide variety of short-tongued insects, including many species of flies. It is often considered to have a tang of stale (human) dung which is probably an attractant to some fly species.

Regeneration strategy Produces many fruits/seeds which, when dry, are easily transported by wind or water.

Weed control Green manuring, hand-weed, or dig out before seed set and compost or, for larger invasions, mowing is an effective method of control.

Herbal, culinary, cultural and folklore In spite of the innocent pleasure it provides today, it was previously associated with the Devil and some of its many common names reflect this: Devil's Meat (Yorkshire) and Devil's Parsley (Cheshire). Happily, it also enjoys more complimentary epithets such as Honiton Lace (Devon) and Moonlight (Wiltshire), though this last name may well reflect earlier associations with the occult.

1) Young plants 2) typical May population 3) young flower buds 4) flowers 5) green fruits 6) dry seed heads

Hemlock *(Conium maculatum)*

Native. Biennial. Height up to 2 m. Hollow purple-spotted stems, smooth, compound ferny leaves up to 30 cm long. Main flower head (*umbel*) 2-5 cm across, with 10-20 secondary stemmed umbels, individual flowers hermaphrodite, very small, white. Paired fruits rounded ovoid, strongly ribbed and slightly warty. Flowering June-July. Occurs in damp places, roadsides, often on heavy fertile soils throughout most of British Isles, often abundant in the south, becoming more coastal northwards and in Wales.

Pollination Mainly various species of flies and beetles.

Regeneration strategy Seed which mostly germinates in autumn, giving rise to overwintering rosettes of large, much dissected leaves, which have a 'sickly, mousey odour' if crushed.

Weed control Handle with care (and gloves), and follow current best practice for removal (see Bibliography and internet). Interestingly, rabbits are reported to browse Hemlock with impunity.

Herbal, culinary, cultural and folklore The toxicity of this species was known to the Ancients, and it is from this species that a fatal draught was made to be administered to the Greek philosopher Socrates. There are a number of records of this species from Roman occupation sites in the UK, providing strong evidence of its ancient introduction to Britain.

Toxicity All parts of plant are highly toxic and contain several alkaloids, the major one being coniine.

47

1) Habit 2) purple spotted stem 3) leaf 4) flowers 5) ripe seed head 6) ripe fruits

Giant Hogweed *(Heracleum mantegazzianum)*

Introduced neophyte, first record early-late 19th Century (opinions vary) from the Caucasus. Usually biennial, living longer if fruiting stage not achieved in second year. Height up to 3.5 m, sometimes as high as 5 m. Stems 5-10 cm in diameter, frequently red-spotted, with short, fine, stiff hairs. Lower compound, pinnate leaves up to 250 cm long. The flower head is a very large compound umbel up to 80 cm across; individual flowers hermaphrodite, small, white. Paired fruits ovate, flattish with three to four long, club-shaped dark lines (*vittae*) on the outer (*dorsal*) faces. Flowering June-July. Naturalised in a number of places throughout the British Isles, especially on waste ground, roadsides and along rivers. It also grows in open woodland, nutrient-rich natural grassland, and nutrient poor habitats. (Recent research suggests two closely related species are present: *Heracleum mantegazzianum* and *H. lehmannianum*.)

Pollination The floral table provided by the large umbel probably attracts a similar variety of insects to those visiting *Heracleum sphondylium*; certainly flies and bees and occasionally beetles.

Regeneration strategy Produces masses of seeds (9-11 mm long) which can blow in the wind for 2-10 m; longer-distance dispersal is achieved by water: seeds can float for up to 68 hours. Seed may remain viable for up to 15 years when stored dry, but field life is much shorter. It has been shown to germinate at c. 600 m above sea level in north-east England (in the Caucasus it occupies a wide habitat gradient of 70-1950 m above sea level).

Weed control Giant Hogweed is listed under Schedule 9 in the Wildlife and Countryside Act 1981, and it is an offence to plant or otherwise cause it to grow in the wild. It is also classified as controlled waste. For small, unestablished invasions, dig out and destroy young plants and their roots (every last piece!), cut off flowering stems before they set seed, and destroy. For large invasions seek professional advice immediately and follow current best practice (see Bibliography and internet). Report occurrences of this species to the landowner and your local Wildlife Trust.

Herbal, culinary, cultural and folklore Originally introduced into UK as a garden ornamental. Decorative use of seeds and flower heads.

Toxicity Chemicals in the sap can cause photo-dermatitis: the skin becomes very sensitive to sunlight, which may cause blistering, pigmentation or long-lasting scars.

48

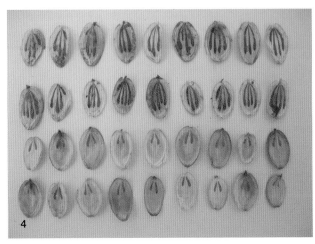

1) Young green leaves 2) habit and flowers 3) seed heads 4) dry fruits and vittas (outer and inner)

Hogweed *(Heracleum sphondylium)*

Native. Biennial-perennial. Height 50 cm-2 m, sometimes as high as 3 m. Stems with short stiff hairs. Leaves large with one to three paired leaflets. The flower head is a large, flat, compound umbel, 5-10 cm, sometimes up to 15 cm across. Individual flowers hermaphrodite, very small, white, greenish-white or, less commonly, pink. Paired fruits ovate, flattish with usually four narrow, longish club-shaped dark lines *(vittae)* on the outer *(dorsal)* faces, extending roughly half the length of the fruit. Flowering June-September. Occurs in grassy areas, banks, roadsides, may show a preference for chalk and open woodland. Widespread throughout the British Isles. Its flowering comes just after Cow Parsley – a handsome, more robust plant, following the former plant's more delicate 'froth'.

Pollination Of all flower inflorescences, these are probably the most fascinating for insect watching: the floral table provided by the large compound umbel attracts a wide variety of insects, including many species of thrips, beetles, sawflies, flies, bees, wasps. Some are visiting for pollen or nectar, some to hunt other insects, and some just for a rest. It is also self-fertile.

Regeneration strategy Produces masses of seeds (7-8 mm long) which can blow in the wind for 2-10 m. Longer-distance dispersal is achieved by water: seeds can float for up to 68 hours. Experimental testing suggests that the seed does not have long dormancy, it is unlikely to germinate after five years.

Weed control Weed out or green manure young plants. For large invasions mowing is an effective method of control. Otherwise follow current best practice for large invasions (see Bibliography and internet).

Herbal, culinary, cultural and folklore Was used for cattle fodder and fattening hogs. The stems were sometimes dried to extract a sugary substance. More recently, early 20th Century, attempts were made in the UK to produce sugar from the stems but results were not cost-effective – 40 lbs of stalks produced 1 lb of sugar.

Toxicity Like Giant Hogweed (see previous entry), chemicals in the sap can cause photo-dermatitis.

49

1) Young leaves 2) enlarged sheathing leaf stalks 3) flowers with insect visitors 4) flowering 5) pink flowers 6) ripe fruiting head

ARALIACEAE *(Ivy Family)*

Ivy *(Hedera helix)*

Native. Perennial. Climbing stems up to 30 m in height. Climbing stem leaves vary somewhat in appearance between populations, although basically they are palmate, and three- to five-lobed, each lobe being more or less triangular. The leaves of the flowering branches are different, having an ovate or rhombic outline. Flowers are very small, hermaphrodite, petals light green and radially symmetric, in semi-rounded inflorescences. Fruits 6-9 mm long, globose, with a lid-like top. Flowering September-November, though not flowering in shade. Widely distributed throughout the British Isles in hedges and woodland. Very shade tolerant, but found in a wide variety of habitats to altitudes of c. 600 m, except for the most waterlogged or acidic soils.

Additional notes *Hedera helix* is one of two British species of Ivy, the Irish Ivy, *Hedera hibernica*, being more frequent in the west. The variability of outline between the palmate climbing stem leaves of different Ivy populations, plus the difference between the palmate leaves and the simpler ovate-rhomboid outline of the flowering branch leaves has encouraged the erroneous idea that there are a number of British species, not just two.

Pollination Various flies, including the rare thick-headed fly *Leopoldius signatus* (family Conopidae), late-flying bees, ichneumon wasps, wasps, and butterflies. Ivy provides an important source of early winter nectar.

Regeneration strategies By seed, but more problematically, the stems have adhesive roots that allow them to attach to trees, rocks and walls with remarkable efficiency. Allowing Ivy to grow on a healthy tree is unlikely to kill it – Ivy-clad trees are more often trees already diseased or in decline.

Weed control After cutting back, Ivy can be shredded, composted, or burned. For best practice in managing large scale invasions seek expert advice and guidance (see Bibliography for a selection of useful websites).

Herbal, culinary, cultural and folklore As a reputed cure for whooping cough, children were given milk in cups made from Ivy wood (Shropshire) or Holly (parts of Hampshire); Ivy is strongly associated with Holly (*Ilex aquifolium*) in winter rituals and celebrations, and both are considered to have protective properties from evil. Ivy is also associated with fidelity in marriage, and has a long standing tradition of re-birth and immortality. Leaves (yellow) and berries (pink, greens, and brown) used for producing a range of dye colours.

Toxicity The berries are poisonous, and other parts of the plant may cause dermatitis.

50

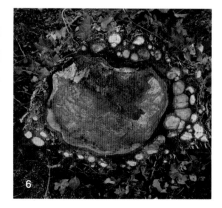

1) Seedling 2) climbing leaves 3) flowering shoot leaves 4) flowers 5) fruits 6) stems surrounding felled Oak tree

ASTERACEAE *(Daisy Family)*

Corn Chamomile *(Anthemis arvensis)*

Native. Annual. Height 12-50 cm. Stems and feathery leaves softly hairy, grey-green. Overall diameter of inflorescence: 2-3 cm, scarcely scented. Ray florets white, numerous, female (c.12-14 mm), disc rounded-conical, florets yellow, tubular and hermaphrodite. Fruits (*achenes*) 2-3 mm long, horn-shaped, ribbed. Flowering June-July. Scattered through southern England, though rare in the west, Scotland and Ireland. Prefers well-drained sandy, or even better, calcareous soils. Of the four annual mayweeds of cereal crops, this is the least frequent.

Pollination A wide variety of insects, notably flies and beetles. Also self-pollinates.

Regeneration strategy By seed only, scattered locally near plant; germination said to be improved if it has passed through the digestive tract of a bird.

Weed control Generally a field, rather than garden, weed: follow best organic practice. In common with other mayweeds, this species is susceptible to many herbicides. Take advice on correct identification and local distribution before spraying herbicide, as this is the least frequently encountered of the four annual mayweeds.

Herbal, culinary, cultural and folklore Flower heads of this species can, like Dyer's Chamomile (*Anthemis tinctoria*), be used to obtain yellow dye tones.

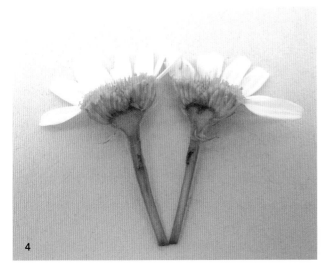

1) Flowering habit 2) leaf close-up showing slightly hairy leaves 3) habit – flowers and leaves 4) flower sectioned to show solid centre of receptacle
5) old flower head with hermaphrodite flowers (left) and ribbed achenes (centre)

Stinking Chamomile, Stinking Mayweed *(Anthemis cotula)*

Native. Annual. Stems 20-60 cm, stems and leaves green and sparsely hairy. Plant has a generally foetid scent when crushed. Overall diameter of inflorescence: 1.2-2.5 cm. Ray florets white, usually sterile, disc domed, conical in older flowers, florets yellow, tubular and hermaphrodite. Fruits (*achenes*) c. 2 mm long, elongate, warty (*tubercled*). Flowering May-September. Locally common in England and Wales, but rare in Scotland and Ireland. Favours arable land, heavy soils, base rich clays and loams, farm yards and waste ground.

Pollination Chiefly hoverflies.

Regeneration strategy By seed alone; 550-12,000 seeds per plant are scattered locally, or spread by clothing, feet and wheels. They germinate between autumn and spring.

Weed control Hand-weed or green manure young plants before flowering. The species is more or less resistant to phenoxyacetic acids but can be controlled by more recently introduced herbicides.

Herbal, culinary, cultural and folklore The juice is very acrid and is said to have blistered the hands, arms, feet and chests of the men working in the fields, scything and gathering the corn into stooks. Apparently the pain from skin blisters could be so bad that those affected could not work again for some days. Growing and dried, the plant is said to repel mice and fleas. Flowers can, like Dyer's Chamomile (*Anthemis tinctoria*), be used to obtain yellow tones of dye.

Toxicity Considered toxic to horses, dogs, cats and guinea pigs; can cause skin allergies.

52

1) Flowering habit 2) stems and leaves 3) habit – flowers and leaves 4) flower heads, above and below
5) old flower head with hermaphrodite florets and ripe, warty seeds

Scentless Mayweed *(Tripleurospermum inodorum)*

Native. Annual to biennial. Height 10-60 cm. Leaves finely divided into numerous fine, almost thread-like, green, glossy segments. Flower heads scarcely scented, overall diameter: 1.5-4 cm, sometimes up to 5 cm. Ray florets female, white and spreading, disc conical, florets yellow, tubular, hermaphrodite. Fruit *(achene)* 2-3 mm long, distinguished by a rim at its top which has two circular darkish spots (oil glands) on one side, while the opposing side of the seed has three broad corky ribs. Flowering July-September, sometimes as late as October. Widely distributed throughout most of the British Isles, excepting parts of the Scottish Highlands and central Ireland, but less frequent on chalk. Recorded growing up to 230 m above sea level.

Additional notes *Tripleurospermum maritimum* is a closely related species but is perennial with rather more fleshy leaf segments and seeds with broad, inflated, contiguous ribs and two elongated oil glands. It has a more or less coastal distribution, infrequently appearing on roadside verges.

Pollination Strongly self-incompatible. Insect-pollinated and a source of nectar and pollen for several beneficial insects. Host to several insect pests.

Regeneration strategy Seed alone: flowers produce huge amounts of seed, which fall in the vicinity of the plant. The seeds have long dormancy/viability.

Weed control For small outbreaks, hand-weed before flowering stage and compost. For advice on managing larger invasions check selected websites in the Bibliography.

Herbal, culinary, cultural and folklore The sap contains an anti-viral agent that inhibits the growth of polio and herpes viruses. It is a weed of man-made environments, not palatable to livestock, and avoided by hens. Flower heads of this species can be used to obtain yellow dye tones.

53

1) Young plants 2) flowering habit 3) flower size variation 4) old flower head with hermaphrodite flowers and ribbed seeds (achenes)

Scented Mayweed, Wild Chamomile *(Matricaria chamomilla/M. recutita)*

Native. Annual. Hairless stems 10-40 cm in height, sometimes up to 60 cm. Feathery leaves, pleasant smelling. Overall diameter of inflorescence: 1.2-2.2 cm, sometimes up to 2.5 cm. Ray florets white, female, central disc hollow, conical from outset, disc florets yellow, tubular and hermaphrodite. Fruit *(achenes)* 1-2 mm long, slightly curved, four or five ribs on inner face. Flowering June-July, sometimes as late as September. Widely distributed throughout most of England, but scarce in the south-west and Wales and rare in Scotland and Ireland. A frequent weed of arable land and waste ground. Prefers sandy or loamy soils.

54

Pollination Various bees and flies, including soldier flies (family Stratiomyidae).

Regeneration strategy By seed only. Seed shed locally to the plant.

Weed control For small outbreaks, hand-weed before flowering stage and compost.

Herbal, culinary, cultural and folklore Also known as German Chamomile, it is sometimes used as a substitute for true Chamomile *(Chamaemelum nobile)* as an aid to sleep, it has anti-inflammatory and bactericidal qualities.

1) Large population in wheatfield 2) flowering stems 3) flower heads 4) flower head sectioned to show hollow receptacle
5) old hermaphrodite flowers and curved four- to five-ribbed seeds (achenes)

Pineapple-weed, Rayless Mayweed *(Matricaria discoidea)*

Introduced neophyte, first recorded in 1871. Probable origin north-east Asia, but now well-established in many temperate regions around the world. Annual. Fibrous roots, erect smooth stems, height 5-30 cm, much-branched. Mid-green stemless leaves, smooth, oblong, strongly indented with central midrib, strong acrid smell when crushed. Overall diameter of inflorescence: 0.5-1 cm, sometimes up to 1.5 cm. Florets all alike, yellow, ray-less, hermaphrodite. Fruit *(achenes)* 1-5 mm long, with four shallow ribs. Flowering June-July. Common throughout the British Isles. An abundant weed of verges, tracks, waysides and waste places.

Pollination Hoverflies (Syrphidae), bees.

Regeneration strategy A single flower head produces c. 135-160 seeds, these are dispersed locally from the plant by rain wash and mud, and subsequently spread by feet and wheeled vehicles.

Weed control For small outbreaks, hand-weed before flowering stage and compost.

Herbal, culinary, cultural and folklore Although present in some counties prior to 1900, the national spread of this weed is directly linked to the rise in popularity of the motor car and to muddy roads and the increasingly long distances more people could travel. The common name, Pineapple-weed, originated prior to its introduction to the UK. The name is usually attributed to its acrid smell, but to many, not at all like the scent of pineapple. Another possibility is that the name refers to the flower heads, which look rather like tiny pineapples. Flower heads of this species can, like Dyer's Chamomile (*Anthemis tinctoria*), be used to obtain yellow dye tones.

55

1) A young plant 2) habit 3) flower heads 4) old flower head with hermaphrodite florets and four-ribbed seeds (achenes)

Corn Marigold *(Glebionis segetum)*

Native. Annual with tap root. Stems smooth, height 20-50 cm. Leaves 2-8 cm long, smooth, bluish-green, slightly fleshy, coarsely toothed, and mostly deeply lobed. Overall diameter of inflorescence: 3.5-6.5 cm. Ray florets yellow, female, disc florets yellow, tubular and hermaphrodite. Fruits (*achenes*) 2.5 mm long, pale, strongly ribbed. Flowering June-August. Locally common, chiefly as a weed of root and broad-leaved crops, particularly on fertile, light acidic, sandy or loamy nitrogen-rich soils. Less troublesome than previously due to increased use of herbicides.

56

Pollination In common with all daisy-like flowers, this species attracts a wide range of insects.

Regeneration strategy Seed only: flowers produce huge amounts of seed, which fall in the vicinity of the plant. The seeds have long dormancy/viability.

Weed control Mostly occurring as a field weed. Follow current best practice for large invasions (see Bibliography and internet).

Herbal, culinary, cultural and folklore A striking flower, worth growing in the garden. However, this species must have been a serious weed during the 13th Century: in Scotland a law of Alexander II stated that if a farmer allowed so much as a single plant to produce seed among his crops he would be fined a sheep! Garlands were hung up for Midsummer, probably for St. John's Eve.

1) Adult leaves 2) a large drift of flowers 3) flower heads, above and below 4) old flower head with hermaphrodite flowers and strongly ribbed seeds (achenes)

Daisy *(Bellis perennis)*

Native. Perennial with stout roots. Height (flowering stems) 3-8 cm, sometimes up to 12 cm. Oval (spoon-shaped) leaves 2-4 cm long, sometimes up to 8 cm, mid-green with more or less straight or slightly wavy margins. Overall diameter of inflorescence: 1.5-2.5 cm. Ray florets female, white (often pink underneath), disc florets yellow, tubular and hermaphrodite. Characteristically inflorescences close at night, and in dull weather. Fruits *(achenes)* 1.5-2 mm long, oval, flat. Flowering January-December. Common throughout the British Isles (to altitudes of 900 m). Found in short grassland on a wide range of soils. Highly tolerant of being trampled on or mown.

Pollination Chiefly by hoverflies. Also pollinated by short-tongued flies and solitary bees such as *Halictus* species. The Tawny Mining-bee *(Andrena fulva)* often visits in spring.

Regeneration strategy Short prostrate shoots develop from the axils of some of the rosette leaves and short horizontal shoots may also develop, expanding daisy patches, notably in lawns. The flowers produce numerous seeds which are shed locally.

Weed control Shallow-rooted so dig out where not wanted, preferably before flowering stage, and compost.

Herbal, culinary, cultural and folklore Much beloved weed of childhood, notably for making daisy-chains. Often tolerated in lawns for its prettiness. In the Victorian era the Daisy signified innocence in their fashionable *Language of Flowers*. Robert Burns immortalised this species in *To a Mountain Daisy* (1786). The species is only found in Europe as far east as the Caucasus.

57

1) Young foliage 2) flowering habit 3) a flower head 4) closed flower heads – sometimes the reverse of the outer florets is pink
5) seed heads – note seeds (achenes) lying on the green bracts

Smooth Hawk's-beard *(Crepis capillaris)*

Native. Usually annual, occasionally biennial. Erect, branching smooth flower stems, height 20-90 cm. A basal rosette of long, narrow, slightly hairy, light-to-mid-green leaves (5-25 cm long), with smooth or slightly lobed/toothed margins. Overall diameter of inflorescence: 1-1.3 cm (less frequently larger than 2.5 cm). Florets all hermaphrodite, bright yellow, orange-tinted on reverse. Fruits (*achenes*) 1.5-2.5 mm long, ribbed, with stalkless pappus. Flowering June-September. Frequent throughout the British Isles, a common plant of grassland, roadsides, heaths, commons and waste places.

58

Pollination Mainly flies and bees. Self-incompatible.

Regeneration strategy Masses of parachute seeds easily carried by wind currents. Seeds germinate in spring or autumn.

Weed control For small outbreaks, hand-weed before flowering stage and compost.

Herbal, culinary, cultural and folklore Young leaves can be used in salads.

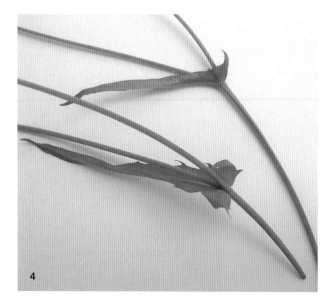

1) Well-established basal leaves 2) flowering group 3) flowering stem 4) flower stem and leaves 5) seed heads and seeds (achenes) with stalkless pappus

Cat's Ear *(Hypochaeris radicata)*

Native. Perennial. Main leaves 7-25 cm long, with short, rough, simple hairs, and arranged in a basal rosette, from which one or several 20-60 cm long smooth flower stems arise more or less vertically. The stems usually have a few scales near the flower heads. Overall diameter of inflorescence: 2.5-4 cm. Ray florets only, all hermaphrodite, bright yellow with a greenish-purple tinged underside. Fruits *(achenes)* 4-4.5 mm long, orange, ribbed, finely warty, with long-stalked pappus. Flowering June-September. Common throughout the British Isles in meadows, pastures, grassy dunes, waysides, parkland and lawns. A preference for mildly acidic sands and clays, less common on chalk.

Pollination Pollinated by a variety of insects including slender, long-legged snipe flies of sub-order Brachycera (family Rhagionidae). Self-incompatible.

Regeneration strategy Seed alone. The parachute seeds are easily carried by wind currents. Ants have been observed carrying the seeds.

Weed control For small outbreaks, hand-weed before flowering stage and compost. It can be a serious problem in cut grass, as it survives regular mowing, and will spread and survive as rather flattened leaf rosettes.

Herbal, culinary, cultural and folklore Sheep browse the shoots and pigs will dig up the plants to eat the roots. Used in traditional medicine as an anti-inflammatory, anti-diuretic and anti-cancer medication, and for treating kidney problems.

59

1) Basal leaves 2) flowering group 3) flower head – note sparse stem scales 4) seed head and seeds (achenes) with long-stalked pappus

Mouse-ear Hawkweed *(Pilosella officinarum)*

Native. Perennial. Root a long slender rhizome and, in addition, numerous above-ground stolons terminating in overwintering rosettes. Flowering stems 5-30 cm long. Leaves small, ovate, with pointed tips, downy white on lower surface, green above, also with sparse stiff white hairs on upper and lower surfaces, particularly noticeable on upper surface. Flower heads are a clear lemon yellow, outer florets often streaked dull crimson below (c. 1-2 cm diameter). Ray florets only, may be female-only in *apomictic* clones, or hermaphrodite. Fruit (*achenes*) 2 mm long, with stalkless pappus. Flowering May-August, sometimes as late as October. Locally common throughout the British Isles, but scarce in the fenlands of East Anglia and parts of northern Scotland. Occurs in grassy pastures, heaths, short turf, walls, banks and rocks, on dry well-drained acidic or calcareous soils.

60

Pollination In polyploid races (virtual clones of the parent plant) seed is produced without sexual fusion (*apomixis*), or by insect-pollination in outbreeding plants. Sexually reproducing flowers are self-incompatible, and are visited by a variety of insects, including beetles, for example *Oedemera nobilis*, and the Flea Bee (*Phthiria pulicaria*).

Regeneration strategy Seed or vegetative spread. Parachute seed produced sexually from heteromorphic flowers, or without sexual fusion. Also leafy rosettes arise from above ground stolons.

Weed control For small outbreaks, hand-weed before flowering stage and compost.

Herbal, culinary, cultural and folklore Traditionally used in herbal medicine for its astringent, expectorant and diuretic properties. Used for respiratory problems, e.g. asthma, bronchitis, coughs, diarrhoea and inflamed kidney infections. It was said that if a horse were given Mouse-ear before being shod, the animal would feel no pain.

1) Low-spreading foliage 2) leaf rosette – note long, stiff hairs 3) flowers 4) seed head

Dandelion *(Taraxacum officinale)*

Native. Perennial with long tap root, on which 'adventitious' shoots readily develop. The root exudes milky juice when cut or damaged. Flowering stem hollow, smooth or hairy, height c. 30-50 cm, depending on soil and exposure. Leaves soft, mid-to-deep green, variously deeply lobed, sometimes with pinkish midrib, especially near base. Flower heads bright yellow, 2-5 cm diameter, florets all hermaphrodite. Fruits (*achenes*) 2-3.5 mm long, cylindrical, ribbed, long-stalked pappus (two to four times the length of the achene). Flowering mainly March-May, but can be found all year. *Taraxacum* is a widespread, much studied, genus of well over 200 microspecies, known throughout the British Isles to an altitude of 1175 m. Most common in meadows and pastures, roadsides, waste places and lawns.

Pollination All set seed *apomictically* i.e. without need for pollination.

Regeneration strategies Masses of windborne parachute seeds, and deep tap roots which sometimes seem almost impossible to dig out.

Weed control For small outbreaks, hand-weeding before flowering stage, deep-dig out tap roots and destroy or, follow current best practice for large invasions (see Bibliography and internet).

Herbal, culinary, cultural and folklore Dandelions need full sun to flower: pick a bunch, put them in a jar of water indoors and they will close up. They are, perhaps, best known as a diuretic – to the delight of children one of the Dandelion's commonest local names is Piss-in-the-bed or, in France *Pis-en-lit*. Dandelion is derived from the French name *Dent-de-lion* (meaning Lion's tooth). The roots are used for making Dandelion 'coffee', at least since the mid-19th Century. In continental Europe the leaves, often blanched, are used as a salad ingredient. In the UK the flower heads are used for making Dandelion wine. It is one of the weeds introduced into the USA by British immigrants.

61

1) Tap roots and young leaves 2) young leaf rosette 3) flower head 4) habit 5) seed head

Goat's-beard, Jack-go-to-bed-at-noon *(Tragopogon pratensis)*

Native. Annual to perennial. Long brownish tap root that exudes milky juice. Flowering stems erect, 30-70 cm long. Leaves grass-like, somewhat sheathing at base, mid-green with a conspicuous white midrib; the first leaves (cotyledons) of the seedlings are the longest and narrowest known for any British member of the Daisy family. Flower heads yellow, or pale yellow, 3-5 cm diameter. Ray florets only, all hermaphrodite, outer florets usually larger/longer than inner florets, but notably shorter than the long pointed green bracts of the involucre. Fruits (*achenes*) 10-12 mm long, with very large, long-stalked (10-12 mm long) feathery pappus. Flowering June-July. Distributed through most of England (less common in the south-west), Wales and southern Scotland. Scarce in the Highlands and in Ireland. It favours rough grassland, roadside verges, hedge banks, meadows, pastureland and sand dunes. In the Pennines it is recorded to an altitude of 370 m.

62

Pollination A variety of generalist bees and flies. Also self-pollination.

Regeneration strategy Seed alone: masses of windborne parachute seeds.

Weed control For small outbreaks, hand-weed before flowering stage, making sure to dig out tap roots and destroy.

Herbal, culinary, cultural and folklore The flowers close around midday, hence many of its local names, including Jack-go-to-bed-at-noon. Closely related to Salsify (*Tragopogon porrifolius*) which has mauve flower heads, and has long been grown for its roots which are boiled and eaten with butter or cream, especially in continental Europe.

1) Seedlings 2) young plant 3) habit 4) flower head 5) seed heads 6) achenes with long-stalked pappus

Creeping Thistle *(Cirsium arvense)*

Native. Perennial. Spreads via rapid growth of long underground stems, height 30-90 cm, sometimes up to 150 cm. Leaves long and narrow, mid-to-deep green, smooth, or slightly cottony above, deeply lobed and spiny, notably at tips of lobes. Plants generally dioecious, although hermaphrodite florets occur occasionally. Overall diameter of inflorescence: 1.5-2.5 cm. Flower heads short-stalked, dull pale purple or whitish: male flower heads (disc-type florets only) much more rounded and with more projecting flowers than female flower heads (disc-type florets only). Fruits *(achenes)* c. 4 mm long, dark brown, with a stalkless feathery pappus. Flowering July-September. Widely distributed throughout the British Isles in a wide range of habitats, excepting the most acidic.

Pollination Visited by a wide variety of insects.

Regeneration strategies By seed and vegetative spread: masses of parachute seeds easily carried by wind currents, and rapidly spreading underground rhizomes.

Weed control A serious agricultural pest, one of the five harmful weeds controlled by law: follow current official advice (see Bibliography for useful websites). Rhizomes should be dug out with the utmost care and destroyed.

Insect weed control *Urophora cardui* (the Canada Thistle Gall Fly) is, in fact, an indigenous European fruit fly introduced to North America from Europe to control populations of its host plant *C. arvense*. The flies lay their eggs on the thistle stems. As the larvae hatch they burrow inside the thistle stem and form a gall (these can be quite large – 4-6 cm or more) where they will continue their development, reaching 98% of their body weight before appearing as adult flies. Pupation takes 24-35 days. From June-October the adult flies leave the galls by tunnelling their way out.

Herbal, culinary, cultural and folklore A British weed, probably introduced to the USA by British emigrants.

63

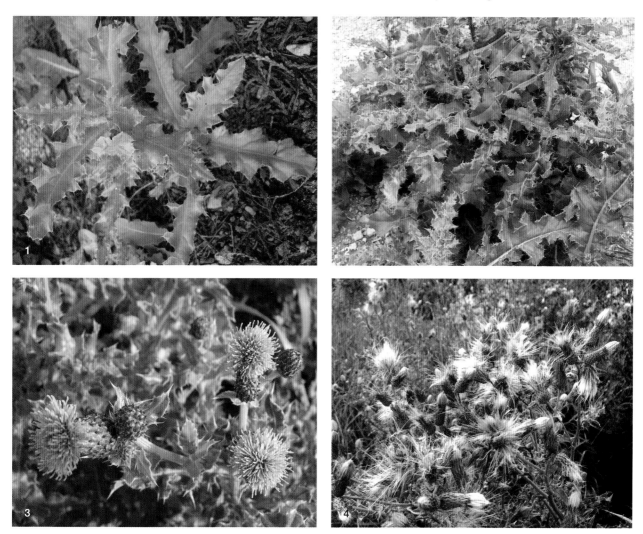

1) Young plants 2) pre-flowering habit 3) flower heads 4) seed heads

Marsh Thistle *(Cirsium palustre)*

Native. Usually biennial. Stem height 30-150 cm. Leaves narrow, mid-green, spear-shaped and continuously spiny-winged, narrowing to a short stalk-like base, with toothed, spiny lobes and undulate hairy margins. Overall diameter of inflorescence: 1.5-2 cm. Florets all tubular, deep reddish-mauve, all hermaphrodite. Fruits *(achenes)* c. 3 mm long, pale beige, with a stalkless feathery pappus. Flowering June-September, sometimes as early as May or as late as October. Abundant throughout the British Isles in marshes, damp grassland, often at a spot where spring water occurs, hedgerows and woods. A widely distributed species in the northern hemisphere as far as Asiatic Russia.

64

Pollination Can self-pollinate, but visited by a wide variety of insects, including bees, flies and butterflies. A good late-flowering resource for a number of insects.

Regeneration strategy Seed only: masses of parachute seeds easily carried by wind currents.

Weed control Follow current best practice, especially for large invasions (see Bibliography and internet).

Herbal, culinary, cultural and folklore Like the Spear Thistle, its seeds are attractive to Goldfinches, Linnets and other small birds. This species is sometimes suggested as the model for the Scottish Thistle but, although spiny, it lacks the sword-like characteristics of *Cirsium vulgare*.

1) Large overwintering leaf crown 2) habit 3) spiny winged stem 4) flower head 5) seed head

Spear Thistle *(Cirsium vulgare)*

Native. Biennial with long tap root. Height 30-150 cm. Basal leaves 15-30 cm long, oblong, lobed with stout, spiny tips, mid-green and hairy. Leaves narrow into short, stalk-like base. Overall diameter of inflorescence: 3-5 cm. Florets pale reddish-mauve, all hermaphrodite. Fruits *(achenes)* c. 3.5 mm long, blotchy yellow-black, with a stalkless, feathery pappus. Flowering July-October. Common throughout the British Isles in fields, waysides, gardens and waste places.

Pollination Visited by a wide variety of insects, notably long-tongued bees, flies and butterflies.

Regeneration strategy Masses of parachute seeds easily carried by wind currents.

Weed control A serious agricultural pest, one of the five harmful weeds controlled by law. Follow current official advice (see Bibliography for useful websites). Insect weed control using *Urophora stylata*, another species of European fruit fly (which feeds on the developing seeds in the flower heads of Spear Thistle) was trialled in North America, Australia and South Africa, during the 1990s. Although effective in some conditions, overall the results have had a mixed reception in terms of sustainable efficacy.

Herbal, culinary, cultural and folklore This species is generally considered to be the model for the Scottish emblem, in spite of the Scotch (or Woolly) Thistle being the common name of another species: *Onopordum acanthium*. The reasons are twofold: 1) *Onopordum acanthium* has always been rare in Scotland, and 2) the characteristics of the heraldic Scottish Thistle are much more akin to those of the Spear Thistle. Furthermore, although the Woolly Thistle is a handsome plant, it is much less spiny, and the leaves are not sword-like in appearance. Goldfinches and Linnets feed on the seeds.

65

1) Young plant 2) young flower bud 3) flower head 4) flower heads and seed heads

Lesser Burdock, Common Burdock *(Arctium minus)*

Native. Biennial. Long stout tap roots. Flowering stem height 60-120 cm, sometimes up to 130 cm; large mid-green leaves, felted white underneath. Overall diameter of inflorescence: 1.5-3 cm, florets all tubular and hermaphrodite. Fruits (*achenes*) c. 5 mm long, speckled, dark brown, elongate-ovoid, slightly curved with a stalkless, bristly pappus. Flowering July-September. Widely distributed throughout the British Isles except for parts of the Scottish Highlands. Common in scrub and open woodland, wood margins, clearings, roadsides, canal banks and waste places.

Pollination Bees and butterflies.

Regeneration strategy By seed only. The spiny, seed-filled fruiting heads catch on animal fur and clothing, and are then dispersed.

Weed control Green manure, or weed out small invasions. Follow current best practice for large invasions (see Bibliography and internet).

Herbal, culinary, cultural and folklore Once a favourite with small boys who threw the prickly buds (burs) to stick on each other's clothes, its spiny hooked fruits were the inspiration for Velcro (invented in 1941 by Georges de Mestral). The herbalist John Gerard records that the young stalks can be peeled and eaten raw or boiled in meat broth to "increase seed and stir up lust"; Dandelion and Burdock, a popular drink consumed in the British Isles since the Middle Ages, was originally a type of light mead, but has evolved into a non-alcoholic soft drink. Valued in herbal medicine and rich in minerals, especially iron. Used medicinally as a diuretic and blood cleanser.

66

1) Young plants 2) leaves of pre-flowering plants 3) flowering plant habit 4) a very tall plant 5) flower heads 6) seeds (achenes) with short, bristly pappus

Perennial Sow-thistle, Field Milk-thistle *(Sonchus arvensis)*

Native. Perennial. Erect hollow stems 60-150 cm in height, covered in short, yellow, glandular hairs. Stems exude white latex when freshly cut. Leaves elongate-triangular and deeply lobed, very prickly, glossy and deep green above, paler and dull below. The leaf bases clasp the stems. Of the three weedy Milk-thistles, this species has the largest and showiest flower heads: bright yolk-yellow, 4-5 cm diameter, ray florets only, hermaphrodite. Fruits *(achenes)* 4-5 mm long, horn-shaped, faces strongly ribbed, mid-brown with a stalkless long-filamented pappus. Flowering July-October, often a happy last reminder of summer on roadside banks. A lowland plant, common throughout most the British Isles, but scarcer or absent further north and in the Scottish Highlands. Can be found on banks, roadsides, arable land, stream sides, drift lines, on salt and brackish marshes.

Pollination Bees, flies, butterflies, beetles. Also self-pollinated.

Regeneration strategies Seed and vegetative spread: parachute seeds which ripen August-October, and far-creeping, bud-bearing roots. The second characteristic is not shared with the annual species of Milk-thistle.

Weed control For small outbreaks, hand-weed before flowering stage and compost. Follow current best practice for large invasions (see Bibliography and internet).

Herbal, culinary, cultural and folklore The leaves of Milk-thistles were used for their anti-inflammatory properties, and a tea made from the roots was used traditionally for relief of asthma and coughs. One of the weeds introduced to the USA by British immigrants.

67

1) Young plants 2) habit 3) stem leaves 4) flower and involucre glands 5) seed head

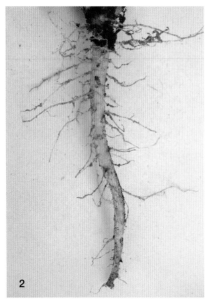

Prickly Sow-thistle, Spiny Sow-thistle *(Sonchus asper)*

Native. Annual, often overwintering, with long pale tap root. Stout, erect, smooth stems that exude white latex when freshly cut, height 20-150 cm. Leaves dark, glossy green above, deeply lobed with short prickly edges. The elaborately rounded, ear-like leaf bases clasp the stems. Flower heads bright yellow, 2-2.5 cm diameter: ray florets only, hermaphrodite. Fruits *(achenes)* 2.5-4 mm long, light mid-brown, curved elongate-ovate, flattish with stalkless long-filamented pappus. Flowering June-August, sometimes as late as December. Common throughout the British Isles, apart from the Scottish Highlands, especially typical of cultivated soil, waysides and waste places. Often found growing near *Sonchus oleraceus*.

Pollination Mostly pollinated by bees and hoverflies.

Regeneration strategy Seed alone: parachute seeds.

Weed control For small outbreaks, hand-weed before flowering stage and compost. Follow current best practice for large invasions (see Bibliography and internet).

Herbal, culinary, cultural and folklore Another common name of this species is Field Milk-thistle and alludes to the white latex from the cut stems, characteristic of all four British species (the fourth species, *Sonchus palustris,* is uncommon and not considered a weed).

68

1) Young plant 2) tap root 3) habit 4) stem leaves 5) flower head and involucre 6) seed heads, achenes with stalkless pappus

Smooth Sow-thistle, Milk-thistle *(Sonchus oleraceus)*

Native. Annual, often overwintering, with long pale tap root. Stout, erect, smooth stems, sometimes purplish, exuding white latex when freshly cut, height 20-150 cm. Leaves soft, light-to-mid-green above, not glossy, sometimes with a purplish midrib, deeply lobed. Upper part of leaf frequently broader and less-deeply lobed. Leaf margins softly toothed, never prickly; the leaf bases acute, and clasp the stems. Flower heads yellow, or pale yellow, 2-2.5 cm diameter: ray florets only, hermaphrodite. Fruits *(achenes)* curved elongate-ovate, flattish, light mid-brown with stalkless long-filamented pappus. Flowering June-August. Common throughout the British Isles, apart from the Scottish Highlands, especially in cultivated soil, waysides and waste places. Often found growing near *Sonchus asper*.

Pollination Mostly pollinated by bees and hoverflies.

Regeneration strategy Seed alone: parachute seeds.

Weed control For small outbreaks, hand-weed before flowering stage and compost. Follow current best practice for large invasions (see Bibliography and internet).

Herbal, culinary, cultural and folklore A favourite food of rabbits and hares, as reflected in some of its local names: Hare's Colewort, Hare's Lettuce, Hare's Thistle, Hare's Palace, Rabbit's Meat and Rabbit's Victuals.

1) Young plant 2) tap root 3) habit 4) stem leaves 5) flower head and involucre 6) seed heads, seeds (achenes) with stalkless pappus

69

Prickly Lettuce *(Lactuca serriola)*

Native. Annual or biennial. Stiffly erect, leafy stem, height 30-200 cm. Stems and leaves exude white latex. Leaves light-to-mid-green, oblong-ovate, upper leaves smooth with finely toothed margins, lobed bases and white midribs, spiny on underside. Overall diameter of inflorescence: 8-13 mm. Ray florets only, light yellow, often violet-tipped, all hermaphrodite. Fruits (*achenes*) elongate-ovate, angled-ribbed, light brown when ripe, long-filamented, with stalked pappus. Flowering July-September. Locally abundant in waste ground and dry stony places, roadsides, on walls, banks and dunes in southern and eastern England and in Wales. Rare or absent in Scotland, western Wales and Ireland.

Pollination Usually self-pollinated.

Regeneration strategy Seed only: parachute seeds easily carried by wind currents.

Weed control For small outbreaks, hand-weed before flowering stage and compost.

Herbal, culinary, cultural and folklore Young leaves can be used as salad, older leaves are bitter and with spiny midrib. Milky sap contains lactucarium which has pain-relieving, anti-spasmodic properties, but should not be used without medical supervision.

70

1) Seedling 2) young plants 3) adult leaves 4) flower heads 5) seed heads, seeds (achenes) with stalkless pappus

Nipplewort *(Lapsana communis)*

Native. Annual to biennial. Erect stems 20-90 cm in height. Leaves light-to-mid-green, lower leaves long-stalked and lyre-shaped, with small side lobes and a large terminal lobe. Upper leaves short-stalked, ovate-pointed. Overall diameter of inflorescence: 1.5-2 cm. Ray florets only, light yellow, hermaphrodite. Fruits *(achenes)* elongate-ovate, finely ribbed, without pappus. Flowering June-September. Common throughout the British Isles, occurs on arable and waste land, and in hedgerows. Favours heavier soil types.

Pollination Small bees and flies.

Regeneration strategy Seed only, shed locally to the plant as it is without a pappus.

Weed control For small outbreaks, hand-weed before flowering stage and compost.

Herbal, culinary, cultural and folklore Common name refers to shape of flower buds. Although bitter to taste, this species was formerly used as a salad leaf. According to the Doctrine of Signatures, the resemblance of the flower buds to nipples recommended its use for the treatment for breast ulcers.

71

1) Seedlings 2) pre-flowering plant 3) flower heads 4) young seed heads 5) seeds

Common Ragwort, Ragwort *(Senecio jacobaea)*

Native. An autumn germinating biennial to short-lived perennial. Stems often reddish, height 30-150 cm, with short, erect rootstock. Leaves mid-green, young leaves in a basal rosette, adult leaves 20-40 cm high, almost ferny. Overall diameter of yellow flower heads: 1.5-2 cm, sometimes up to 2.5 cm. Ray florets female, disc florets hermaphrodite. Fruits (*achenes*) c. 2 mm long, cylindrical, slightly curved, ribbed with stalkless, long-filamented pappus. Flowering June-October, sometimes as late as November. Distributed throughout the British Isles. Abundant on grassland, roadsides, waste or disturbed land, and neglected, or over-grazed, pastures, and on almost all soil types excepting the most acidic peats and sands.

Pollination Flowers attractive to as many as 178 different species of insect, including many species of butterflies and moths, of which the Cinnabar Moth (*Tyria jacobaeae*) is probably the best known pollinator, due to its striking black and yellow striped larvae. Attracts flies, notably St. Mark's Flies (*Bibio marci*, family Bibionidae) – large black flies that emerge in swarms around St. Mark's Day (25 April) – also soldier flies (family Stratiomyidae), biting midges (family Ceratopogonidae), thick-headed flies (family Conopidae), gall wasps (families Cynipidae and Lamprotatidae), and solitary wasps (family Sphecidae).

Regeneration strategy Overwintering rosettes of leaves, and parachute seed for efficient wind dispersal – an average-sized plant can produce 50-60,000 seeds, with a germination rate of c. 80%.

Weed control For small outbreaks, hand-weed before flowering stage and compost; however, this is a serious agricultural pest, and is one of the five harmful weeds controlled by law. Ragwort contains toxins harmful to livestock, therefore follow current official advice for large invasions, especially on grazing land (see Bibliography for useful websites).

Herbal, culinary, cultural and folklore Irish fairies, and fairies of the Highlands and Islands are reputed to ride on stems of Ragwort between the islands. In the centuries of witch mania, it was witches who rode these herbal nags. Ragwort is also the Herba Sancti Jacobi (the Herb of St. James), a name which persists in several European countries.

Toxicity Can cause liver damage, but animals tend to eat around it when fresh, however, if Ragwort gets into hay unnoticed, it could then be ingested by horses and other livestock with seriously harmful effects. Its high pollen production causes allergic reaction in susceptible individuals, especially those similarly affected by other members of the Daisy family, such as Canadian Goldenrod.

1) Young plant 2) habit 3) flower heads 4) young seed heads 5) seed head, seeds (achenes) with stalkless pappus
6) Cinnabar Moth (*Tyria jacobaea*) caterpillars on Common Ragwort

Oxford Ragwort *(Senecio squalidus)*

Introduced neophyte from southern Europe, from Sicily to Oxford Botanic Garden in late 17th Century; almost certainly escaping from there and spreading later, notably via railway networks. Overwintering annual. Height 20-40 cm. Adult leaves mid-to-deep green, with a central midrib, deeply dissected and sparsely hairy. Overall diameter of yellow flower heads: 1.5-2.5 cm. Ray florets female, disc florets hermaphrodite. A characteristic for identification are the black tips to the bracts of the involucre – the calyx-like ring of green bracts below the bright yellow petals. Fruits *(achenes)* 1.5-2 mm long, cylindrical, slightly curved, ribbed, greyish-beige with stalkless, long-filamented pappus. Flowering June-December. A common plant of waste ground, old walls, railways, and roadsides through most of England and Wales, although it is still uncommon or rare in Scotland and Ireland. When not flowering, the general appearance of stems and leaves allows Oxford Ragwort to be mistaken for another weed: Groundsel *(Senecio vulgaris)*.

Pollination Long-snouted hoverflies: *Rhingia* species (family Syrphidae) are among the main insect visitors.

Regeneration strategy By seed only: parachute seeds for efficient wind dispersal of the 40-120 seeds produced by each flower head. Average seed production per plant each year is c. 10,000.

Weed control For small outbreaks, hand-weed before flowering stage, and compost or follow current best practice for large invasions (see Bibliography and internet).

Herbal, culinary, cultural and folklore The species name *squalidus* refers to the favoured habitats, rather than the plant itself.

1) Young plant 2) flowers – note black-tipped green bracts 3) flowering habit 4) seed heads, seeds (achenes) with stalkless pappus

Groundsel *(Senecio vulgaris)*

Native. Annual, often overwintering. Rather weak soft stems, more or less erect, height 8-45 cm, smooth or with non-glandular hairs. Leaves mid-green, hairless or slightly cottony, pinnate, with blunt-oblong, irregularly toothed lobes. Flower heads in dense yellow clusters, overall diameter of flower heads: c. 4 mm. A variable plant, usually no ray florets but, infrequently (notably in coastal areas), ray florets may be present; disc florets hermaphrodite. Fruits *(achenes)* 1.5-2 mm long, cylindrical, slightly curved, ribbed, greyish-beige with stalkless, long-filamented pappus. Flowering January-December. Abundant throughout the British Isles, except some parts of the Scottish Highlands. Particularly frequent on cultivated ground and in waste places, with a preference for heavier, damper soils.

74

Pollination Although the flowers contain nectar, insect visitors are few, and automatic self-pollination is frequent. It may cross-pollinate with Oxford Ragwort.

Regeneration strategies Parachute seeds. Often self-pollinated although it has been shown that cross-fertilised flowers produce larger, more fertile plants. One of a few very common weeds that can come into flower at any time of year, unaffected by day length.

Weed control For small outbreaks, hand-weed before flowering stage and compost.

Herbal, culinary, cultural and folklore In the past Groundsel was widely used as a cure-all for anything from 'the king's evil' (scrofula, a very unpleasant infection of the lymph nodes, which the King's touch was reputed to clear), to de-worming young children. A British weed introduced to North America by immigrants. A good plant for rabbit food (leaves), and caged birdfood (seed). This species can host a fungus that causes black rot in a range of commonly grown vegetable crops, including tomatoes, peas and beans.

1) Seedlings 2) solitary plant 3) flower heads, no ray florets 4) seed heads, seeds (achenes) with stalkless pappus

Mugwort *(Artemisia vulgaris)*

Native. Perennial. Stems erect, sparsely hairy, reddish, 60-120 cm in height. Leaves dark green, 6-8 cm long, more or less smooth above, white-woolly beneath. Overall diameter of flower heads: 2-3 mm. Florets yellow, often turning reddish or mauve at maturity, outer florets long slender, female, inner short florets hermaphrodite. Fruits *(achenes)* c. 1 mm long, brown, elongate-ovoid, slightly angled, without pappus. Flowering July-September. Common throughout the British Isles, especially in waste places, roadsides, waysides and hedgerows. Present on most soils except the most acidic, frequent on fertile or calcareous soils.

Pollination Wind-pollinated.

Regeneration strategy Reproduces very freely from seed.

Weed control In gardens, remove young plants before flowering stage and compost.

Herbal, culinary, cultural and folklore An important element of mediaeval medicine and sorcery, one of the oldest herbs known (active compounds are terpenoids and sesquiterpene lactones). Used to aid digestion, relieve depression, restore menstrual flow, and for easing childbirth. Smoked as a tobacco substitute in Berkshire until late 19th Century. It was also used as an antidote to gangrene in horses. Pollen may cause hayfever allergy (this species is widely known as Ragweed in the medical profession). Flowers worn on Tynwald Day in the Isle of Man.

75

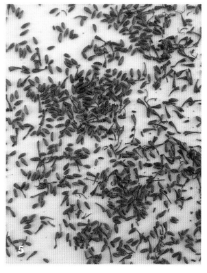

1) Young plants 2) young adult foliage 3) flowering habit 4) flower heads 5) old florets and seeds without pappus

Canadian Goldenrod *(Solidago canadensis)*

Neophyte, first introduced into cultivation in Britain in 1648. Signs of naturalising by 1888 in Oxfordshire, though serious spread not recorded before 1930. Rhizomatous perennial. Stems slightly hairy, 1.8 m in height, sometimes up to 2.5 m. Leaves 1-5 cm wide, mid-green, long and narrow. Flower heads very small, with many (nine to 17 or more) tiny yellow, mainly hermaphrodite ray florets and tubular disc florets, arranged on small arching stems emanating from the central main stem. Fruits *(achenes)* elongate, slightly curved, few ribbed with stalkless, long-filamented pappus. Flowering August-October. Frequent throughout lowland England, less widespread in Devon and Wales, rare in Ireland and the Scottish Highlands. A coloniser of open land, roadsides, dry to damp thickets, slopes and clearings; avoids acidic soils.

Additional notes *Solidago gigantea,* a similar species from North America, and probably introduced into the UK via nurseries and/or botanic gardens, is also becoming a menace in the UK. It is somewhat taller than Canadian Goldenrod (up to 2.5 m), the flower heads droop slightly, and the stems are hairless. Like Canadian Goldenrod, there are a number of garden cultivars. Interestingly, there is only one British native Goldenrod – the smaller (up to 75 cm), daintier, *Solidago virgaurea,* a variable species common to many parts of the British Isles, although it has been in decline in some areas. It is not a weedy species.

Pollination This species is self-sterile. Nevertheless, it produces high amounts of pollen and nectar, attracting many species of insects. It is a good nectar plant for bees. It is also visited by some species of the largest group of British solitary wasps (family Sphecidae), and is among the flowers most visited by butterflies.

Regeneration strategies Seed and vegetative spread. Produces parachute seeds for wind dispersal. Birds also like feeding on the seed, which probably helps dispersal. Spreads by rhizomes to form patches.

Weed control For small outbreaks, hand-weed before flowering stage and compost, or follow current best practice for large invasions (see Bibliography and internet).

Herbal, culinary, cultural and folklore Often tolerated and/or enjoyed in gardens. In combination with other dye agents, used to produce a range of colours, notably golden yellow and a strong orange colour. In herbal medicine it was known to have anti-inflammatory properties, and a tea made from the leaves may be taken for relieving sore throats and urinary tract infections. It is also considered to help staunch blood flow from wounds. In its native Canada it is traditionally considered to be a sign of good luck if, uninvited, it is found growing by your front door.

Toxicity The high pollen production may cause an allergic reaction to recognition proteins contained in the pollen wall in susceptible individuals, especially those similarly affected by other members of the Daisy family, such as Ragwort.

76

1) Young leaf shoots 2) adult leafy stems 3) roadside stand of flowering stems 4) flowering stem 5) close-up of flower heads 6) seed heads

Canadian Fleabane, Horseweed *(Conyza canadensis)*

Introduced neophyte, native of North America, first noted in Britain between 1640-1690. Annual. Stiffly erect, leafy stems, height 20-150 cm, often as short as 8 cm. Leaves light-to-mid-green, long, narrow and pointed, sparsely hairy; basal leaves soon die. Overall diameter of inflorescence: 3-5 mm. All florets hermaphrodite, outer florets white, inner florets white/yellowish. Fruits (*achenes*) pale yellow, with stalkless, short-filamented pappus. Flowering July-October. Widespread in the south-east and south central England, more scattered in the north. Favours light, well-drained, sandy soils, waste ground and other neglected niches.

Additional notes Two similar species, *Conyza floribunda*, apparently from South America, but well-established in the northern hemisphere, and *Conyza sumatrensis* (Guernsey Fleabane, first noted in London in 1983), are now both very widespread throughout southern Britain.

Pollination Small insects.

Regeneration strategy Spreads via its light parachute seeds, easily carried by wind currents.

Weed control Remove seedlings or young plants prior to flowering by hand-weeding, hoeing or, if they are in the path or driveway, a flame weeder could be used. Note that the plants can flower when very small.

Herbal, culinary, cultural and folklore The British seem to have been atypically unenterprising with this early introduction. Geoffrey Grigson reports it as having, "done extra well on the ruins and the waste left by the air raids" (following WWII).

77

1) Young plants 2) Canadian Fleabane as an urban opportunist 3) flowering and seeding 4) flower heads and seed heads

Yarrow, Milfoil *(Achillea millefolium)*

Native. Patch-forming perennial with far-creeping stoloniferous roots. Leaves mid-to-deep green, feathery. Flowering stem height 8-45 cm, sometimes up to 60 cm. Overall diameter of inflorescence (*corymb*): 2-7 cm, sometimes up to 8 cm; ray florets very small, female (c. 3 mm long), usually five in number, disc florets tubular, hermaphrodite. Fruits (*achenes*) 2 mm long, elongate-ovoid-triangular. Flowering June-August but sometimes even as early as January, or as late as December. Common throughout the British Isles, especially in meadows, pastures, grassy banks, hedgerows and waysides, on all but the poorest soils.

Pollination A wide variety of insects, including butterflies and gall midges.

Regeneration strategies Abundant flowering heads and prolific seeds with at least 75% germination. Also spreads by far creeping stolons that root at the nodes.

Weed control Mulch, hoe or dig up and compost before flowering, or follow current best practice for large invasions (see Bibliography and internet).

Herbal, culinary, cultural and folklore Used as a wound herb by mediaeval herbalists; receiving its Latin name because Achilles was said to have used it to treat "those that had been wounded with iron". It is one of the Herbs of St. John. Traditionally farmers considered it a valuable 'condiment' in good nutritious herbage for browsing cattle. Colourful cultivars of the wild species are widely grown in herbaceous borders.

78

1) Roots and runners 2) flowering habit 3) flower heads 4) pink flowers sometimes occur 5) finely cut leaves that give the species its name
6) seed heads, seeds (achenes) without pappus

Gallant Soldier, Kew-weed *(Galinsoga parviflora)*

Introduced neophyte from Peru, arriving at the Royal Botanic Gardens, Kew c. 1796. First recorded as an escape (locally) from Kew c. 1863. Annual. Height 10-75 cm. Stems hairless, or shortly hairy. Basal leaves broadly ovate-pointed, short fine hairs and more or less toothed margins, upper leaves narrower and less toothed, not hairy. Overall diameter of inflorescence: 3-5 mm. Five white female ray florets, disc florets yellow, tubular, hermaphrodite. Fruits *(achenes)* ovoid, black and bristly, with a circlet of white pappus scales. Flowering May-October; a frequent weed of gardens, waste ground and arable land, especially in southern UK.

Additional notes A similar but larger species, *Galinsoga quadriradiata* (which has a scientific synonym, *G. ciliata*), was introduced in 1909 and is now common in southern Britain. The main differences, apart from a more upright habit and greater height of adult plants, are the longer narrower leaves with glandular hairs, subtending the flowers.

Pollination Self- or insect-pollinated.

Regeneration strategy Seed only, via parachute seeds from the ray florets. Average seed output per plant ranges from 2,000-15,000 and is carried by the wind.

Weed control For small outbreaks, hand-weed before flowering stage and compost.

Herbal, culinary, cultural and folklore The name Gallant Soldier is a local British conversion of the botanical name *Galinsoga* (named after Ignacio Mariano Martinez de Galinsoga who founded the Spanish Real Academia Nacional de Medicina and was Director of the Jardin Botanico de Madrid). The name Gallant Soldier even became Soldiers of the Queen. This species was introduced into the Paris Botanical Gardens in 1785, and from there and Kew it has subsequently spread all over Europe.

79

1) Young plant 2) habit 3) flower heads 4) seed head and seeds with scaly, stalkless pappus

Butterbur *(Petasites hybridus)*

Native. Perennial. Rhizomes stout and far-creeping. Leaves at first downy on both sides, then green above and greyish below. Mature leaves very large, c. 10-90 cm in diameter, rounded. Flowering stems thick, height 10-40 cm (up to 80 cm in fruit). Flowers are either male or female, and are borne on separate plants (*dioecious*); individual flowers very small, unscented, and dull lilac, and grouped in small clusters on the thick stems. Fruits (*achenes*) 2-3 mm long, yellowish-brown with stalkless, long-filamented pappus. Flowering March-May. The flowering stems are succeeded by the leaves. Male plants locally common and widely distributed throughout the British Isles, while female plants are most frequent in central to northern England. Favours damp meadows, copses, stream banks, roadsides and ditches.

Additional notes Another species of *Petasites*, *P. fragrans* (Winter Heliotrope or Wintersweet), is often cultivated in the wilder parts of gardens. It also has lilac flower heads but is scented, some say sweetly. It flowers earlier than Butterbur, from January to March, and the evergreen leaves are present with the flowers.

Pollination The early flowering time makes it attractive to early bumblebees and honey bees. In Sweden, farmers traditionally plant it near their bee-hives. The Butterbur Moth (*Hydraecia petasitis*) lays its eggs on the remains of the plant. The larvae hatch April-July and eat through the stems to pupate among the roots.

Regeneration strategies By seed or by vegetative spread: parachute seeds are easily carried by wind currents, and stout far-creeping rhizomes form extensive, up to 1 m large patches.

Weed control For small invasions dig out the rhizomes and burn. For large invasions follow current best practice (see Bibliography and internet).

Herbal, culinary, cultural and folklore Recent studies (2011-2013) by Swiss and British researchers have confirmed the antihistamine qualities of Butterbur leaf extracts in treating symptoms of asthma and hay fever. The giant leaves of Butterbur have often been used as umbrellas, hence the name *Petasites* which is from the Greek *petasos*, meaning a covering for the head. The common name, Butterbur, refers to the old use of the leaves for wrapping pats of butter. The emerging flower heads looked, to some country folk, like clusters of tiny, rather livid-coloured mushrooms, remembered by a Dorset name for Butterbur: Early Mushroom.

80

1) Runners, six months old 2) young flower head (these emerge before the leaves) 3) close-up of flowers in one flower head
4) young leaves (these emerge after the flowers have died)

Coltsfoot *(Tussilago farfara)*

Native. Perennial. Leaves 20-30 cm in diameter, white-felted above and below. Flowering stems 5-15 cm in height, appearing in small clusters before the leaves. Overall diameter of flower head: 15-35 mm. Ray florets female and seed-producing; central florets male. Fruits *(achenes)* elongate, light brown with stalkless, long-filamented pappus. Flowering March-April, followed by leaves. Distributed through the whole of the British Isles. A common plant of roadsides, hedge banks, arable fields and waste ground, especially heavy calcareous clays, chalk quarries, sand and shingle. In Scotland, Coltsfoot will grow up to an altitude of 1070 m.

Pollination The male florets secrete nectar at the bases of the stamens and are visited by the relatively short-tongued Andrena bees, and by some flies. Self-pollination is possible when heads close at night, or during cold weather.

Regeneration strategies Parachute seeds, although Coltsfoot seedlings are unusual as seed viability is quite short-lived. This species usually increases via very long, underground root runners that send up new shoots. These can not only penetrate to a depth of several metres, but can also extend radially to a distance of 3 m or more in a single season.

Weed control For minor invasions deep-dig out runners and roots, and burn. For large invasions follow current best practice (see Bibliography and internet).

Herbal, culinary, cultural and folklore Traditionally (and currently) used as a herbal cough remedy *(Tussilago* is derived from *tussis* – Latin for cough). The smoking of the plant leaves was strongly recommended by old writers. The cottony down is reputed to have sometimes been used for filling pillows or cushions, although this seems very labour-intensive by modern standards. In the 17th Century it was also used for tinder: "rapped in a rag and boiled in a little lee with a little salt-petre added". The down is also often used as nest-lining by Goldfinches. An old name for the plant was *filius ante patrem* (son before the father) because the flowers precede the leaves. In fact, some of the older botanists, including Pliny, thought that Coltsfoot didn't have any leaves – very poor field observations and notes!

81

1) Flower heads (these emerge before the leaves) 2) detail of flower head 3) seed heads 4) young leaves and part of the roots (the runners are extensive) 5) young adult leaves

BALSAMINIACEAE *(Balsam Family)*

Indian Balsam, Himalayan Balsam, Policeman's Helmet
(Impatiens glandulifera)

Introduced from India (Himalayas) about 1839, first noted as "another terrible weed" by a Mrs Earle in 1898. Annual. Height 1-2 m. Stems thick, reddish-green, ribbed. Leaves 6-15 cm long, ovate, with finely toothed margins and pointed tip. Flowers hermaphrodite, strongly bisymmetric; five petals, purplish pink, pink or white: one large hooded petal embraces a pair of smaller petals above, and a pair of large, downward pointing petals below; the calyx comprises a pair of small sepals at the base of the upper petal, and a highly specialised large, helmet-like spurred sepal, which is often strongly blotched, protrudes almost horizontally behind the petals. The flowers have a curious, but not unpleasant, resinous smell. Flowering July-September, sometimes as late as October. Widespread throughout the British Isles, it can rapidly form tall, dense monocultures along riverbanks or in damp places.

Pollination Bumblebees. It also self-pollinates. A larval food plant for the Elephant Hawkmoth.

Regeneration strategy Seed alone. Strongly projectile seed pods with a firing range of up to 11 m. An average-sized plant will produce c. 800 seeds, and these are subsequently spread further by water movement.

Weed control This species is controlled by law and must not be planted in the wild or caused to spread. Control is most effective by uprooting plants before they fruit. They can also be cut very low (they may resprout if cut above the lowest node). Seeds may be dormant for two years so control in subsequent years might be needed. A rust fungus is currently being investigated as a possible biological control agent. Because it is an annual species the bare soil is easily eroded after the plants die back in winter.

Herbal, culinary, cultural and folklore The projectile seeds have been responsible for one of the most well-known common names *Noli-me-tangere*, or Touch-me-not. Since its arrival in the UK it has always had its supporters – children love the fun of popping the fruits. It has been encouraged in industrially polluted backwaters where nothing else will grow, or flower so delightfully.

1) Colonising habit 2) leaves 3) flowers 4) seed heads and sprung capsules with a seed still in place

BORAGINACEAE *(Borage Family)*

Bugloss, Small or Lesser Bugloss *(Anchusa arvensis)*

Native. Annual or short-lived perennial. Height 15-50 cm. Short straight tap root, stems, leaves and calyx covered with short swollen-based hairs. Leaves narrowly ovate with undulate margins. Flowers hermaphrodite, in clusters on the stems, small, sky blue, tubular and radially symmetric, opening a few at a time; calyx with five narrow hairy lobes, the four-loculed capsule at the base contains four slipper-shaped seeds (nutlets). Flowering June-September. Widely distributed throughout the British Isles to altitudes of c. 500 m. A weed of arable crops, field margins, roadsides, grassy banks, disturbed ground, grassy banks or heaths, on dry, well-drained calcareous or light sandy soils.

Pollination Inside the flower, below the petals, is a ring of hair-like scales. Below this is a curved flower tube at the base of which is a four-lobed ovary, where nectar is secreted nearby to entice insects to enter the tube. Above the ovary are five anthers arranged in a circle around the wall of the flower tube: visiting insects are unavoidably dusted with pollen, even if they cannot reach the nectar. Insects known to visit include small bees and butterflies. In the absence of insects, self-pollination is achieved by the corolla falling off, during which process some of the pollen is drawn off across the pistil.

Regeneration strategy Seed alone. Capsules get caught in animal

fur or clothing and may spread some distance. Seeds also fall locally, and are adapted to be spread by ants.

Weed control For small outbreaks, hand-weed before flowering stage and compost, or follow current best practice for large invasions (see Bibliography and internet).

Herbal, culinary, cultural and folklore The name Bugloss is of Greek origin, from *bouglóssos* meaning ox tongue: a reference to its bristly leaves and stems.

83

1) Young plant 2) plant habit 3) flowers 4) flowers and green fruit 5) ripe seeds

BORAGINACEAE

Field Forget-me-not *(Myosotis arvensis)*

Native. Annual, often overwintering. Stems 15-20 cm in height, sometimes up to 30 cm, both stems and leaves softly hairy. Leaves ovate with straight margins. Flowers hermaphrodite, very small (less than 5 mm diameter) and radially symmetric, in small loosely coiled clusters at the top of the stems, mid-blue with a small bright yellow centre, petals sometimes slightly mauve or pink; calyx covered with spreading hooked bristles. A four-loculed capsule at the base contains four small glossy seeds (nutlets). Flowering April-September. Common throughout almost all of the British Isles, excepting parts of northern and north-west Scotland, in most more or less open, but not wet, habitats.

84

Pollination Attracts long-headed flies (family Dolichopodidae) and bee flies (Family Bombyliidae), and is well-adapted to butterflies.

Regeneration strategy Seed alone. The hairy seed capsules readily attach to animals or clothing, and may spread some distance, but are also shed locally, frequently dispersing close to the parent plants and forming colonies. Seeds germinate rapidly.

Weed control For small outbreaks, hand-weed before flowering stage and compost, or follow current best practice for large invasions (see Bibliography and internet).

Herbal, culinary, cultural and folklore Forget-me-not as a common name is applied to a number of species of *Myosotis*, however, the romantic symbolism of the name apparently originates from Germany where, legend has it, a knight was walking with his lady by a river, gathering Water Forget-me-nots (*Myosotis palustris*) for her. Unfortunately he lost his footing and fell into the river but, as he was being swept away by the current, he threw the flowers to her crying "Vergiss mein nicht!" ("forget me not!"). Far less romantically, in Britain it was known as Scorpion Grass – a name commonly applied to any species of *Myosotis*. Happily in north-east Europe and in France, generally the German name caught on, and the British embraced it too.

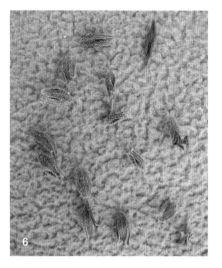

1) Seedlings 2) young plant 3) flowering plants 4) flowers 5) seed heads and seed 6) seed pods caught on fabric

Green Alkanet, Alkanet, Evergreen Alkanet *(Pentaglottis sempervirens)*

Native, or of very early/obscure introduction from Europe. Perennial. Stems 30-100 cm in height, with short, stiff hairs. Leaves broadly ovate, also covered with short stiff hairs; leaf margins slightly undulate with some longer hairs. Flowers hermaphrodite, radially symmetric, small (c. 10 mm diameter), intense bright blue with a small white centre, usually opening in groups of two, sometimes three, at top of stems; calyx with five narrow longish lobes, covered with untidy hairs, the four-loculed capsule at the base produces four mitten-shaped seeds (nutlets). Flowering May-July. The species has become completely naturalised throughout the British Isles as far as northern Scotland, but with rather localised distribution, apart from in the south-west. Favours shaded hedge banks, road verges, damp woodland borders, allotments and fertile ground near walls and buildings.

Pollination Mainly bees, including honey bees and bumblebees (notably *Bombus pascuorum* – the Common Carder Bee), and hoverflies such as the long-snouted *Rhingia rostrata*.

Regeneration strategies Seed and vegetative spread. Seed capsules get caught in animal fur or clothing and may spread some distance, although seeds often fall locally to the parent plants, forming colonies.

Weed control For small outbreaks, hand-weed and dig out roots before flowering stage and compost, or follow current best practice for large invasions (see Bibliography and internet).

Herbal, culinary, cultural and folklore The roots can produce a brownish-red dye which was used as a substitute for the far superior dye obtained from *Alkanna tinctoria* (Dyer's Alkanet); Alkanna/Alkanet are corruptions of the Spanish *alcanna*, which comes from the Arabic *al-henna* – the henna plant (the North African *Lawsonia inermis*, family Lythraceae), used since antiquity for colouring hair, fingernails and toenails.

85

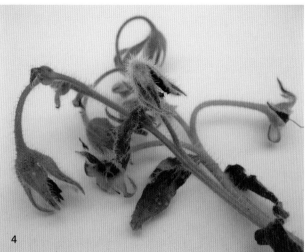

1) Seedling 2) habit 3) flowers 4) fruiting head 5) old calyx and seeds (nutlets)

Lacy Phacelia, Purple Tansy *(Phacelia tanacetifolia)*

Introduced from south-western USA and northern Mexico, cultivated in UK since 1832. First recorded in the wild in 1885. Annual. Maximum height c. 100 cm. Leaves are mostly divided into smaller leaflets, deeply and intricately cut into toothed lobes, giving them an almost ferny appearance. Flowers hermaphrodite. The very hairy inflorescence is a one-sided coil of bell-shaped, radially symmetric flowers, blue to lavender, white-throated, slightly less than 1 cm diameter, with very long whiskery stamens. Calyx teeth, five in number, very long, narrow and hairy. The four-loculed capsule produces four ovate glossy seeds. Flowering April-May, sometimes as late as September. The current UK distribution indicates that most populations are casual but it is increasingly used as a small crop on farms, especially in southern England.

Pollination Nectar-rich flowers encourage bees and hoverflies.

Regeneration strategy Seed alone. Germinates at low temperatures, readily self-seeds, and has an extensive root system.

Weed control Hand-weed, dig in as green manure pre maturity, or follow current best, preferably organic, practice for large invasions (see Bibliography and internet).

Herbal, culinary, cultural and folklore Used as a cover crop, an ornamental and a 'bee plant'. Popular with organic farmers and gardeners to attract honey bees for pollination and hoverflies for aphid control, and as green manure. It also occurs in birdseed and in pheasant feed. In Jersey, it is planted after potatoes to deter eelworm. In recent years, with declining pollinator populations, it has become a popular plant to attract honeybees. Despite this range of uses, some recent studies have expressed serious concerns about its possible negative effects on our native floras and faunas.

1) Young plant 2) habit 3) flowers 4) growing in grassland 5) seed heads and seeds

BRASSICACEAE *(Cabbage Family)*

Garlic Mustard, Hedge Garlic, Jack-by-the-hedge *(Alliaria petiolata)*

Native. Mostly biennial with tap root. Stems 20-120 cm in height, smooth, or nearly so. Main leaves long-stalked, light-to-mid-green, broadly heart-shaped with toothed margins, emitting garlic-odour when crushed. Flowers hermaphrodite, c. 6 mm diameter, grouped in loose terminal heads. Individual flowers four-petalled, white, with six stamens and radially symmetric, petals c. twice as long as sepals. Seed pods *(siliquae)* narrow, elongate (30-65 mm long), on short stalks from central stem. Flowering April-June. Distributed throughout most of the British Isles, though rare or absent over large areas of northern and western Scotland and Ireland. Common in hedgerows, wood margins, roadsides and deciduous woodland or shady places on nutrient-rich soils.

Pollination Self-pollinated, and also visited by hoverflies and other insects. A food plant of Green-veined White and Orange-tip Butterflies. The female Orange-tip lays her eggs on this species.

Regeneration strategy Seed alone. When the seed pods ripen and dry, the seeds are ejected in the vicinity of the parent plant. If the main stem is damaged early in a new season of growth the plant can develop root shoots from the tap root.

Weed control For small outbreaks, hand-weed before flowering stage and compost, or dig in as green manure, but remove and destroy any tap roots. Follow current best practice for large invasions (see Bibliography and internet).

Herbal, culinary, cultural and folklore One of its common names is Sauce Alone because, like many pungent members of the Brassicaceae (notably mustard and horseradish), it was formerly used as a condiment or spring sauce to enhance meat or fish dishes.

87

1) Seedling 2) young leaves 3) flowers 4) ripe fruits, some open with seeds still attached to central septum

Thale Cress *(Arabidopsis thaliana)*

Native. Usually short-lived annual with tap root. Flowering stems slender, erect, 5-50 cm in height, slightly hairy below flowering part of stem. Stem leaves small and few. Leaves in a basal rosette, narrowly ovate, stem leaves small and few; stems and leaves grey-green. Flowers hermaphrodite, very small (c. 3 mm diameter), at tips of elongating stems: four white petals and six stamens; long, narrow seed pods (*siliquae*), 6-16 mm in length, develop from old flowers on the stem below. Mostly flowering April-July, but also at other times of the year. Distributed throughout the British Isles to c. 850 m above sea level, but becoming scarcer in the west and in Ireland. Occurs in gardens, on banks, hedgerows waste places, dry soils, footpath edges, walls and rocks.

Pollination Self-pollinated.

Regeneration strategy Seed alone. When the seed pods ripen and dry, the seeds are ejected in the vicinity of the parent plant. In ideal conditions the development rate from seedling to mature seed-bearing plants can be very rapid, a young mature plant can set seed within four weeks of its own germination.

Weed control For small outbreaks, hand-weed before flowering stage and compost, or dig in as green manure.

Herbal, culinary, cultural and folklore Because of its rapid annual life cycle, this species is used by plant geneticists for reproductive studies. It is the botanical counterpart of the rapidly reproducing fruit fly *Drosophila melanogaster*, used by animal geneticists.

88

1) Young plants 2) basal leaves 3) flower head 4) fruiting head 5) fruits, some opened with seeds still attached to the central septum

Oil-seed Rape, Rape, Turnip Rape *(Brassica napus* subsp. *oleifera)*

Probably originated in cultivation in 16ᵗʰ Century Europe. Annual or biennial with often strong or tuberous tap root. Flowering stems smooth, up to 1-1.5 m in height. Leaves bluish-green, deeply scalloped and sparsely bristly; bases of upper leaves clasp the stem. Flowers hermaphrodite, carried in dense heads at the tip of the main stem, or side branching stems. Individual flowers 1.5-2 cm diameter, four-petalled and bright yellow with six stamens; petals almost twice as long as sepals. Elongated seed pods (*siliquae*) develop below flowering heads. Flowering May-August. Widely distributed along roadsides, banks, and field margins, as an escape from cultivation.

Pollination Bees, and self-pollinated.

Regeneration strategy Seed alone. When the seed pods ripen and dry, the seeds are ejected in the vicinity of the parent plant.

Weed control For small outbreaks, hand-weed before flowering stage and compost, or dig in as green manure. Follow current best practice for large invasions (see Bibliography and internet).

Herbal, culinary, cultural and folklore The use of rapeseed oil in cooking, frying and baking increased during the later 20ᵗʰ Century, because it has the lowest saturated fat of any edible oil. An esterified form of rapeseed oil is used as a lubricant for jet engines. Seed residue, after oil extraction, is used in animal fodder.

89

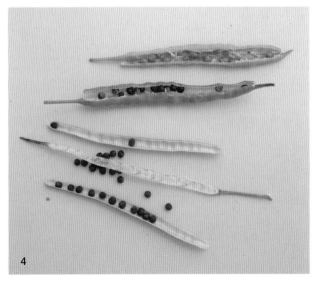

1) Young plants 2) flowers 3) ripe fruits 4) fruits, green to ripe

Shepherd's-purse *(Capsella bursa-pastoris)*

Native. Annual or occasionally biennial. Flowering stem 3-50 cm in height, sometimes up to 70 cm, erect and branching, smooth or with sparse hairs. Leaves elongate and variable. The basal leaves arranged in a loose rosette; leaf margins vary from more or less un-indented to highly indented or very divided, almost fern-like; bases of upper leaves clasp the stem. Flowers hermaphrodite, tiny (c. 2.5-3 mm diameter), with six stamens, four-petalled and white, held in small dense flower heads at the tip of the main stem or side branching stems. Small triangular seed pods *(siliculae)*, c. 4-10 mm long, develop below flowering heads. Flowering January-December. Common on cultivated ground, waysides and waste places throughout the British Isles, apart from mountainous areas. One of our most common garden or field weeds.

Pollination Usually self-pollinated, although producing some nectar and sometimes visited by small insects.

Regeneration strategy Seed alone. When the seed pods ripen and dry, the seeds are ejected in the vicinity of the parent plant. One of a few very common weeds that can come into flower at any time of year, unaffected by day length.

Weed control For small outbreaks, hand-weed before flowering stage and compost, or dig in as green manure. Follow current best practice for larger invasions (see Bibliography and internet).

Herbal, culinary, cultural and folklore The common name refers to the shape of the pouch or purse worn by mediaeval peasants, hung on a belt. This species has been introduced throughout the temperate world. It also may be one of a number of British or European weeds introduced to the USA by immigrants. Chaffinches and other wild birds eat the seeds. In herbal medicine, it is used fresh or dry as a herbal infusion: it is valued for the control of internal bleeding, or on surface wounds to promote healing. It is also used for skin rashes. Seeds of this species were among those found in the stomach of Tollund Man (Denmark, early Celtic Iron Age – c. 400BC-200AD).

Toxicity Do not use any herbal remedy without consulting qualified herbalists or your doctor.

90

1) Young plants 2) young adult plant 3) flower head 4) green fruits 5) ripe fruits

Wavy Bitter-cress, Wood Bitter-cress *(Cardamine flexuosa)*

Native. Annual, biennial or perennial. Leafy stem 7-50 cm in height, usually with at least a few side branches, sparsely hairy, and wavy/flexuose (not straight), especially during fruiting stage. The basal leaf rosette not strongly defined, and the basal leaves terminate with a kidney-shaped leaflet. Four to ten, sometimes less than three, composite leaves, 15-20 cm in length, alternately arranged on the stem; each leaf comprises two to seven pairs of small, slightly hairy, elliptic leaflets. Flowers hermaphrodite, held in small dense flower heads at the tip of main stem, or side branching stems. Individual flowers with four white petals (2.2-4.3 mm long, sometimes up to 5 mm), and four to six stamens. Small, elongate, upward pointing seed pods *(siliquae)*, 12-26 mm long, sometimes as small as 8 mm. Flowering May-September. Common throughout Britain and Ireland in moist shady places, damp woodland, by streams or ditches. Also frequent in gardens and damp waste ground. Extends to an altitude of 1190 m in Scotland. A British native now widespread throughout the temperate world.

Additional note Not always easy to distinguish from *Cardamine hirsuta*.

Pollination Self-pollination. Flower visitors include hoverflies (notably, *Platycheirus albimanus*), butterflies, e.g. Green-veined White (*Pieris napi*) and Orange-tip (*Anthocharis cardamines*) and flea beetles (notably *Phyllotreta nigripes* and *P. tetrastigma*).

Regeneration strategy Seed alone. When the seed pods ripen and dry, the seeds are explosively ejected in the vicinity of the parent plant. Seed dormancy/viability up to seven years. Seeds can spread through waterways, on hikers' boots, on water birds and animals.

Weed control For small outbreaks, hand-weed before flowering stage and compost, or dig in as green manure. Follow current best practice for large invasions (see Bibliography and internet). (A serious weed of paddy fields in China and Japan.)

Herbal, culinary, cultural and folklore Leaves and flowers have a peppery, cress-like flavour and can be used as a tasty ingredient in salads.

91

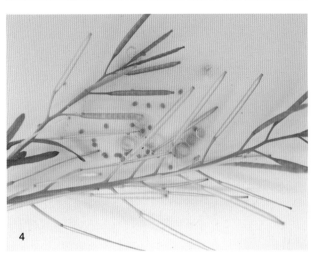

1) Young plant 2) flowers 3) habit 4) green and ripe fruits

Hairy Bitter-cress *(Cardamine hirsuta)*

Native. Annual. Stems 5-30 cm in height, sometimes as short as 3 cm, smooth or almost smooth, and erect or spreading. Basal compound leaves in a compact, well-defined rosette, 10-13 cm diameter. All leaves smooth, or almost smooth, young leaves terminate with a more or less kidney-shaped leaflet. The flowering stems may be leafless but usually have from one to four, occasionally five, alternately arranged composite leaves, these are smaller than the basal rosette leaves. Flowers hermaphrodite, white and held in small dense flower-heads at the tip of the main stem or side branching stems; four-petalled (2.7-4.8 mm long, sometimes up to 5.2 mm), and four (less often six) stamens. The elongate seed pods (*siliquae*) are small and 10-21 mm long, sometimes as small as 9, or as large as 25 mm. Flowering nearly all year but mainly March-July. A common weed of gardens, greenhouses, flowerpots, paths, railways, sand dunes, rocks, screes, walls and waste ground throughout Britain and Ireland. Native throughout most of the northern hemisphere. A cosmopolitan weed.

92

Additional note Not always easy to distinguish from *Cardamine flexuosa*.

Pollination Automatically self-pollinated.

Regeneration strategy Seed alone. When the seed pods ripen and dry, the seeds are explosively ejected, in still air up to 0.75 m above the parent plant. The seeds germinate early in the year allowing the plant to complete its life cycle ahead of summer drought.

Weed control For small outbreaks, hand-weed before flowering stage and compost, or dig in as green manure. Follow current best practice for large invasions (see Bibliography and internet).

Herbal, culinary, cultural and folklore Leaves and flowers have a peppery, cress-like flavour and can be used as a tasty ingredient in salads.

1) Seedlings 2) young adult plant 3) habit 4) flower heads 5) green and dry fruits

Hoary Cress, Thanet Cress, Pepper Cress *(Lepidium draba)*

Introduced to Swansea in 1802. Independently introduced to a number of other ports, including Thanet, at about the same time. Perennial. Deep tap root and fine, spreading roots bearing adventitious stem buds. Erect stems 20-60 cm in height, sometimes up to 90 cm, mid-green, smooth or with short dense hairs. Leaves mid-green, ovate, up to 10 cm long and 4.5 cm wide; leaf margins irregularly toothed; leaf bases clasp the stem. Flowers hermaphrodite, in large, dense, flat-topped flower heads: individual flowers white, 3-4 mm diameter; petals elongate, twice the length of sepals, six stamens, anthers yellow. Seed pods *(siliculae)* very small, broadly triangular, widest diameter 4-6 mm, with just two seeds. Flowering April-July, sometimes as late as November. A variable species best distinguished from other *Lepidium* species by the shape of its seed pods. Common in southern England, less common further north. A plant of roadsides, railways, docks, waste ground, salt marshes and arable land.

Pollination The flowers serve as pollen and nectar sources for many insects, including bees. The plant is also weakly self-fertile.

Regeneration strategies Seed and vegetative spread. Seed pods are more or less indehiscent and fall close to the parent. It also reproduces efficiently from root fragments.

Weed control For small outbreaks, hand-weed before flowering stage and compost, or dig in as green manure. Follow current best practice for larger invasions (see Bibliography and internet).

Herbal, culinary, cultural and folklore Like many plants in the cabbage family, the young leaves are sometimes used as salad, condiment or as a potherb, however, there are weakly substantiated reports suggesting that young plants contain hydrogen cyanide, so it is probably unwise to eat. Cattle and sheep will eat it, where it is abundant, and goats will eat it, but goats are famous for their robust digestions and will consume almost anything!

1) Habit 2) flower heads 3) close-up of leaf base 4) fruiting stems and fruits

Lesser Swine-cress *(Coronopus didymus)*

Introduced, first recorded in early 18th Century, origin uncertain, often cited as South America. Annual or biennial. Low-growing plant with spreading or ascending stems (5-35 cm in height, sometimes up to 50 cm), with small bright green, fern-like leaves. Stems and leaves more or less smooth, slightly lighter green, and less coarse than those of Swine-cress. The plant is often described as having a foetid odour. Flowers hermaphrodite, tiny, c. 1-1.5 mm diameter and arranged in small groups on short flowering stems: the white petals are smaller than the sepals, and sometimes absent; stamens six in number, anthers pale yellow, sometimes absent. Lower down the flower stem, young, green seed pods (*siliculae*) develop rapidly from the flowers. The pods (c. 2.5 mm long and 1.5 mm wide) are slightly wrinkly, paired and kidney-shaped, each half containing one seed. Flowering June-September, sometimes as late as October. A widespread weed of cultivated and waste ground, but avoids well-drained or acidic soils. Especially common through the southern regions of England Wales and Ireland, less common in northern areas.

Pollination Self-pollination (perhaps erroneously, ant-pollination has also been suggested).

Regeneration strategy When the seed pods ripen and dry, the seeds remain in the pods and germinate locally to the parent plant.

Weed control For small outbreaks, hand-weed before flowering stage and compost, or dig in as green manure. Follow current best practice for larger invasions (see Bibliography and internet).

Herbal, culinary, cultural and folklore The leaves are sometimes used as a pot herb.

94

1) Young plant 2) habit 3) leaves and flowers 4) green fruits

Swine-cress *(Coronopus squamatus)*

Probably native near the coast in south-east England, or introduced pre-1500. Annual or biennial. Low spreading plant with tap root. Stems 5-30 cm in height, spreading, with small stalked, deeply cut, slightly fern-like leaves. Stems and leaves coarser, and slightly deeper green than Lesser Swine-cress. Flowers small, hermaphrodite, c. 2.5 mm diameter and arranged in small groups on short flowering stems: the white petals are longer than sepals and always present; stamens six in number, anthers present, pale yellow. Lower down the flowering stems young seed pods (*siliculae*) develop rapidly after the flowers. The pods (c. 3-4.5 mm long and 2.3-3.5 mm wide) are very wrinkly/warty, paired and kidney-shaped, and each half contains one seed. Flowering May-September, sometimes as late as October. A common plant preferring nutrient-rich waste ground and trampled places, such as farmyards, paths and pastures. Particularly common in southern England. Further north, and in Scotland, Wales, and Ireland, it is more common in coastal areas.

Pollination Usually self-pollinated.

Regeneration strategy When the seed pods ripen and dry the seeds remain in the pods, and germinate locally to the parent plant.

Weed control For small outbreaks, hand-weed before flowering stage and compost, or dig in as green manure. Follow current best practice for larger invasions (see Bibliography and internet).

Herbal, culinary, cultural and folklore The seeds have been used as a peppery condiment.

95

1) Young plant 2) habit 3) flowers; 4) fruits

Danish Scurvy-grass *(Cochlearia danica)*

Native. Overwintering annual. Stems spreading to ascending 5-25 cm in height, frequently at the shorter end of this range, sometimes as low as 2 or as high as 50 cm. Leaves small, slightly fleshy, mid-green, long stalked and rounded-triangular, or ivy leaf-shaped. Flowers hermaphrodite, dense heads of small flowers, 4-5 mm diameter, four-petalled, white with light-to-deep pink/mauve reverse, and six stamens. Seed pods *(siliculae)* ovoid raindrop-shaped (3-5 mm long and 2.5-4 mm wide, sometimes up to 7 mm long and 5 mm wide), containing two to five, sometimes up to seven seeds. Flowering January-June. Originally a locally common coastal species all around the British Isles; however, winter salting of roads has made this plant a common and striking sight nationwide, on many inland roadside and motorway verges, during late winter and early spring.

96

Pollination Automatically self-pollinated, although visited by a number of small insects.

Regeneration strategy When the seed pods ripen and dry, the seeds fall in the vicinity of the parent plant.

Weed control For small outbreaks, hand-weed before flowering stage and compost, or dig in as green manure. Follow current best practice for larger invasions (see Bibliography and internet).

Herbal, culinary, cultural and folklore This is an especially striking modern example of a native plant being 'turned into a weed' by human intervention in the landscape. It was reputedly eaten by sailors as protection against scurvy.

1) Flowering habit 2) leaves 3) flowers 4) fruits

Treacle Mustard *(Erysimum cheiranthoides)*

Doubtfully native but known in England since the 16th Century. Annual. Stems erect,15-90 cm in height, slightly hairy. Lower leaves slightly hairy, elongate-ovate, leaf margins slightly undulate with wide-spaced teeth; upper leaves smaller, elongate-ovate. Flower heads crowded with bright yellow hermaphrodite flowers, c. 6 mm diameter, with six stamens, petals twice as long as sepals. Seed pods *(siliquae)* long and narrow,12-25 mm long and 1 mm wide, on slender upward angled stalks. Flowering June-August. Distribution local, especially in south-eastern England, less frequent in the south-west, Wales and the Midlands. Also occurs in central Ireland, elsewhere rare or casual. A weed of cultivated ground and waste places, it prefers light sandy soils.

Pollination Self-pollinated.

Regeneration strategy When the seed pods ripen and dry, the seeds are ejected in the vicinity of the parent plant.

Weed control For small outbreaks, hand-weed before flowering stage and compost, or dig in as green manure.

Herbal, culinary, cultural and folklore Treacle Mustard is a relative of our garden wallflowers (which are hybrid cultivars of *Erysimum cheiri*). Originally from continental Europe, Treacle Mustard spread eastward to the UK and then to North America where a common name for it is Wormseed Wallflower, an epithet alluding to its former use for treating intestinal worms.

97

1) Habit 2) close-up of flowers 3) old flower stem and young fruits 4) dry fruits and ripe seeds

Wild Radish, White Charlock, Runch *(Raphanus raphanistrum* subsp. *raphanistrum)*

Accepted with reservations as native. Annual (occasionally biennial). Slender, with whitish tap root and erect stem 20-60 cm in height, sometimes up to 100 cm, with short bristles, especially on lower stem. Leaf stems shortly hairy; leaves mid-green, shortly hairy on underside; basal leaves smaller than adult leaves, but all leaves deeply lobed, except near tip, which is more complete. Flower heads vary in size, but crowded. Individual flowers hermaphrodite, c. 2 cm diameter, sometimes from 1.5 up to 3 cm, with four spoon-shaped, white, yellow or, rarely, purple petals, usually with very clear veining, and six yellow stamens, four long and two shorter. Seed pods (*siliquae*) long and narrow (2.5-8.6 cm long, sometimes as small as 1.3 cm) on slender, upward-angled stalks. The pods, which contain from one to ten seeds, but usually c. four to seven, have pointed tips and show slight to pronounced constrictions between each enclosed seeds. Flowering time June-October, sometimes as early as May. A common weed throughout the British Isles, especially on acidic soils, but avoids markedly calcareous habitats. The white-flowered form is rare in the north.

98

Pollination Although self-pollination takes place it is ineffective, which is unusual within the British weedy species of the cabbage family (Brassicaceae). Instead Wild Radish is a significant source of pollen and nectar for a variety of pollinators, especially honey bees during the spring, butterflies (*Pieris* species) and hoverflies (*Eristalis* species).

Regeneration strategy When the seed pods ripen and dry, the seeds remain in the pods, and germinate locally to the parent plant.

Weed control For small outbreaks, hand-weed before flowering stage and compost, or dig in as green manure. Follow current best practice for large invasions (see Bibliography and internet).

Herbal, culinary, cultural and folklore Although never conclusively substantiated, this species is sometimes suggested to have played a role in the parentage of modern radishes (cultivars of *Raphanus sativus*), one of the earliest cultivated vegetables. In herbal medicine it is sometimes used to relieve rheumatic pain.

1) Young plant 2) habit 3) flowers 4) green fruits 5) ripe fruits and seeds

Charlock, Wild Mustard *(Sinapis arvensis)*

Probably native in Europe to North Africa and Asia. Annual. Height 20-100 cm, sometimes from 5 up to 220 cm. Stems and leaves darkish green with short stiff hairs; main leaves ovate, 8-20 cm long, with coarsely toothed margins. Flowers hermaphrodite, four-petalled, bright yellow, c. 30-40 mm diameter, sometimes up to 45 mm, with six stamens. Seed pods *(siliquae)* long (c. 22-57 mm), smooth or slightly hairy. Seeds c. four to 24 in number, spheroidal, dark brown or black. Flowering time May-July. A very variable species. Widely distributed in the British Isles with the exception of north-west Scotland. An abundant weed of arable land, less frequently roadsides and waste places, it favours calcareous and heavy soils.

Pollination Various bees and flies. Also host to some small butterflies, including the Small White *(Pieris raphae)*.

Regeneration strategy Seed only. When the seed pods ripen and dry, the seeds are ejected in the vicinity of the parent plant. An average plant produces between 1000-4000 seeds and these can persist in the soil for as much as 50 years.

Weed control Intolerant of shade, easily controlled by selective herbicides. Follow current best, preferably organic, practice for large invasions (see Bibliography and internet).

Herbal, culinary, cultural and folklore Oil extracted from the seeds is edible, it is also used in soap manufacture and, in the past, for oil lamps. The seeds can be ground to produce a hot mustard. Young leaves may be cooked as a vegetable.

Toxicity Care should always be taken before preparing seeds or leaves for human consumption: when flowering the whole plant is an irritant. Ingested seed may cause inflammation of the intestine.

99

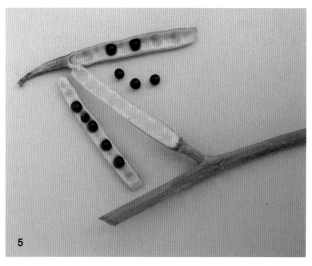

1) Young plant 2) adult flowering plant 3) flowers and leaves 4) fruits 5) ripe fruits and seeds

Hedge Mustard *(Sisymbrium officinale)*

Native. Annual, overwintering or biennial. Stiffly erect, branching stems 15-100 cm in height, sometimes up to 140 cm, lend a rather wiry appearance to old or dead plants. Stems have short, downward pointing hairs. Annual plants much smaller and less branched. Stems and leaves mid-green, the leaves have short soft hairs; basal rosette leaves are deeply lobed; the smaller, less lobed stem leaves and the upper leaves often have only a basal pair of lobes, or none. Flowers hermaphrodite, closely packed in groups at the tip of each inflorescence stem, four-petalled, light yellow (2-4 mm diameter, sometimes up to 5 mm); the petals are about half as long again as the sepals, there are six stamens. As the stem lengthens with age, thin pod-like fruits (*siliquae*) develop and align closely to the stem, while new flowers continue to open at the stem tip. Flowering mainly June-July, although it may be found in flower somewhere at almost any month of the year. Widely distributed throughout the British Isles with the exception of Shetland. It is closely associated with human activity, and a common plant of farmland, hedges, roadsides and waste places.

100

Pollination Self-pollinated.

Regeneration strategy When the seed pods ripen and dry, the seeds are ejected in the vicinity of the parent plant. For caterpillars of some butterflies, including the Small White Butterfly (*Pieris raphae*), it is a valuable food source.

Weed control For small outbreaks, hand-weed before flowering stage and compost, or dig in as green manure. Follow current best practice for larger invasions (see Bibliography and internet).

Herbal, culinary, cultural and folklore Native to Europe and North Africa, this species is now well-established throughout the world. In folk medicine it was once valued for soothing sore throats (in France a common name for this species is Singer's Plant because it was considered an infallible remedy for loss of voice). An old local name for this species is Lucifer Matches, apparently referring to the appearance of the ripe seed pods.

1) Habit 2) flowers and leaves 3) closed fruits 4) open fruits and seeds

Field Penny-cress *(Thlaspi arvense)*

Native. Annual. Smooth, erect leafy stem 10-60 cm in height, sometimes a little less or up to 80 cm. Leaves smooth, mid-green, elongate with stalk-like bases, margins either straight or wavy-edged with widely-spaced teeth; basal rosette leaves up to 7 cm long. Flowers hermaphrodite, closely packed on groups at the tip of each flowering stem: c. 2.5 mm diameter with four white petals which are twice as long as the sepals, there are six stamens. As the stem lengthens with age broad, almost circular, pod-like rimmed fruits *(siliculae)* (c. 6-20 mm wide) develop at the tips of the old flower stalks, which are angled c. 45-90° from the main stem. Flowering May-July, sometimes as early as March or as late as October. A weed of arable land and waste places, particularly abundant in the south and east of Britain, more scattered in the north and west.

Pollination Small insects, including bees and flies, or self-pollinated.

Regeneration strategy When the seed pods ripen and dry, the seeds are ejected in the vicinity of the parent plant. The longevity of buried seed in general does not seem to exceed more than a few years.

Weed control For small outbreaks, hand-weed before flowering stage and compost, or dig in as green manure. Follow current best practice for larger invasions (see Bibliography and internet).

Herbal, culinary, cultural and folklore A weed widespread in Europe, North Africa and Asia. Its presence in the USA is probably a result of European migration. It has long been regarded as a nuisance weed. It is said by many to have an unpleasant odour when bruised, leading to its other widespread common name, Stinkweed. Like many other species of family Brassicaceae its leaves may be eaten, and its seeds used for mustard. The generic name *Thlaspi* is a combination of the Greek words *thlao* (to flatten) and *aspis* (a shield).

101

1) Habit, young plant 2) flower heads 3) green fruits 4) dry fruits and seeds

CANNABACEAE *(Hemp Family)*

Hop *(Humulus lupulus)*

Native. Herbaceous climbing perennial. Clockwise climbing stems (bines) 3-6 m in height with short downward pointing hairs, leaves 10-15 cm long, sometimes as small as 4 cm, three or five-lobed or not lobed; leaf margins toothed. Flowers dioecious: male flowers have five *tepals* (a cross between a petal and a sepal) and five stamens of similar length to the tepals, c. 5 mm long. Female flowers, grouped in very small, long-stalked ovoid inflorescences comprising overlapping green bracts, each with two stalkless highly reduced flowers at the base, comprising an ovary with a long two-branched style; at maturity the bracts enlarge, forming a soft, light green cone-like structure, c. 2-3 cm, with a pair of rounded fruits (c. 2 mm long). The outer bases of the bracts and the fruits are more or less covered in tiny yellow glands, and it is these glands which give the flavour to beer. Flowering July-August. Widely distributed throughout the British Isles, especially in hedgerows and banks, the wild occurrences mostly considered to be from escapes back into the wild, following widespread cultivation for the beer industry since the 16th Century.

102

Additional notes It is amusing to note that, of the three botanically accepted species of north temperate Hops, the European *Humulus lupulus* twines clockwise, while the far eastern *Humulus japonica* twines anticlockwise – Flanders and Swann (see Bindweed for more detail) would have been delighted to discover such a misalliance between two closely related species.

Pollination Wind.

Regeneration strategies Mainly by rampant climbing semi-woody vines, but also from seed.

Weed control Usually restricted to hedgerows and banks. Remove at young stage, prior to fruit/seed development. Follow current best practice for large invasions (see Bibliography and internet).

Herbal, culinary, cultural and folklore The female inflorescences are used in beer-making. Hopped ale or beer was first brewed in England in the 15th Century, and was initially regarded as adulterated, however, the product was accepted when it was realised that the resinous compounds in the Hops helped preserve the ale longer in warm weather. Prior to late 19th and early 20th Century innovations in Europe leading to clean drinking water, beer was the favoured drink of the masses. The brewing process sterilises the water it uses, making it a very healthy alternative to the foul and infected water previously on offer in most urban communities.

  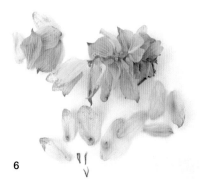

1) Habit, female plant in fruit 2) male inflorescences 3) young female flowers 4) close-up of male flowers
5) female fruits, scales with basal resinous glands 6) scales with basal seeds and the old (detached) paired styles

CARYOPHYLLACEAE *(Campion & Pink Family)*

Common Mouse-ear *(Cerastium fontanum)*

Native. Perennial with slender, creeping rootstock. Non-flowering shoots up to c. 15 cm in height, tending to be more or less prostrate. Flowering shoots erect, up to 45 cm in height. Stem leaves opposite, ovate, dark green, stalkless, densely covered in short hairs. Flowers hermaphrodite, short-stalked, in groups of c. three to seven, on short stems, 12-25 mm diameter: five white petals, elongate, deeply cleft, with ten stamens and five styles. Sepals green, similar length to petals, pointed ovate, with translucent white margins. Seed pods 9-12 mm long, distinctly curved, with toothed margins. Seeds tiny (c. 0.35 mm long), droplet-shaped. Flowering April-September. A common weed throughout the British Isles, favouring well-drained calcareous and neutral soils, especially arable and grassland. Also common on roadside verges, wasteland, sand dunes and shingle.

103

Pollination Flies or self-pollinated.

Regeneration strategy Seed dispersal locally, or short distances by wind.

Weed control For small outbreaks, hand-weed before flowering stage and compost, or dig in as green manure.

Herbal, culinary, cultural and folklore Leaves edible either raw or cooked. This species is not confined to Britain; it occurs in many other temperate regions.

1) Habit and flowering stems 2) close-up of flower 3) stems and stem leaves 4) seed heads and seeds

Sticky Mouse-ear *(Cerastium glomeratum)*

Native. Annual. Stems 5-45 cm in height, stem leaves opposite, ovate, small, pale yellowish-green and covered with short translucent hairs. Flowers hermaphrodite, in compact clusters, short-stalked, with five elongate deeply cleft white petals, (c. same length as sepals or longer); ten stamens, five styles. Sepals glandular with long translucent hairs. Seed pod 7-10 mm long and curved with toothed margins. Seeds tiny (0.35 mm long), droplet-shaped. Flowering most of the year. A common weed throughout the British Isles, on arable land, pathways, in gardens, roadsides and waste places, on walls, banks and sand dunes, especially light sandy soils.

Pollination Self-pollinated.

Regeneration strategy Seed only, locally dispersed, or short distances by wind.

Weed control For small outbreaks, hand-weed before flowering stage and compost, or dig in as green manure.

Herbal, culinary, cultural and folklore Juice of leaves and stems was applied to the forehead to relieve headaches, or dropped into nose to stop nosebleeds.

104

1) Seedlings 2) habit and flowers 3) close-up of flowers 4) young seed pods

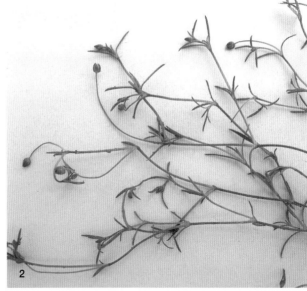

Annual Pearlwort *(Sagina apetala)*

Native. Annual. A variable species, often very delicate ('lanky') in appearance. Non-rooting stems with several angled or ascending branches, 3-18 cm in height. Loose central rosette of leaves which soon withers; stem leaves long (3-7 mm) and very narrow, in groups of two to four at well-spaced junctions on stem. Flowers hermaphrodite, borne on long, thin, smooth stems, emerging at leaf junctions. Petals minute (or absent), often falling early. Sepals four or five ovate, with slightly 'hooded' tips. Seed capsules thin, sepia coloured when ripe (could be mistaken for old petals). Seeds very tiny (c. 0.25 mm long), droplet-shaped. Flowering May-August. Common throughout most of British Isles, rare or local in northern Scotland, absent from Shetland and the Orkneys. Often occurs on well-drained bare or gravelly ground, verges, paths and walls.

Pollination Small insects or self-pollinated.

Regeneration strategy Local and wind dispersal of tiny, dust-like seeds.

Weed control For small outbreaks, hand-weed before flowering stage and compost, or dig in as green manure.

Herbal, culinary, cultural and folklore None recorded.

105

1) Variation between plants 2) plant habit 3) flowers and seeds

Procumbent Pearlwort *(Sagina procumbens)*

Native. Perennial. Main stem short and non-flowering, lateral stems up to 20 cm in height, prostrate and rooting below, then ascending. Distinctive central leaf rosette; leaves narrow, elongate, 5-12 mm long, mid-to-deep green and glossy. Flower stalks 2-4 cm long, smooth, erect at first, then curving down at the tip before straightening again. Flowers hermaphrodite, four to five white or very pale blue petals. Sepals four or five in number, green, hooded and closely covering green seed pod but becoming horizontal to ripe pods. Seeds very tiny (c. 0.25 mm long), droplet-shaped. Flowering May-September. Common throughout the British Isles on grassy verges, waste ground, paths, lawns, banks, wall tops and stream-sides. It generally tolerates moister habitats than *Sagina apetala*.

Pollination Self-pollinated.

Regeneration strategy Local and wind dispersal of tiny, dust-like seeds.

Weed control For small outbreaks, hand-weed before flowering stage and compost, or dig in as green manure.

Herbal, culinary, cultural and folklore This species of Pearlwort is considered to have special powers in the Highlands and Islands of Scotland, where there is a belief that it was the first plant Christ stepped on when he came to Earth. It is traditionally revered, and gathered to use as protection against evil spirits, as well as for its magic powers.

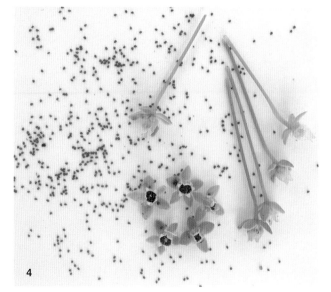

1) Young plant 2) flowers 3) close-up of flowers 4) fruits and seeds

Red Campion *(Silene dioica)*

Native. Biennial to perennial with slender creeping rootstock and numerous flat-lying shoots. Stems erect, softly hairy, sometimes sticky; flowering stems 30-90 cm in height. Leaves opposite, broadly ovate, lower and upper leaves stalkless. Flowers numerous, dioecious, 18-25 mm diameter, scentless: five deeply divided, bright rose pink petals with short, paler, toothed flanges at their bases. Male flowers with ten stamens and a hairy, slightly sticky cylindrical calyx tube; pistil of female flowers with five styles, a broadly ovoid seed capsule and calyx tube. Seed capsule opening widely to disperse ripe, kidney-shaped seeds (c. 1.5 mm long) with regular lines of tubercles. The teeth on the rim of the open capsule are down-curled. Flowering mostly May-July. Locally abundant throughout the British Isles, especially in the west, in woodland, woodland clearings, roadside banks, cliff ledges and scree. Favours base-rich or calcareous, well-drained soils (up to altitudes of 1070 m in Scotland). *Silene dioica* and *Silene alba* are not commonly found growing together because of differences in their habitat requirements.

Pollination Long-tongued flies and bees, butterflies.

Regeneration strategy Seed only, locally dispersed.

Weed control For small outbreaks, hand-weed before flowering stage and compost, or dig in as green manure. Follow current best practice for larger invasions (see Bibliography and internet).

Herbal, culinary, cultural and folklore
The roots contain saponins, mildly toxic glycosides used as foaming agents, and formerly often used as a soap substitute for washing clothes and/or hair. Red Campion was also considered protection against snake bites. The botanical genus name *Silene* refers to the Greek woodland god Silenius. In folklore fairies used *Silene* to protect their honey stores; however, many of the folklore references to *Silene* refer to the stickier Catch Fly species, for example *S. noctiflora* (Night-flowering Campion) and *S. nutans* (Nottingham Catchfly). It was said that throwing a Red Campion plant at a scorpion rendered the animal harmless. Although the UK has no native scorpions, the Sheerness Docks is home to a flourishing colony of Yellow-tailed Scorpions introduced about 200 years ago.

107

1) Young leaves 2) male flowers 3) sections through female (left) and male (right) flowers 4) dry seed pods

White Campion *(Silene latifolia* subsp. *alba)*

Native. Annual or short-lived perennial with thick creeping rootstock and a few flat-lying shoots. Stems erect, softly hairy, sometimes sticky; flowering stems 30-100 cm in height. Leaves opposite, broadly ovate; lower and upper leaves stemless. Flowers few, dioecious, 25-30 mm diameter, slightly and sweetly night-scented: five pure white petals, deeply divided with short, paler, toothed flanges at their bases. Male flowers with ten stamens and a cylindrical calyx tube; pistil of female flowers with five styles, a broadly ovoid seed capsule and calyx tube. Seed capsule opens widely to disperse ripe, kidney-shaped, warty seeds (c. 1.5 mm long). The pointed teeth on the rim of the open capsule straight or curving, not curling as in Red Campion. Flowering May-September. Common throughout most of the British Isles but less frequent in the west, and scarce or local in Ireland and parts of northern Scotland. Occurs in hedgerows, waste places and cultivated land on dry, especially calcareous, soils. *Silene alba* and *Silene dioica* are not commonly found growing together because of differences in their habitat requirements.

108

Pollination Long-snouted hoverflies (*Rhingia* spp.), butterflies and moths, notably the Silver Y Moth (*Plusia gamma*).

Regeneration strategy Seed only, locally dispersed.

Weed control For small outbreaks, hand-weed before flowering stage and compost, or dig in as green manure. Follow current best practice for larger invasions (see Bibliography and internet).

Herbal, culinary, cultural and folklore Like Red Campion, the roots contain saponins, mildly toxic glycosides used as foaming agents, and formerly often used as a soap substitute for washing clothes and/ or hair. Called Mother-dee in the Western Isles of Scotland due to the superstition that if you pick the flowers your mother will die.

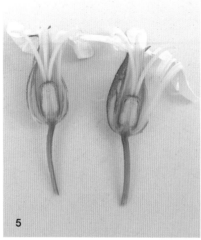

1) Habit 2) adult stem leaves 3) female flower 4) section through male flower 5) section through female flower 6) seed capsule and seeds

Corn Spurrey *(Spergula arvensis)*

Native. Annual. Stems slender; flowering stems 7.5-40 cm in height, with 'knee' joints which allow the fruiting heads to point downwards after flowering. Short glandular hairs on stems and leaves; leaves very long, narrow, needle-like and grass-green, arranged in whorls on lower stems. Flowers with 1-2.5 cm long stalks: hermaphrodite, 4-7 mm diameter, with five white petals, slightly longer than the ovate-glandular sepals, stamens ten or fewer. Seed capsule ovoid, up to twice sepal length. Seeds blackish, smooth, clam-shaped, with tiny pale *papillae* (small, soft, nipple-like protuberances) near the rim. Flowering June-August. Locally abundant throughout the British Isles. An often troublesome, lime-intolerant weed of arable land, favouring light, acidic, sandy soils, or gravelly habitats. Its altitudinal limit coincides with the limits of arable farming.

Pollination Mostly self-pollinated when flowers (which only open for three to five hours a day) are closed. When open, the flowers have an unpleasant odour which attracts flies and bees.

Regeneration strategy Seed only, dispersed locally from the downward pointing ripe fruiting heads.

Weed control For small outbreaks, hand-weed before flowering stage and compost, or dig in as green manure, A persistent and troublesome weed in market gardens and farmland. Follow current best practice for large invasions (see Bibliography and internet).

Herbal, culinary, cultural and folklore A British weed introduced to North America by immigrants. In some parts of Europe this species is grown as a crop for fodder; sheep are fond of it, and cows fed on it are said to give good milk. Like Fat Hen and Black-bindweed, these seeds also formed part of the last meal of Tollund Man, recorded from the stomach contents (Denmark, early Celtic Iron Age – c. 400BC-200AD).

109

1) Young plant 2) habit 3) flowers 4) seed capsule and seeds

Common Chickweed *(Stellaria media)*

Native. Annual. Stems prostrate and ascending, 5-40 cm in height with a single line of hairs between each leaf pair. Leaves mid-green, smooth: lower leaves 3-20 mm long, narrowly ovate, with pointed tips, long-stalked; upper leaves broadly ovate with pointed tips and stems short or absent. Flowers hermaphrodite, with five white petals, deeply divided to base, not exceeding sepal length, stamens two to eight; sepals with a narrow translucent margin. Fruit capsules ovoid-oblong, a little longer than the sepals, with stalks curving downwardly. Seeds kidney-shaped, c. 0.5 mm long and covered with regular lines of tubercles. Flowering January-December. Widespread throughout the British Isles. An abundant weed of cultivated ground and waste places. Particularly troublesome because it flowers and produces seeds in a very short time, throughout the year, unaffected by day length.

Pollination Self-pollinated.

Regeneration strategy High seed production. Spreads locally and by bird-dispersed seed.

Weed control For small outbreaks, hand-weed before flowering stage and compost, or dig in as green manure. Follow current best practice for larger invasions (see Bibliography and internet).

Herbal, culinary, cultural and folklore A British weed introduced to North America by immigrants. The seeds provide a valuable food source for small birds nearly all year round and were a well-known food source for caged birds for hundreds of years. Rich in minerals and trace elements essential to man. 'Chickweed water' is an old wives remedy for obesity as it helps to prevent water retention.

110

1) Habit on pavement edge 2) flowering habit 3) flowers and young fruits 4) dry seed capsules and seeds

CONVOLVULACEAE *(Bindweed Family)*

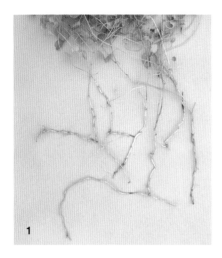

Field Bindweed, Bindweed, Cornbine *(Convolvulus arvensis)*

Native. Perennial. Stems 20-75 cm long, pinkish-green or green, scrambling or climbing anticlockwise around the stems of other plants, or spreading horizontally across clear stretches of ground. Roots penetrate into the earth to a depth of 3 m or more. Leaves mid-green, broadly arrow-head shaped. Flowers hermaphrodite, delicately scented, trumpet-shaped, white or pink (or striped white and pink), 2-2.5 cm diameter. Rounded ovate fruits contain four shallowly triangular seeds. Flowering time June-September. Widespread and common throughout most of England, except on the poorest soils. Less common in the north of England and absent from northern Scotland.

Pollination Various long-tongued insects, hoverflies, or self-pollinated. The leaves are the larval food plant for the Convolvulus Hawkmoth (*Agrius convolvuli*).

Regeneration strategies Seed and vegetative spread. Long winding or creeping stems, and underground roots with runners that break quite easily when pulled. Four-seeded fruits, which are shed locally to the plant.

Weed control Careful removal and burning of over-ground stems, and deep-digging of underground runners, or follow current best, preferably organic, practice for large invasions (see Bibliography and internet).

Herbal, culinary, cultural and folklore Leaves and stems have been shown to have high nutritional value as fodder, and were popularly used as rabbit food. The enchantingly pretty flowers belie the troublesome nature of this serious and persistent weed of arable crops and gardens, which is known in some parts of the British Isles as Devil's Guts. Bindweed is the co-subject (with Honeysuckle) of *Misalliance*, a delightfully funny song about the clockwise or anticlockwise habits of climbing plants by Flanders and Swann (1957). A British weed that was introduced to the USA by immigrants.

1) Young root runners 2) young stem runners 3) pink-flowered plant colonising road verge 4) flowers 5) fruits and seeds

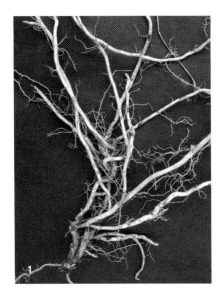  

Hedge Bindweed, Bellbine, Larger Bindweed *(Calystegia sepium)*

Native. Perennial. Stems 1-3 m long, reddish or green, scrambling or climbing anticlockwise around the stems of other plants, or spreading horizontally across clear stretches of ground. Rhizomes seldom more than 30 cm deep, although the roots penetrate into the earth to a depth of 3 m or more. Leaves mid-green, elongate, heart-shaped. Flowers hermaphrodite, unscented, 5-7 cm diameter, twisted in bud and trumpet-shaped when open, five-lobed, usually pure white, occasionally pale pink or with a narrow pink stripe up the centre of each lobe. At the base of the flower tube two large green bracts cover the calyx. Rounded ovate fruits contain four shallowly triangular seeds. Flowering June-September. Abundant and widespread throughout most of the British Isles, but scarce or absent from northern Scotland and the Shetland Isles.

112

Pollination Self-incompatible. Pollination by various long-tongued insects, hoverflies and bumblebees. Flowers remain open on moonlit nights, and are reputed to be visited by the diurnal Convolvulus Hawk-moth (*Agrius convolvuli*); however, there seems to be some doubt about this as records of visits are very rare. The species name of the moth apparently alludes to the diet of its larvae, which feed on both *Calystegia* and *Convolvulus* leaves.

Regeneration strategies Seed and vegetative spread. Long winding stems, deep underground roots and underground root runners (rhizomes) that break quite easily when pulled. Seed shed locally from capsules.

Weed control Careful removal and burning of over-ground stems, and deep-digging of underground runners, or follow current best, preferably organic, practice for large invasions (see Bibliography and internet).

Herbal, culinary, cultural and folklore Traditionally children, notably in the counties surrounding London, popped the white flowers out of the bracts chanting "Granny pop out of bed" or "Lazy Maisie pop out of bed".

Toxicity The roots especially have been used as an extremely effective purgative. It is unadvisable to follow this practice without knowledge or supervision.

1) Root runners 2) stem runners taking hold 3) rampant flowering habit 4) flower 5) fruits, each with four seeds

CUCURBITACEAE *(Bryony & Cucumber Family)*

White Bryony *(Bryonia dioica)*

Native. Perennial rootstock, can grow to very large size. A climber. Stems very long, branching from near the base, brittle with rough hairs. Tendrils develop from the stem-leaf junctions in a fascinating manner: they start out straight, then tightly coil; however, to avoid self-twisting, the coiled tendril then straightens itself for a short length, before coiling in the opposite direction – this is termed *tendril perversion*. Leaves mid-green with three to five strongly pronounced lobes. Flowers dioecious: petals white with three to five green veins, and much longer than sepals. Male flowers with short stalks, 12-18 mm diameter, in groups of three to eight; stamens five, often united; female flowers without stalks, 10-12 mm diameter, in groups of two to five, pistils split into two. Young berries (fruits) green, turning red when ripe, three- to six-seeded. Flowering May to September. Widespread in lowland England, except in the extreme west, but rare or unknown in Scotland and Ireland. A frequent plant of copses, woodland margins, hedges and scrub, especially abundant on calcareous soils.

Additional notes The only other British Bryony, Black Bryony *(Tamus communis)*, is not related to White Bryony. Black Bryony is the only British species of the Yam family (Dioscoreaceae) and is a monocotyledon, whilst White Bryony is a dicotyledon. The comparison between the two species is mainly because both species are dioecious climbers, and have very large thick roots (tubers), and produce very poisonous red berries.

Pollination Bees and other insects.

Regeneration strategy Seed only. A rapidly spreading climber blanketing hedgerows. It is stimulated into root shoot growth if the stems or roots are damaged.

Weed control Careful removal of young growth prior to flowering, and especially digging out of rootstocks. Follow current best, preferably organic, practice for large invasions (see Bibliography and internet).

Herbal, culinary, cultural and folklore This species is the only member of the Bryony & Cucumber family native to the UK. One of its chief uses was as a substitute for the more celebrated mandrake (a Mediterranean plant, which does not occur naturally in Britain), which was supposed to help women conceive if they carried it near their body, following the story of Rachel and Leah in the Old Testament (Genesis). The roots were trimmed to look like a child and even given grassy hair, then hung in English herb shops into the 19th Century.

Toxicity The large, starchy tubers and the red berries are poisonous: the main toxin is the glycoside bryonin, a drastic purgative.

113

1) Large rootstock 2) male flowers 3) fallen vine of ripe red fruits, resembling a bead necklace

ERICACEAE *(Heather Family)*

Rhododendron *(Rhododendron ponticum)*

Introduced in 1763. First recorded in the wild in 1894. Perennial shrub. Maximum dimensions c. 6-8 m high and 6 m wide. Spreads mainly by lateral branching and rooting. Bark of branches almost smooth. Leaves ovate with pointed apices and un-toothed margins, short-stalked, deep green and leathery. Flowers hermaphrodite, c. 5 cm across, funnel-shaped, bisymmetric, mauve, central upper petal usually flecked with light brown spots; stamens ten; pistil long and narrow, c. twice the length of elongate (sausage-shaped) ovary. Seeds numerous, very small (c. 1.5-1.8 mm long). Flowering May-June. This species is a serious non-native invader. It favours sandy or peaty soils and has thoroughly naturalised in many areas, notably in Wales and parts of East Anglia, often to the detriment of less vigorous native species.

Pollination The pollen is presented not loose, but in long threads. The flecked spots of the upper central petal are an attractant for insect visitors, mainly bumblebees, and social wasps (subfamily Vespinae).

Regeneration strategies A very invasive shrub which spreads rapidly by horizontal layering and rooting branches, and also from wind-dispersed seed. A flower head can produce 3-7000 seeds. A single plant can cover many metres of ground within a few years, effectively cutting out light for growth for other species.

Weed control For small invasions root out and burn. Seek up to date professional advice for major eradication (see Bibliography and internet).

Herbal, culinary, cultural and folklore Originally introduced as a fashionable new shrub, it was later found by gamekeepers to be excellent ground cover for pheasants. The native geographic range for this species includes Portugal, Spain, the Caucasus, Turkey, Lebanon and Bulgaria. Its changing distribution since the Last Glacial Maximum, c. 20,000 years ago, is well-documented.

Toxicity Animals such as sheep and cattle may be poisoned by toxic chemicals after ingesting *Rhododendron ponticum*, but this is rare as the plant is not typically eaten by these animals unless they are desperate for food. Human poisoning from this species does occur, albeit rarely, if honey containing nectar or pollen from *Rhododendron ponticum* has been consumed. This is known as Honey-intoxication or Mad Honey Disease. For this reason most beekeepers do not site their beehives within bee-foraging range of *Rhododendron ponticum* plantations and, furthermore, all commercially sold honey is subject to pollen checking prior to marketing to confirm floral sources.

114

1) Young plants 2) invasion 3) seed capsules and seeds 4) flower heads

4

EUPHORBIACEAE *(Spurge Family)*

Dwarf Spurge *(Euphorbia exigua)*

Native. Annual with a short tap root. Stems erect, smooth, waxy bluish-green, 5-30 cm in height. Leaves narrow, stalkless, spirally arranged, linear and mid-grey/green (0.5-3 cm long). Flowering stem branching with three to five rays; stems exude a milky sap when broken. Flowers small, monoecious: five tiny male flowers, each with a single stamen, surrounded by a ring of five oval, green-horned, reddish-brown glands and a thick-stalked female flower. The female flower comprises a green, smooth lobed, rounded, three-celled ovary with a three-branched style at the top, like a little tassel. The thick stalk (*pedicel*) of the female flower elongates in fruiting stage. Each flower group is flanked by a pair of large, elongate leafy bracts and, at an angle to these, one or two more pairs of stalked bracts subsequently develop. Ripe seeds are tiny, brown and oval, with a reticulate surface and a small whitish blob (*aril*) at one end. Flowering April-November. A plant of lowland Britain, more or less confined to the south. It is scarce or local in the south-west, Wales, Ireland and southern Scotland. A frequent weed of arable crops on dry, base-rich or calcareous soils. Its small stature allows the plants to survive the cutting of the corn.

116

Pollination Flies, notably *Dilophus febrilis* (Fever Fly) and *Bibio hortulanus* (similar to St. Mark's Fly but the female is rich brown, not black).

Regeneration strategy The seeds colonise locally via expulsion from the ripe pods. Seeds are further dispersed by ants who are attracted by the nutritious arils.

Weed control Before fruiting stage, hand-weed or hoe out young plants, or use as green manure by digging in. Follow current best, preferably organic, practice for large invasions (see Bibliography and internet).

Herbal, culinary, cultural and folklore None found.

Toxicity The sap should not be ingested, or placed in contact with the skin for prolonged periods.

1) Habit 2) close-up of male flowers and female fruits 3) plants and stems 4) ripe fruits (centre)

Caper Spurge, Mole Weed *(Euphorbia lathyris)*

Arguably, in botanical literature, an introduction. Biennial. Stem erect, waxy bluish-green, up to 1.5 m in height. Narrow spear-shaped stem leaves (5-15 cm long) are bluish-green with greenish-white midrib and veins. Stem leaves arranged in opposite but successive pairs, presenting a strikingly regular arrangement of four-rowed leaves in young plants. Stems and leaves exude a milky sap. Flowers small, monoecious: five tiny male flowers, each with a single stamen, surrounded by a ring of five bluntly lobed greenish-yellow glands, and a thick-stalked female flower. The female flower comprises a smooth lobed, rounded-triangular, three-celled ovary with a three-branched style at the top like a little tassel. The stalk of the female flower elongates in fruiting stage. Each flower group is flanked by a pair of large leafy bracts and, at an angle to these, one or two more pairs of stalked bracts develop. Seeds are brown and oval, with a reticulate surface and a small whitish blob (*aril*) at one end. Flowering time June-July. Widely distributed in England and Wales as an escape from cultivation, or as a garden weed.

Pollination Flies, notably *Dilophus febrilis* (Fever Fly) and *Bibio hortulanus* (similar to St. Mark's Fly but the female is rich brown, not black).

Regeneration strategy Projectile seeds which can land as much as three metres from the parent plant. Seeds are further dispersed by ants who are attracted by the nutritious arils.

Weed control Before fruiting stage, hand-weed or hoe out young plants, or use as green manure by digging in.

Herbal, culinary, cultural and folklore A stylish border plant (if kept under control); sometimes the seeds are pickled as ersatz capers (true capers are the pickled flower buds of *Capparis spinosa*, a Mediterranean species not related to Euphorbiaceae) but, given the toxic properties of the plant, it might be wise to refrain from pickling without expert guidance. Enjoyed or tolerated by gardeners as it is considered to deter moles. Used in folk medicine as a purgative, antiseptic poison, and a remedy for cancer, corns and warts.

Toxicity All parts poisonous. The seeds yield a violently purgative oil, the toxic principles being euphorbin and oil of euphorbia. Handling may cause skin irritation as the plant produces latex.

117

1) Two seedlings 2) two mature plants 3) large maturing fruit (left), young fruit and male flower (upper right) 4) fruits and seeds

Petty Spurge *(Euphorbia peplus)*

Native. Annual. Height 10-30 cm. Stems and leaves smooth and light green. Leaves oval-elongate (0.5-5 cm long), short-stalked with smooth margins. Stems and leaves exude a milky sap when broken. Flowering stems branching in threes from main stem. Flowers small, monoecious: five male flowers, each with a single stamen, surrounded by a ring of five crescent-shaped, horned glands, and a thick stalked female flower. The female flower comprises a green, ridged, three-celled ovary, rounded triangular in shape, with a three-branched style at the top like a little tassle. The stalk of the female flower elongates in fruiting stage. Each flower pair is flanked by a pair of large, leafy bracts and, at right angles to these, a stem supporting another pair of bracts that enclose developing flowers. Seeds mid-grey, oblong with distinctive oval to round pits and a small white blob *(aril)* at one end. Flowering July-October, sometimes as early as April or as late as November. Widely distributed in the British Isles but less common further north. Rare or absent in large parts of northern and western Scotland. An abundant weed of fertile soils; occurs in gardens, arable crops and disturbed ground, to an altitude of c. 400 m.

Pollination Flies, notably *Dilophus febrilis* (Fever Fly) and *Bibio hortulanus* (similar to St. Mark's Fly but the female is rich brown, not black).

Regeneration strategy The seeds can colonise locally via seed propulsion from parent plant, to a distance of more than one metre. Seeds further dispersed by ants who are attracted by the nutritious arils.

Weed control Before fruiting stage, hand-weed or hoe out young plants, or use as green manure by digging in. Follow current best, preferably organic, practice for large invasions (see Bibliography and internet).

Herbal, culinary, cultural and folklore The milky sap is toxic to rapidly replicating human tissue. It has long been used in traditional medicine for common skin lesions, and is being investigated for curing some cancers. The active component of the sap is a diterpine ester: ingenol mebutate.

Toxicity The sap should not be ingested, or placed in contact with the skin for prolonged periods.

118

1) Seedlings 2) flowering plant 3) male flowers and female fruits 4) fruits and seeds

Sun Spurge *(Euphorbia helioscopia)*

Native. Annual. Height 10-50 cm. Stems and leaves smooth, light green. Leaves oval-elongate (1.5-5 cm long), short-stalked with toothed margins. Stems and leaves exude a milky sap when broken. Flowering stems branching in fives from main stem. Flowers small, monoecious: male flowers with a single stamen on a jointed stalk, surrounded by five oval green glands, and female flowers comprising a three-branched style on a smooth, rounded three-celled ovary with a stalk that elongates in fruiting stage. Each flower pair is flanked by a pair of large leafy bracts and, at right angles to these, the next pair of developing flowers, still enclosed in leafy bracts. Seeds raindrop-shaped with a raised network-like pattern and a small blob (*aril*) or a small flat area – the aril scar – at the pointed end. Flowering May-October, sometimes as late as November. Widely distributed throughout the British Isles, but becoming increasingly scarce and more coastally distributed in Scotland. A common weed of arable crops, waste ground, roadsides and gardens. Most frequent on calcareous or base-rich soils.

Pollination Flies, notably *Dilophus febrilis* (Fever Fly) and *Bibio hortulanus* (similar to St. Mark's Fly but the female is rich brown, not black).

Regeneration strategy Numerous seeds which can colonise locally via seed propulsion from parent plant, to a distance of more than two metres. Seeds further dispersed by ants who are attracted by the nutritious arils.

Weed control Before fruiting stage, hand-weed or hoe out young plants, or use as green manure by digging in. Follow current best, preferably organic, practice for large invasions (see Bibliography and internet).

Herbal, culinary, cultural and folklore Other common names include Mad Woman's Milk.

Toxicity The sap should not be ingested, or in skin contact for prolonged periods.

119

1) Seedlings 2) young plant habit 3) a large plant (c. 1 m in height) 4) male and female flowers 5) fruits and seeds

Annual Mercury *(Mercurialis annua)*

Native. Annual. Stems smooth, erect and branching with a prominent rib, 10-50 cm in height. Leaves opposite and oval with toothed margins, 1.5-5 cm long. Leaf stalk 2-15 mm long. Flowering stems arise from stem leaf junctions. Flowers usually dioecious. In male plants the flowers are borne in long spike-like clusters and have four ovate sepals with no petals but numerous stamens producing copious amounts of pollen. Female plants also have four thin, pale brownish sepals but no petals. The fruit is a bristly capsule (2-3 mm diameter) which splits in two halves when ripe and contains one oval seed. Flowering July-October. In the UK it is largely restricted to southern England, though scattered further north, and in southern Scotland, south Wales and south-east Ireland. Mostly in waste places and gardens.

Pollination The loose panicles and copious pollen of male flowers are typical of a wind-pollinated plant. It is not self-fertile.

Regeneration strategy Female plants produce numerous seeds which fall locally. Notably, the two sexes sometimes occur on the same plant: this unusual situation has made the species an ideal model for studying sexual systems in plants.

Weed control Before fruiting stage, hand-weed or hoe out young plants, or use as green manure by digging in. Follow current best, preferably organic, practice for large invasions (see Bibliography and internet).

Herbal, culinary, cultural and folklore A weed that is also a widespread native elsewhere in Europe, in North Africa and the Middle East. In herbal medicine it has emetic, emollient and purgative value.

Toxicity The juice is considered to be emetic and the seeds dangerously purgative but heat usually destroys the poisonous principles: mercurialine and oil of euphorbia. Its unpleasant smell usually makes it unpalatable to animals.

120

1) Seedlings 2) plant habit – male 3) plant habit – female 4) male flowers and pollen
5) small buff female flowers in leaf axils and soft prickled fruits 6) fruits and seeds

FABACEAE *(Pea Family)*

Meadow Vetchling, Yellow Meadow Vetchling *(Lathyrus pratensis)*

Native. Perennial with creeping rootstock, climbing or scrambling to a height/spread of 30-120 cm. Stems and leaves slightly hairy. Leaves in pairs: mid-green, long-stalked, lance-shaped, 1-3 cm long, and smooth-edged, with large arrow-shaped basal bracts, and a long terminal tendril. Flower heads long-stalked: flowers hermaphrodite, bright yellow (c. 2 cm long) and bisymmetric, with ten stamens all united by a tube-like structure surrounding the pistil. Fruit a slightly hairy, elongated green pod, black when ripe, containing five to ten smooth, pea-like seeds. Flowering May-August. Widespread and common throughout the British Isles except for part of northern Scotland. Common in meadows, grassland, hedges, roadside verges and rough ground on a range of soils.

Pollination Not conclusive – studies suggest it may be at least partially self-pollinated via bee intermediaries activating ('rubbing') the surface of the pistil to make it receptive to pollen from the surrounding stamens.

Regeneration strategies Spread by rhizomes and by seed. Seed locally shed, or more widely spread by animals.

Weed control Carefully remove all runners, compost or dry and burn.

Follow current best, preferably organic, practice for large invasions (see Bibliography and internet).

Herbal, culinary, cultural and folklore The species has a wide distribution through Europe, and from the Mediterranean to Afghanistan.

Toxicity Ingestion of seeds can cause violent headaches and severe vomiting.

121

1) Flowering habit 2) flowering stems 3) flowers 4) green pods 5) ripe pods and seeds

Black Medick, Black Hay *(Medicago lupulina)*

Native. Annual. Stems spreading, 5-50 cm in length. Leaves short-stalked, mid-green, slightly toothed and softly downy, each comprising three ovate leaflets (3-20 mm long) with a small green scale-like structure (*stipule*) surrounding the base of the shared leaf/flower stems. Flower heads long-stalked (c. 0.5-1 cm long) and globose. Flowers hermaphrodite, tiny (2-3 mm long), bright yellow and bisymmetric, with ten stamens: one free, the other nine united by a tube-like structure surrounding the pistil. Fruit comprising a one-seeded, kidney-shaped pod with a strongly reticulate surface, green in colour and turning black when ripe (c. 2 mm long). Flowering April-August. Generally distributed throughout England and Wales (up to an altitude of 370 m) except on poorest soils, scarce in northern Ireland and absent from Scotland. Common in meadows and grassland, short grass (including lawns) and waste places but avoids strongly acidic conditions.

122

Pollination Usually self-pollinated, but as it flowers early in the season, honey bees visit while other flowers are more scarce.

Regeneration strategies Plentiful seed and spreading stems.

Weed control Carefully remove all stems (and roots), compost or dry and burn.

Herbal, culinary, cultural and folklore Like all pea family species it is a nitrogen fixer, often a component of fodder crops. Formerly, leaves were used as a potherb. A favourite food plant of the Common Blue Butterfly (*Polyommatus icarus*).

1) Young leaves 2) flowering habit 3) flower heads 4) heads of green seed pods 5) ripe pods

Lesser Trefoil, Lesser Yellow Trefoil *(Trifolium dubium)*

Native. Annual. Stems spreading to 0.5 m in length. Leaves short-stalked, mid-green, slightly toothed and smooth, each comprising three ovate leaflets (3-20 mm long) with a small green scale-like structure (*stipule*) surrounding the base of the shared leaf/flower stem. Flower heads 0.5-1 cm diameter, globose. Flowers hermaphrodite, tiny, pale yellow and bisymmetric with ten stamens: one free, the other nine united by a tube-like structure surrounding the pistil. Seed pods are tiny lidded capsules (2-3 mm long), each containing one ovoid brown seed, enclosed in a dead flower. Flowering June-September, sometimes as early as May. Occurs throughout the British Isles except for parts of the Scottish Highlands. Common in areas of short grassland, usually on well-drained soils in meadows, grassland, heaths, commons, tracks, roadside verges and lawns.

Pollination Self-fertile.

Regeneration strategies By seed and by long over-ground runners.

Weed control Carefully remove all stems (and roots), and compost before seed set to prevent spread.

Herbal, culinary, cultural and folklore This is the species generally accepted as the primary plant to represent the traditional Irish Shamrock, used by St. Patrick as a metaphor for the Holy Trinity (not to be confused with 'lucky' four-leaved clovers). Although native to Europe, it is also found in many parts of the world as an introduced species. It is considered to have originated as a cross between *Trifolium campestre* and *Trifolium micranthum*.

123

1) Young leaves 2) long, prostrate flowering stems 3) flower heads 4) fruiting head and tiny one-seeded pods

Red Clover *(Trifolium pratense)*

Native. Short-lived perennial. Stems upright, up to 60 cm, sometimes 80 cm in height. Leaves and stems more or less hairy. Leaves comprise three ovate leaflets (10-30 mm long), each marked with a faint lighter green chevron. A green scale-like structure (*stipule*) surrounds the bases of the leaf stems. Flower heads (up to 3 cm diameter) globose, pink or less commonly pure white. Flowers hermaphrodite, tiny and bisymmetric, pink-tipped, bases paler or white, and ten stamens: one free, the other nine united by a tube-like structure surrounding the pistil. Seed pods are tiny lidded capsules, each containing four to six ovoid seeds, enclosed in a dead flower. Flowering May-September. Widely distributed throughout the whole of the British Isles. A common plant of pastures, meadows and rough grassland, roadside verges and cultivated ground on calcareous to weakly acidic soils. Widely grown as a fodder crop, as green manure, and for its nitrogen fixation properties which increase soil fertility.

Additional notes This species may be confused with a similar species, *Trifolium medium*. Despite the common names, a good way to distinguish the two species is that *Trifolium pratense* has a faint light green chevron on the leaflets, while *Trifolium medium* or Zig-zag Clover has plain green leaflets.

Pollination Highly self-incompatible. An important bee flower; natural pollinators are various species of bumblebees, mainly in the following *Bombus* species groups: *B. hortorum*, *B. lapidarius* and *B. terrestris*, and the Common Carder Bee *(Bombus pascuorum)*. Honey bees also forage for nectar on this species.

Regeneration strategy Locally shed seeds, or seed excreted by browsing herbivores.

Weed control Hand-weed or hoe out young plants before fruiting stage and compost, or use as green manure by digging in. As is characteristic of legumes, the roots are excellent nitrogen fixers: cut pre-flowering tops and compost but leave roots in ground to over-winter for a free dressing of nitrogen.

Herbal, culinary, cultural and folklore An important species for honey production. An old remedy against whooping cough, asthma and bronchitis was to make an infusion with the flower heads. Dietary amounts of Red Clover are safe, but medicinal amounts may cause bad reactions. The flowers may also be used to enhance a salad.

124

1) Habit 2) flower head and leaves 3) pink and white flower heads 4) old flowers persist, encasing seed pods

White Clover, Dutch Clover *(Trifolium repens)*

Native. Perennial. Stems up to 50 cm in length. A creeping plant, rooting at leaf nodes. Leaves and stems may be smooth or slightly hairy. Leaves comprise three leaflets (10-30 mm long), broadly oval or slightly heart-shaped, usually with a whitish chevron. A green scale-like structure *(stipule)* surrounds the bases of the leaf stems. Flower heads up to 2 cm diameter. Flowers hermaphrodite, tiny (8-10 mm long), usually white, sometimes pale pink, rarely purple, bisymmetric, and with ten stamens: one free, the other nine united by a tube-like structure surrounding the pistil. Seed pods 4-5 mm long, containing three to six seeds and enclosed in a dead flower. Flowering June-September. Abundant in grassy places throughout the whole of the British Isles. A very polymorphic species with numerous physiological races which enable it to grow in a wide range of habitats: meadows, pastures, limestone grassland, lawns and grass tracks on a wide range of soils but most successfully on rich loam. The most commonly cultivated clover for fodder.

Pollination Highly self-incompatible. An important bee flower; pollinators are various species of bumblebees, mainly in the following *Bombus* species groups: *B. hortorum*, *B. lapidarius* and *B. terrestris* but also Common Carder Bees *(Bombus pascuorum)*. Honey bees also forage for nectar on this species.

Regeneration strategies Very efficient runners, as well as locally shed seed or seed excreted by browsing herbivores.

Weed control Hand-weed or hoe out young plants before fruiting stage and compost, or use as green manure by digging in. As is characteristic of legumes, the roots are excellent nitrogen fixers: cut pre-flowering tops and compost but leave roots in ground to over-winter for a free dressing of nitrogen.

Herbal, culinary, cultural and folklore An important species for honey production. Traditionally country children know that the white flowers can be pulled off and sucked for the tiny nectar drop, hence the common name Bee-bread. Another common name is Dutch Clover, a name which came into use when British farmers began to follow the Dutch farmers' example of cultivating it as a fodder crop.

125

1) Young prostrate stems 2) flowering habit 3) flower head 4) group of seed heads 5) old flowers persist, encasing seed pods

Gorse, Furze, Whin *(Ulex europaeus)*

Native. Perennial. Bushy habit with height/spread 60-200 cm, sometimes more. The stiff, ferocious dark green spines on main stems are modified leaves. Flowers hermaphrodite, bright yellow and bisymmetric with ten stamens: one free, the other nine united by a tube-like structure surrounding the pistil. Seed pods with one to three, sometimes four to six seeds, with small yellow arils. Flowering throughout the year but mainly March-June. Widespread throughout the whole of the British Isles, notably on open areas of common land, less frequent on calcareous soils.

Pollination Like many members of the pea family, Gorse has an explosive pollen release system that is triggered by insect visitors, mostly bumblebees and honey bees.

126

Regeneration strategy On hot summer days, the ripe seed pods twist and crack open and the seeds are dispersed very efficiently into the surrounding area: "…the high moor where the sun cracked the pods of the furze, and bees scrambled over the bells of the heather." – Henry Williamson (1957): *The Golden Virgin*

Weed control Consult your local branch of FWAG (Farming and Wildlife Advisory Group). Traditionally a plant of great economic value, and currently of considerable ecological importance, its management should be thoughtfully undertaken. It burns easily, and can present a fire risk in urban areas. As a method of control, burning is counter-productive because Gorse is a species which responds positively after fire.

Herbal, culinary, cultural and folklore It can be a scourge on common land and pastures, and can be a menace to clear from arable land due to its thorny modified leaves. Despite this, the glory of its yellow flowers when it is blooming in large areas have allowed Gorse to become much loved, with iconic status on British moors and common lands. When the great Swedish botanist Carl Linnaeus first saw it, he is said to have fallen to his knees in rapturous joy. Also an important habitat for a number of different birds, reptiles, spiders and moths.

1) Habit 2) green branches with modified spiny leaves 3) close-up of flowers 4) ripe and green pods 5) hairy pods and seeds

Hairy Tare *(Vicia hirsuta)*

Native. Annual. Slender, weakly stemmed, climbing or scrambling to a height/spread of 20-30 cm, sometimes up to 70 cm. Stems and leaves almost hairless. Leaves mid-green with a long, usually branched, tendril. Six to ten, sometimes four to 18 pairs of narrow leaflets (10-20 mm long), often indented at the tip. Basal bracts (*stipules*) very small and pointed. Flower heads short-stalked, comprising one to nine flowers. Flowers hermaphrodite, tiny (4-5 mm long), bisymmetric and white or dull whitish-purple in colour, with ten stamens: one free, the other nine united by a tube-like structure surrounding the pistil. Fruit comprises a small hairy green pod (8-12 mm long), black when ripe and containing usually two roundish, mottled seeds. Flowering June-August. Once a troublesome arable weed, it is fairly widespread throughout the British Isles, but rare in western and northern Scotland, north-west England, and much of Wales and Ireland. Common in rough grassland, pasture, open scrub, hedges and roadside verges. Favours dry, weakly acidic, neutral or calcareous soils.

Pollination The small whitish flowers secrete abundant nectar, which collects in the form of a large drop and emerges on each side of the base of the free stamen. Insect visitors are numerous, and include bees, moths and butterflies. It is also able to self-pollinate.

Regeneration strategies Locally shed seed or more widely spread by animals. Also scrambling habit, with tendrils to anchor progress.

Weed control: Hand-weed or hoe out young plants before fruiting stage, and compost, or use as green manure by digging in.

Herbal, culinary, cultural and folklore A real menace to pre-mechanised agriculture. Bible-reading farmers were not slow in appreciating the harvesting problems that Old Testament farmers had with rampant weeds or *tares* so to them *Vicia hirsuta* was indeed another, albeit hairy, tare.

127

1) Habit 2) flowering stems 3) flowers 4) fruiting stems 5) green and ripe seed pods

Common Vetch *(Vicia sativa* subsp. *segetalis)*

Alien, widely cultivated throughout the world, but its exact native range is obscure, however, it is thought to be native to parts of Europe and Asia. It was recorded growing wild in Britain by c. 1660, but previous to this was mainly grown for fodder. Annual or biennial. Climbing or scrambling to a height/spread of 15-120 cm. Stems and leaves only slightly hairy. Leaves mid-green with a long terminal, sometimes branched, tendril. Four to seven, sometimes eight pairs of leaflets (10-20 mm long), each with a tiny point at the tip and short basal bracts (*stipules*), often arrow-shaped (1-3 cm long). Flowers hermaphrodite, reddish-purple, bisymmetric, either solitary or in pairs (up to four), on very short stalks in the leaf axils: ten stamens, one free, the other nine united by a tube-like structure surrounding the pistil. Seed pods 5 cm long, sometimes as small as 2.5 or as large as 8 cm, smooth green, black when ripe and twisted after opening. Four to twelve smooth, brownish-speckled, pea-like seeds (2-3 mm long). Flowering May-July, sometimes as late as September. Widespread and common throughout the whole of the British Isles, except for part of northern Scotland. Common in pastures, meadows, hedgerows, roadside verges and rough ground.

Pollination Bumblebees, solitary bees and honey bees and/or self-pollination.

Regeneration strategies Pods twist and crack open, scattering the pea-like seeds locally, or spread further afield via animals.

Weed control Hand-weed or hoe out young plants before fruiting stage and compost, or use as green manure by digging in. As is characteristic of legumes, the roots are excellent nitrogen fixers: cut pre-flowering tops and compost but leave roots in ground to over-winter for a free dressing of nitrogen.

Herbal, culinary, cultural and folklore Carbonised remains of this species from early Neolithic sites in a wide range of countries including Syria, Bulgaria, Turkey, Hungary and Slovakia. Also from earlier pre-dynastic sites of ancient Egypt, and several Bronze Age sites in Turkmenia and Slovakia. Definite evidence of later cultivation is only recorded from the Roman times.

128

1) Habit 2) flowers and leaves 3) flower 4) young green seed pods 5) dry pods and seeds 6) pods after seeds have been shed

GERANIACEAE *(Geranium Family)*

Cut-leaved Crane's-bill *(Geranium dissectum)*

Native. Annual. Stems 10-60 cm in height. Ascending branches softly hairy. Leaves (2-7 cm long) softly hairy, long-stalked and rounded or kidney-shaped in overall outline: deeply divided into five to seven feathery lobes, c. 2-4 mm across at their bases and five to ten times longer than the undivided central area of the leaf. These primary lobes are subdivided by secondary lobes, which are oblong or linear and may themselves be lobed. The smaller upper leaves are also much divided and feathery but with shorter stalks. Flowers hermaphrodite, radially symmetric (0.5-2 cm diameter, sometimes up to 3 cm), paired on common stalks. Individual flower stalks 0.5-1.5 cm long. Petals c. 5 mm long, bright mauvish-pink, broadly ovate with a central notch in the upper margin. There are ten stamens; the five rounded ovaries are tightly grouped like a tiny pumpkin, and their long styles are united into a vertical glandular-haired column or 'beak' with five small stigmas at the apex (7-12 mm long at fruiting stage). Sepals glandular-hairy. When ripe, the dry beak springs open and the five previously united pistils separate and curl upwards like watch springs. Attached only at the top by their old stigmas, each 'spring' catapults a single seed out of its ovary casing and into the surrounding area. Seeds oval, reticulate. Flowering May-August. Widespread and common throughout the whole of the British Isles, but scarcer in central and northern Scotland. A plant of waste ground, cultivated areas, grassland, hedges and roadsides to altitudes of c. 385 m.

129

Pollination Mostly self-pollinated, although visited by sawflies, and some species of short-tongued solitary wasps (Sphecidae).

Regeneration strategy Spring release mechanism of seed heads ensures good local distribution.

Weed control Before fruiting stage, hand-weed or hoe out young plants, or use as green manure by digging in.

Herbal, culinary, cultural and folklore A brown dye is obtained from the flowers and the leaves are rich in tannin. An infusion from the whole plant or the roots is used to alleviate a number of internal and external conditions, including diarrhoea, dysentery, haemorrhoids and wounds.

1) Flowering habit 2) flower 3) fruits 4) carpels and seeds 5) finely reticulate seeds

Dove's-foot Crane's-bill *(Geranium molle)*

Native. Annual. Stems 10-40 cm in height, branched from base, spreading or ascending, and densely covered with long soft white glandular tipped hairs. Leaves mid-green. Lower leaves (1-5 cm long) long-stalked, softly hairy and rounded or kidney-shaped in outline: irregularly five- to nine-lobed, with lobes close together, up to twice the length of the undivided central area of the leaf, and close together. Upper leaves smaller with shorter stalks and more deeply lobed. Flowers hermaphrodite, numerous and radially symmetric (0.5-3 cm diameter), in pairs on common stalks (0.5-1.5 cm long). Flower stalks often curved upward after flowering. Petals 3-6 mm long, sometimes up to 7 mm, bright rose-purple, less frequently white, with a deep central notch in the upper margin. There are ten stamens; the five smooth, rounded ovaries are tightly grouped like a tiny pumpkin, and their long styles are united into a smooth vertical column or 'beak' (c. 5-8 mm long), with five small stigmas at the apex. Sepals densely glandular-hairy. When ripe, the dry beak springs open and the five previously united pistils separate and curl upwards like watch springs. Attached only at the top by their old stigmas, each 'spring' catapults a single seed out of its ovary casing and into the surrounding area. Seeds smooth or slightly wrinkled. Flowering April-September, sometimes as early as March. Widespread throughout Britain and Ireland in short, open grasslands, often in sandy soils.

130

Pollination Mostly self-pollinated, although visits from various bee species are reported.

Regeneration strategy Spring release mechanism of seed heads ensures good local distribution. Highly tolerant of being trampled on and mown (regularly mown plants may be misidentified due to the miniaturised appearance).

Weed control Before fruiting stage, hand-weed or hoe out young plants, or use as green manure by digging in.

Herbal, culinary, cultural and folklore The herbalist John Gerard found this species "miraculous against ruptures" if it was powdered and drunk in red wine or old claret, but added that for ruptures in the elderly, to this agreeable sounding potion should be added the powder of nine red slugs dried in an oven!

1) Young plant 2) flowers and leaves 3) ripe seed heads 4) ripe carpels (above) and seeds (below)

Small-flowered Crane's-bill *(Geranium pusillum)*

Native. Annual with tap root (strong on overwintered plants). Stems 10-30 cm, sometimes up to 40 cm in height, branched from base, spreading or ascending, and densely covered with soft white glandular tipped hairs. Leaves mid-green. Lower leaves (1-4 cm long) long-stalked, slightly hairy, and rounded or kidney-shaped in outline. Seven, sometimes from five and up to nine clearly separated lobes, c. 2-5 mm at base and two or three times the length of the undivided central area of the leaf. Upper leaves smaller with shorter stalks and more deeply lobed. Flowers hermaphrodite, radially symmetric (0.5-2 cm long, sometimes up to 3 cm), paired on common stalks. Individual flower stalks 0.5-1.5 cm long. Petals 2-4 mm long, pale lilac or lilac-pink, less frequently white, broadly ovate with a shallow central notch in the upper margin. There are ten stamens, only five with anthers; the five rounded ovaries are covered in minute hairs, flattened to the surface of the ovary, and are tightly grouped like a tiny pumpkin, their long styles united into a vertical glandular-haired column or 'beak' with five small stigmas at the apex (7-12 mm long at fruiting stage). Sepals densely glandular with soft longish hairs. When ripe, the dry beak springs open and the five previously united pistils separate and curl upwards like watch springs. Attached only at the top by their stigmas, each 'spring' catapults a single seed out of its ovary casing and into the surrounding area. Flowering June-September. Widespread and quite common in England and Wales, occasionally occurring locally elsewhere.

Pollination Usually self-pollinated.

Regeneration strategy Spring release mechanism of seed heads ensures good local distribution.

Weed control Before fruiting stage, hand-weed or hoe out young plants, or use as green manure by digging in.

Herbal, culinary, cultural and folklore The botanical name, *Geranium*, is derived from the Greek noun *geranos* meaning a Crane – the reference being to the long, beak-like appearance of the fruit.

131

1) Habit 2) leaves 3) typical pinkish flower with five stamens 4) white-flowered form with five stamens 5) ripe fruits
6) ridged hairy carpels encasing smooth seeds

Herb Robert *(Geranium robertianum)*

Native. Usually biennial, sometimes annual. Stems 10-50 cm in height and brittle, usually branched from the base, often red-tinged and covered in soft slender glandular hairs that give off a pungent smell (sometimes described as disagreeable) when touched. Leaves opposite, with short, sparse flat-lying hairs on both sides, broadly triangular and deeply divided into three main segments, these again deeply divided. Flowers hermaphrodite, radially symmetric, usually in pairs on long stems in the axils of the leaves on terminating stems. Petals rounded at the apex, commonly deep rose-pink with paler veins, less often pure white (9-12 mm long, sometimes as small as 8 mm). There are ten stamens, with noticeably orange pollen, arranged in inner and outer rings of five: the inner stamens open and shed their pollen first, then the outer stamens move toward the centre and shed their pollen; the five rounded ovaries are tightly grouped like a tiny pumpkin, and their long styles are united into a vertical glandular-haired column or 'beak' with five small stigmas at the apex (7-12 mm long at fruiting stage). Sepals non-glandular, oblong-ovate with spiked tips, and long sparse hairs. When ripe, the dry beak springs open and the five previously united pistils separate and curl upwards like watch springs. Attached only at the top by their stigmas, each 'spring' catapults a single seed out of its ovary casing and into the surrounding area. Flowering May-September. Widespread and common throughout the whole of the British Isles except for the outer Hebrides, Orkneys and Shetland where it is rare. Found in woods, on banks, among rocks and in shingle.

Pollination Self-pollinated, but visited by the long-snouted hoverflies *Rhingia campestris* and *R. rostrata*.

Regeneration strategy Spring release mechanism of seed heads ensures good local distribution.

Weed control Before fruiting stage, hand-weed or hoe out young plants, or use as green manure by digging in.

Herbal, culinary, cultural and folklore There are well over 100 common regional names for this species, many including Robin in the name – for example: Poor Robin, Robin's Flower and Red Bobby's Eye, probably because it seems to have been associated with the house goblin Robin Goodfellow (or Puck), a mythical character taken very seriously in the past. It was, and is, an important herb medicinally. Traditionally used to ease toothache, nosebleeds, and for wound healing. The strong smelling leaves, which are considered by many to be foul-smelling, could be rubbed on the body to repel mosquitos. Active ingredients include tannins, geraniins and essential oils. It was also carried to attract good luck.

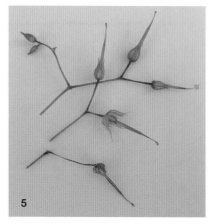

1) Seedlings 2) habit 3) pink and white flowers 4) flower showing five inner and five outer stamens 5) green seed heads
6) reticulate carpels showing typical white hair tuft near apex

HYPERICACEAE *(St. John's-wort Family)*

Tutsan *(Hypericum androsaemum)*

Native. Perennial. Semi-evergreen shrub, 40-100 cm in height. Stems and branches light green, often crimson-tinged. Leaves opposite, 5-10 cm long, short-stemmed and blunt-ovate, with uninterrupted margins and minute translucent glands. Flowers few and arranged in terminal groups, middle one opening first. Individual flowers hermaphrodite, radially symmetric, c. 2 cm diameter. Five bright yellow petals and numerous stamens of similar length to petals; calyx tinged crimson in bud, blunt-ovate (often very unequal), glandular. Fruit yellow-red, turning black. Flowering June-August. Widely distributed through western and southern Britain, rare or scattered elsewhere. Found in damp deciduous woodland on base-rich soil, but avoiding the most acidic conditions. It is a characteristic plant of high Devon banks and Cornish hedges, while in northern England it favours the crevices of limestone pavements.

Pollination Insect visitors, probably fairly generalised, as there is no nectar reward. Also self-fertile. The flowers are visited by small metallic beetles who feed on the pollen, notably *Chrysolina hyperici*, *C. brunsvicensis*, *C. quadrogemina* and *Agrilus hyperici*.

Regeneration strategy Produces numerous small seeds that are shed locally, but are spread by birds and other animals that eat the ripe fruit.

Weed control Hand-weed or hoe out young plants and compost, or use as green manure by digging in; remove older rooted plants before fruiting stage, or cut back larger growth before fruits develop, chop and compost or burn.

Herbal, culinary, cultural and folklore Widely grown as ground cover, especially in large woodland gardens. The name Tutsan is a corruption of the French *toute-saine* meaning heal all, because the leaves were once used in the healing of wounds. In Welsh it is called *Dail y Beiblau* ('Bible leaves') as the sweet-smelling leaves were often used as bookmarks, and the most common book in most households was the Bible.

1) Seedlings 2) habit 3) flowers and fruits 4) semi-ripe and ripe fruits

Perforate or Common St. John's-wort *(Hypericum perforatum)*

Native. Perennial. Smooth, erect, two-ridged stems 30-90 cm in height, with short runners (rhizomes). Leaves opposite, stalkless, mid-green, ovate-oblong (1-2 cm long), with transparent dots (glands) observed by holding leaf against the light, also black dots (glands) often apparent along leaf margins. Flowers (c. 2 cm diameter), hermaphrodite, radially symmetric, arranged in terminal leafy shoots, with the oldest flower at the tip. Five bright yellow petals, often with black gland dots near the petal margin, stamens numerous; calyx with five sepals, margined with glands. Inverted cone-shaped fruits enclose three closely associated segments (*locules*). Each segment houses numerous bluntly elongate seeds (like tiny dark sausages). Flowering June-September. Widespread in Britain and Ireland, especially on calcareous soils, in grasslands, meadows, road and track verges and open scrub.

Pollination Numerous different insect visitors but there is no nectar reward, and the species is self-fertile. No insect-pollinator associations have been conclusively proven and recent research suggests that self-pollination may be the most frequent method of reproduction in this species, however, flowers are visited by bumblebees and small metallic beetles who feed on the pollen, notably *Chrysolina hyperici*, *C. brunsvicensis*, *C. quadrogemina* and *Agrilus hyperici* (see weed control).

Regeneration strategies Rhizomes freely produce new shoots if shoots are injured. Lateral rhizomes may allow new plants to form at some distance to the parent in shallow soils. Numerous seeds are produced (more than 30,000 per plant), and dispersed locally.

Weed control Hand-weed or hoe out young plants and compost, or use as green manure by digging in. Remove older rooted plants before fruiting stage, or cut back larger growth before fruits develop, chop and compost or burn. Two of the beetle visitors listed (*Chrysolina* sp. and *Agrilus hyperici*) are sometimes used for bio-control in places where St. John's-wort has become invasive.

Herbal, culinary, cultural and folklore A range of dye colours, including yellow, light greens and tan, can be obtained from the leaves. This species is the principal plant among the wild flowers traditionally gathered in Britain to celebrate the Eve of St. John the Baptist (23 June) or, in the Orthodox Church, on St. John's Day (24 June). The species has a long history of herbal use, and is a popular alternative treatment for a number of clinical conditions. It is a powerful antidepressant but should not be used without expert advice, especially as it can interact adversely with other drugs.

Toxicity Poisonous to livestock. Skin contact with sap can cause photosensitivity.

134

1) Leaf glands 2) flower, petals bordered by black glands 3) fruits 4) habit

LAMIACEAE *(Dead-nettle Family)*

Common Hemp-nettle *(Galeopsis tetrahit)*

Native. Annual. Square stem, erect, bristly, with some glandular hairs, 10-100 cm in height, swollen at leaf junctions. Stalked leaves 2.5-10 cm long, ovate and hairy with toothed margins. Flowers in dense clusters in the axils of the upper leaves. Flowers hermaphrodite, bisymmetric (13-20 mm long), pink or purplish-pink (less frequently white), with darker markings on lower, square-ish, central lobe: four paired stamens, upper two with longer filaments, and a forked pistil pressed close against the large upper petal; flower tube equal to or longer than petals, reverse of upper and side petals hairy; upper 'hooded' petal more or less vertical to lateral and lower petals. Calyx bell-shaped with five long, more or less equal, prickle-like lobes, bristly with dark purplish ribs. Four seeds (nutlets), droplet-shaped, c. 1 mm long. Flowering August-September, sometimes as early as July. Occurs throughout the British Isles. Frequent on field margins, arable land, hedges and shady banks, less commonly in woods and wet heaths and fenland, in a wide range of soil types.

Pollination Usually self-pollinated.

Regeneration strategy Locally dropped seed, spread from cattle dung, or via the spiny/hairy calyces which attach to clothing and animals.

Weed control Before seeds develop, hand-weed or hoe out young plants and compost, or use as green manure by digging in. Cut back larger growth before fruits develop, and carefully dig out and remove roots, then chop and compost or burn.

Herbal, culinary, cultural and folklore The botanical name *Galeopsis* is from the Greek *gale* (weasel), and *opsis* (appearance), probably because of the sharp spines of the calyx which resemble the teeth or claws of a weasel. Also native to Europe and north-western Asia.

1) Typical stem swelling 2) flowering stem 3) flower 4) flowers, fruits and seeds 5) seeds (nutlets), c. 1 mm long

Ground-ivy (*Glechoma hederacea*)

137

Native. Perennial. Height 10-30 cm. Long, square, creeping and rooting stems, with ascending flowering branches. Leaves opposite, long-stalked and kidney- or ovate heart-shaped (1-3 cm long), mid-to-deep green, often tinged with dull purple and slightly hairy, with 'scalloped' margins. Flowers hermaphrodite or female only (*gynodioecious*). Hermaphrodite plants/flowers are larger than the female only plants/flowers. Flowers (15-20 mm long) bisymmetric, in groups of c. three in leaf axils; petals violet with purple spots on the lower 'lip' petal; under the small upper 'lip' petal are four paired stamens, the upper two with longer filaments, and a purple-tipped, forked pistil (or pistil only); lateral petals small, lower lip petal large, with long white hairs at mouth of the flower tube (which is slightly shorter than the petals). Calyx narrow and bell-shaped with five more or less equal short, pointed lobes. Four droplet-shaped seeds (nutlets), c. 1 mm long. Flowering March-June (one of the earliest spring wild flowers). Found throughout the British Isles but rare or absent from the Scottish Highlands and northern Scotland including the Hebrides, Orkney and Shetland. A common plant of woodland rides, recent coppice, scrub, hedgerows, permanent grassland, waste ground and shady places. A preference for heavy, fertile calcareous soils to an altitude of c. 400 m.

Pollination Female-only flowers depend on pollen from hermaphrodite flowers for pollination. Nectar is secreted at the base of the flower tube, near the ovary. Pollinated by bees and bee flies, notably highly developed nectar feeders such as the long-tongued, furry bee-like *Bombylius* species. The long-tongued hoverfly *Rhingia campestris* (Syrphidae) also visits the flowers.

Regeneration strategies Spreads by long stolons, by stems bending down and rooting at the leaf nodes, or by seeding. A great survivor of mowing, it can form dense mats, which may take over large areas of lawn. Seed dropped locally by parent plants and may be further transported by ants.

Weed control Carefully remove roots and rhizomes before fruiting stage. Before flowers/seeds develop, hand-weed or hoe out young plants and compost, or use as green manure by digging in.

Herbal, culinary, cultural and folklore One of the Herbs of St. John. It has no botanical relationship to Ivy (*Hedera helix*) – the common name simply reflects its long-stemmed creeping habit. It has two other interesting folk names: Ale-hoof and Tun-hoof. These names relate to its use in the brewing trade prior to the introduction of Hops, owing to its bitterness. It was also used in the cheese-making industry as a substitute for rennet. Ground-ivy was imported into America (where it is a now a nuisance weed in some areas) by early European settlers who used it to make a herbal tea rich in vitamin C and also consumed it as a pot herb or salad leaves. There is a popular, similarly invasive garden form, with green and white leaves: *Glechoma hederacea* var. *variegata*. Also native in Europe and south-western Asia, in addition to the UK.

1) Stem runners 2) flower stems – hermaphrodite (left) and female (right) 3) young flowering plants

White Dead-nettle (*Lamium album*)

Native. Perennial. Erect, square, hollow stems (20-60 cm in height) and a creeping stoloniferous rhizome. Stem shortly hairy. Short-stalked leaves 3-7 cm long, light-to-mid-green, ovate, with pointed tip and coarsely toothed margins. Flowers in groups of seven to eight in leaf axils. Flowers (c. 2 cm long) hermaphrodite, bisymmetric and white. The upper 'lip' petal is hood-like and slightly hairy, it lightly conceals two pairs of stamens, and a forked pistil, the uppermost pair of stamens have longer filaments; lateral flower lobes small and toothed, the lower lip broad and deeply split in the middle, sometimes with light beige patterning at mouth of the flower tube. Calyx bell-shaped, green (brownish at base) with five long narrow, more or less equal, prickle-like lobes. Four droplet-shaped seeds (nutlets), c. 1 mm long. Flowering May-December. Common throughout most of the British Isles as far north as the Firth of Forth, but scarce in south-west Scotland, and absent from north-west Scotland, north-west England and western Wales. In Ireland confined to the north-east. A common plant of hedgerows, farmyards, road verges and waste ground, usually on moist fertile soils.

138

Pollination Long-tongued bees, especially bumblebees. A good source of early nectar and pollen. There seems to be no barrier to self-pollination.

Regeneration strategies Creeping rhizomes. Seed dropped locally and carried away by ants.

Weed control Carefully remove roots and rhizomes before fruiting stage. Hand-weed or hoe out young plants and compost, or use as green manure by digging in. Cut back larger growth before fruits develop, chop and compost or burn.

Herbal, culinary, cultural and folklore Young leaves are edible and can be used in salads or as a cooked vegetable. A distillation from the flowers is said to make the heart merry, give good colour to the face and refresh and liven the spirit. A local Somerset name is Adam and Eve in the Bower – the stamens in the hooded upper petals are seen to resemble Adam and Eve lying side by side. It is another flower (cf. White Clover) that country children would pull off the little florets and suck for the tiny nectar droplet. Also native throughout Europe and Asia.

1) Very young plants 2) adult habit 3) flower head 4) flowers and calyces, from above and below 5) calyces and seeds (nutlets) – four seeds per flower, c. 1 mm long

Henbit Dead-nettle, Henbit *(Lamium amplexicaule)*

Native. Annual. Square stems 5-25 cm in height, branching from the base, with short fine hairs. Leaves opposite, 1-2.5 cm long, mid-green, long-stalked (3-5 cm long on lower leaves) and kidney-shaped or rounded, with broad, round-lobed margins. Stalkless bracts on flower stems similar to leaves, sometimes larger. Flowers in small groups (whorls) at distinct intervals up the flowering stem. Flowers hermaphrodite, bisymmetric (c. 15 mm long), frequently small and insignificant (*cleistogamous*). Well-developed flowers are pinkish-purple with a long narrow flower tube that terminates in a small, ovate, hooded upper petal; this petal lightly conceals four paired stamens (upper two with longer filaments) and a forked pistil; the side lobes of the flower tube are small and narrow while the pale bi-lobed lower lip has conspicuous purplish-pink spots. Tubular calyx (5-6 mm long) with five long, narrow, more or less equal, prickle-like lobes covered with short whitish hairs. Four seeds (nutlets), light brown with white flecks, slightly angled, droplet-shaped (c. 1 mm long). Flowering generally April-August, but often found flowering outside this period. Occurs throughout the British Isles, frequent in the east and south, scarce and localised elsewhere. Rare in Ireland, more or less confined to the south-east. Chiefly a weed of arable crops, usually on sandy or calcareous soils, flowerbeds and allotments.

Pollination Primarily long-tongued bees. Plants with cleistogamous flowers self-pollinate.

Regeneration strategy Locally shed seed.

Weed control Before fruiting stage, hand-weed or hoe out young plants and compost, or use as green manure by digging in. Cut back larger growth before fruits develop, chop and compost or burn.

Herbal, culinary, cultural and folklore Probably native to the Mediterranean region but has spread around the world as an arable weed. It is widely naturalised in eastern North America. Traditionally young plants are eaten raw or cooked.

139

1) Young plant 2) habit 3) flowering stem with stalkless bracts 4) cleistogamous (unopening) flowers 5) seeds (nutlets), c. 1 mm long

Red Dead-nettle *(Lamium pupureum)*

Native. Annual (or biennial). Square stems 10-20 cm in height, sometimes as short as 5 or as tall as 45 cm, branching from the base, shortly hairy. Leaves opposite (1-5 cm long), softly hairy, shortly ovate, heart-shaped at base, often purple-tinged, margins bluntly toothed. Lower leaf stalks long, upper leaves crowded and bracts short-stalked. Flowers in dense clusters in axils of leaf bracts. Flowers hermaphrodite, bisymmetric, 10-15 mm long, pale pinkish to purple; upper hooded petal lightly concealing four paired stamens (upper two with longer filaments) and a forked pistil; side lobes small and narrow, front lobe deeply divided, with deep crimson spots. Calyx shortly hairy, bell-shaped (5-6 mm long) with five equal long-pointed lobes. Seeds (nutlets), deep greyish-brown and densely white flecked, slightly angled, droplet-shaped (c. 1 mm long). Flowering March-October, but sometimes found flowering outside this period. Widespread throughout the British Isles, except for parts of the Scottish Highlands and Ireland where it is locally scarce. Usually found in arable fields, grassy meadows, hedge banks, waste places and as a garden weed.

Pollination A valuable early-flowering species for bees foraging for nectar and pollen (unusually red in colour, much more frequently pollen is in the yellow-orange area of the spectrum). Can self-pollinate.

Regeneration strategy Seeds dropped in vicinity of parent plant. Tends to form colonies.

Weed control Before fruiting stage, hand-weed or hoe out young plants and compost, or use as green manure by digging in. Cut back larger growth before fruits develop, chop and compost or burn.

Herbal, culinary, cultural and folklore Also native to mainland Europe and Asia. Its common name of Dead-nettle refers to the absence of the stinging hairs found in Stinging Nettles (to which it is not related, although the leaves have a comparable appearance). Traditionally, the tops of young plants and the leaves are used for salads, or as a cooked vegetable. Medicinally this plant has astringent, diaphoretic, purgative diuretic and styptic qualities.

140

1) Flower head 2) habit 3) seedling 4) seeds (nutlets), c. 1 mm long

Self-heal *(Prunella vulgaris)*

Native. Perennial. Slender, spreading rhizomatous roots. Square, shortly hairy flowering stems, 5-30 cm in height. Leaves 2-5 cm long, short-stalked, ovate with smooth or slightly toothed margins. Flowers hermaphrodite, grouped in dense rounded conical clusters in axils of leafy bracts: (10-14 mm long), bisymmetric, violet (occasionally white or crimson); upper hooded petal lightly concealing four paired stamens (upper two with longer filaments) and a forked pistil; side lobes small and narrow, lower lobe lighter coloured (sometimes white), toothed, spreading and unequally three-lobed. Bracts and calyx greenish-red to deep brownish-red with long white hairs; upper calyx broad, with three short teeth, lower calyx spreading and unequally three-lobed. Four seeds (nutlets), smooth, light brown, slightly angled, droplet-shaped (c. 1 mm long). Flowering July-August, sometimes as early as June or as late as September. One of the most widely distributed native species. Very common in grassland (meadows, commons, pastures and lawns), clearings in woods, roadsides and waste places throughout the British Isles. Tends to avoid acidic conditions, preferring neutral to alkaline soils to altitudes of c. 760 m.

Pollination Honey bees, bumblebees and hoverflies.

Regeneration strategies Locally shed seeds and short spreading rhizomes.

Weed control Carefully remove roots and rhizomes before fruiting stage. Hand-weed or hoe out young plants and compost, or use as green manure by digging in. Cut back larger growth before fruits develop, chop and compost or burn.

Herbal, culinary, cultural and folklore Found throughout Europe and Asia, although it seems to be European in origin. As its common name suggests, it is widely used in herbal medicine, particularly taken as a tea, to help sore throats, fevers, diarrhoea, liver and heart problems and internal bleeding. Poultices of Self-heal were used to alleviate skin irritation and nettle stings. It serves well as an antiseptic wound packing material in extremis. It can also be eaten as a salad leaf or potherb.

141

1) Young plant 2) flower heads, unrestricted habit 3) seeds, c. 1 mm long 4) old flower heads in mown grass 5) young seed heads

Hedge Woundwort *(Stachys sylvatica)*

Native. Perennial. Rootstock with long creeping rhizomes. Square, solid stems 30-100 cm in height, with short stiff whitish glandular hairs. Leaves also with glandular hairs, mid-green, ovate, heart-shaped at basal stem junction, with coarsely toothed margins. Stems and leaves have a pungent smell when brushed. Flowers hermaphrodite, grouped around the stem in rings (whorls) of six to ten, uppermost flowers forming a spike; bisymmetric, dark reddish-purple (13-15 mm long); undivided upper petal forms a hood over the four-paired stamens (upper two with longer filaments) and a forked pistil; lower lobe large, three-lobed with distinct light pink angular markings. Calyx with five equal-sized triangular lobes, with glandular hairs. Four seeds (nutlets), smooth, dark brown-black, slightly angled, droplet-shaped (c. 1 mm long). Flowering June-September. Widespread throughout the British Isles, excepting parts of the Scottish Highlands, where it is scarce. A common plant of hedgerows, banks, shaded gardens and waste places, especially on mildly acidic to calcareous soils, to an altitude of 460 m.

142

Pollination Honey bees and bumblebees, including the Common Carder Bee (*Bombus pascuorum*) and the Wool Carder Bee (*Anthidium manicatum*).

Regeneration strategies Creeping rhizomes and locally dropped seed.

Weed control Carefully remove roots and rhizomes before fruiting stage. Hand-weed or hoe out young plants and compost, or use as green manure by digging in. Cut back larger growth before fruits develop, chop and compost or burn.

Herbal, culinary, cultural and folklore Native to Europe and Central and western Asia. Its medicinal and healing qualities are similar to those of *Prunella vulgaris*, and were much praised and used by the herbalist John Gerard. The once rare but now common Woundwort Shieldbug (*Eysarcoris venustissimus*) is particularly associated with this species.

1) Seedling plant 2) young foliage 3) adult habit 4) flowering stems 5) calyces with four green or ripe black seeds (nutlets) in bases

MALVACEAE *(Mallow Family)*

Musk Mallow *(Malva moschata)*

Native. Perennial. Branching rootstock and several erect, softly hairy stems (30-80 cm in height). Lower leaves 5-8 cm long, light-to-mid-green and almost hairless. Leaves nearly entire or divided almost to the base, alternate, on longish stalks; higher leaves shorter stalked. Flowers hermaphrodite, usually solitary in axils of upper leaves, and in a terminal cluster at top of stem; radially symmetric, with five large petals, light pink, rarely white, with slightly irregular incurved upper margins, petals c. five times as long as sepals; stamens numerous, their filaments united into a staminal tube joined at the base and surrounding the pistil. Within a flower, to avoid self-fertilisation, the anthers shed their pollen and droop before the pistil emerges from the top of the staminal tube, thus ensuring that the pistil will only be fertilised by pollen from another flower or, from another plant. Calyx five-lobed, enlarging at fruiting stage, with a narrowly three-lobed epicalyx below, lobes half the length of calyx lobes. Fruits one-seeded (nutlets), black with white hairs, rounded, notched on one side (c. 2-2.5 mm long), arranged in a circle in the base of the flower and separating easily when ripe. Flowering July-August. Common throughout much of the British Isles, but scarcer in west Wales, northern England, Scotland and Ireland. Absent from Orkney and Shetland. Occurs in pastures and grassy places, field margins, roadsides, hedgerows, banks and has a preference for dry, fertile soils.

143

Pollination Attractive to bees, including long-tongued species, and other insects.

Regeneration strategy Hairy seeds spread locally, but probably also carried further afield on animal fur and feet.

Weed control Before fruiting stage, hand-weed or hoe out young plants and compost, or use as green manure by digging in. Cut back larger growth before fruits develop, chop and compost or burn.

Herbal, culinary, cultural and folklore Native to Europe and south-western Asia. Its musky odour (of the common name) is only noticeable if the flowers are brought indoors. A very pretty plant, cultivars of this species are widely grown in herbaceous borders. Leaves can be used as salad, and flowers sometimes used to decorate salads or desserts.

1) Habit 2) flower – note staminal tube 3) calyx and epicalyx 4) flower and green fruit 5) enlarged dry calyx and hairy seeds 6) seeds (nutlets)

Common Mallow *(Malva sylvestris)*

Native. Biennial or perennial with branching rootstock. Stems several, erect and prostrate and sparsely hairy (30-80 cm in height, sometimes up to 1.2 m). Lower leaves 5-10 cm long, mid-green, slightly hairy, rounded with shallow lobes and long stems. Stem leaves slightly smaller and more obviously lobed. Flowers hermaphrodite, usually solitary in axils of upper leaves and in a terminal cluster at top of stem; radially symmetric, with five large softly triangular petals, pinkish-mauve with darker stripes, upper edge of each petal with a broad shallow notch; petals two to four times as long as sepals; stamens numerous, their filaments united into a staminal tube joined at the base and surrounding the pistil. Within a flower, to avoid self-fertilisation, the anthers shed their pollen and droop before the pistil emerges from the top of the staminal tube, thus ensuring that the pistil will only be fertilised by pollen from another flower or from another plant. Calyx five-lobed, not enlarged at fruiting stage, with a three-lobed epicalyx below, lobes two thirds, or as long as, length of calyx lobes. Fruits one-seeded (nutlets) wedge-shaped (c. 2.5-3 mm long) and tightly arranged in a circle (like segments of a tangerine), the outer face curved, reticulate, sides flat, inner edge notched. Flowering June-September. Common throughout most of the British Isles, but in Scotland it is more or less confined to the east coast, absent from Orkney, Shetland and the Hebrides. In lowland Britain it is a common plant of roadsides, banks and waste ground and shows a preference for dry fertile soils.

144

Pollination Usually bees, including solitary bees (e.g. *Adrena bicolor*), long-tongued bees and Red-tailed Bumblebees (*Bombus lapidarius*), also the Painted Lady Butterfly (*Vanessa cardui*).

Regeneration strategy Locally dispersed seed.

Weed control Before fruiting stage, hand-weed or hoe out young plants and compost, or use as green manure by digging in. Cut back larger growth before fruits develop, chop and compost or burn.

Herbal, culinary, cultural and folklore Local names frequently allude to cheese, because of the ring of tightly pressed wedge-shaped seeds. Perhaps the prettiest of such local names is from Lincolnshire where traditionally the children call them Fairy Cheeses; however, because the plants and their flowers rapidly become victim to insects and rust virus after flowering, the species is also known as Rags and Tatters in the West Country. Leaves and flowers of mallows have a high mucilaginous content and are rich in vitamins, B1, B2 and vitamin C, and have long been valued by herbalists. The confection marshmallows was originally made using mucilage from the roots of the Marsh Mallow (*Althaea officinalis* – a coastal species).

  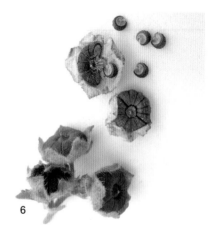

1) Young plant 2) basal leaves, pre-flowering 3) spreading habit 4) flower 5) calyces and epicalyces 6) fruits and seeds

ONAGRACEAE *(Willowherb Family)*

Rose-bay Willowherb *(Chamerion angustifolium)*

Native. Perennial. Stems erect, 30-200 cm in height. Long, horizontally spreading and branching roots give rise to new leafy shoots. Leaves mid-green, slightly bluish on underside, spirally arranged on the stem, long, narrowly ovate, usually straight-edged, or slightly wavy (occasionally slightly toothed). Flowers hermaphrodite, almost radially symmetric (two upper petals usually slightly wider than the two lower ones). Four deep purplish-pink petals, broadly heart-shaped, with narrowly elongate bases and eight stamens: four short and four long; the pistil is divided into four curled stigma lobes. Calyx with four narrow sepals, c. same length as petals, or slightly shorter, pink with greenish tips. Fruits long, four-sectioned capsules that split open and curl back when ripe to release the many-plumed seeds. Flowering June-September. Occurring throughout the British Isles but most common in the south, less common in north-west Scotland and scarce in Ireland. Often forming dense stands in recently disturbed conditions such as felled woodland, road verges, heathland or derelict buildings and railway sidings. Grows best on fertile soils but is tolerant of a wide range of conditions except for waterlogged sites.

Pollination Bees and moths.

Regeneration strategy Much spreading and branching roots.

Weed control Hand-weed young seedlings. Carefully remove older growth making sure to dig out all branching roots as well, before the plants get too big, or reach fruiting stage. Leaves and stems can be composted but do not compost roots – either incinerate or take to local garden waste facility. Follow current best, preferably organic, practice for large invasions (see Bibliography and internet).

Herbal, culinary, cultural and folklore Also known as Fireweed because it thrives and multiplies on sites where the ground has been subject to fires, demolition sites and railway sidings. A larval food plant for the Elephant Hawkmoth.

1) Young plant 2) flowering habit 3) flowers 4) seed capsules and seeds 5) fruiting stems

American Willowherb *(Epilobium ciliatum)*

Introduced, first found in Leicester c. 1891, but then not recorded again until 1932 in Surrey – now widespread in southern UK. Perennial. Stems 30-90 cm in height, sometimes up to 150 cm, stiffly erect, much-branched, covered with short hairs, many of them glandular and slightly sticky. In late autumn almost stalkless, shortly stoloniferous, basal rosettes of smooth, slightly glossy leaves appear, from which normal leaves will develop the following year. Leaves short-stalked (1.5-4 mm long), narrowly ovate, and almost smooth, leaf edges with shallow widely spaced teeth; lower short-stalked stem leaves in opposite pairs, uppermost leaves not opposite. Flowers hermaphrodite, radially symmetric (4-6 mm diameter), single-stalked and grouped at top of stem; four deeply lobed white or light pink petals, eight stamens: four long, four short, pistil with club-shaped stigma. Calyx with four glandular sepals, similar in length to the petals. Fruits long, four-sectioned capsules with many plumed seeds. Flowering June-August. Common throughout lowland England, and with records from Wales and the south-west, in Scotland records from as far north as Angus. In many areas a common plant of waste ground, walls, banks, roadsides, railway banks, damp woods, copses, stream sides and gardens.

Additional notes A useful pointer in identifying this species, and also the other rather less commonly occurring *Epilobium* with sticky glandular hairs – Small-flowered Willowherb (*Epilobium roseum*) – is the presence of aphids (dead or alive) caught on the sticky upper stem glandular hairs.

Pollination Self-pollinated, although it is often visited by hoverflies, who may pollinate, and might account for some the hybridisation recorded for this species.

Regeneration strategies Short stolons and feathery plumed seeds readily carried by wind.

Weed control Hand-weed young stolons and basal leaf rosettes. Carefully remove older plants, making sure to dig out roots and stolons as well, before the plants reach fruiting stage. Leaves and stems can be composted but do not compost roots or stolons – either incinerate or take to local garden waste facility.

Herbal, culinary, cultural and folklore None found.

146

1) Flowering stem 2) glandular hairs on stem 3) flowers – note glandular hairs on flower buds 4) open seed capsule

Great or Great Hairy Willowherb *(Epilobium hirsutum)*

Native. Perennial. Stems 80-150 cm in height, thick, erect, with densely glandular and soft spreading hairs; stems white or pinkish, and fleshy stolons are produced in summer. Leaves without stalks, mostly opposite, elongate-ovate, with toothed edges, and softly hairy on both sides. Flowers hermaphrodite, radially symmetric (15-25 mm diameter), long-stalked and loosely grouped at top of the stem. Four deep purplish-rose petals (occasionally white flowers occur); eight stamens: four long, four short; stigma of pistil with four curved lobes. Calyx with four softly hairy sepals, about half the length of the petals. Fruits long (5-8 cm), four-sectioned capsules with many plumed seeds. Flowering July-August. Widely distributed throughout England, Wales and Ireland. In Scotland more or less restricted to east coast as far north as Caithness, rare or absent elsewhere. Particularly associated with damp places, especially edges of rivers, streams, ponds, lakes and ditches, fens and marshes, on fertile base-rich or calcareous soils. In favourable conditions often forms dense stands. It is not shade tolerant. May be found in altitudes of up to 370 m.

147

Pollination Bees and flies.

Regeneration strategies Far-reaching stolons and feathery plumed seeds readily carried by wind.

Weed control Hand-weed young pre-flowering plants. Carefully remove older growth making sure to dig out roots and rhizomes as well, before the plants get too big, or reach fruiting stage. Leaves and stems can be composted but do not compost roots or stolons – either incinerate or take to local garden waste facility. Follow current best, preferably organic, practice for large invasions (see Bibliography and internet).

Herbal, culinary, cultural and folklore The name Willowherb was first used in the late 16th Century and refers to the similarity of the leaf shape with that of willows. A larval food plant for the Elephant Hawkmoth.

1) Young stolons 2) adult habit 3) flower showing four-lobed stigma and eight stamens, four long and four short
4) less frequent white-flowered form 5) open seed capsules and feathery seeds

Broad-leaved Willowherb *(Epilobium montanum)*

Native. Perennial. Stems 20-60 cm in height, sometimes as low as 5 cm, slender erect, almost smooth to sparsely hairy and with few to numerous, short glandular hairs near apex. In late autumn, at the base of the old flowering stem, almost stalkless, shortly stoloniferous, basal rosettes of smooth, slightly glossy leaves appear, from which normal leaves will develop the following year. Leaves short-stalked (slightly winged), narrowly ovate, or ovate, and almost smooth, leaf edges sharply and irregularly toothed, all leaves more or less opposite. Flowers hermaphrodite, radially symmetric (6-9 mm diameter), single-stalked and grouped at top of stem, buds more or less drooping. Four lobed pale mauve-pink petals (occasionally white): eight stamens, four long, four short; stigma of pistil with four-curved lobes. Calyx with four slightly hairy, elongate sepals, about half the length of the petals. Fruit capsule with four sections, downy, long and thin (4-8 cm in length), with many plumed seeds. Flowering June-August. Common throughout the whole of the British Isles. Occurring in woodland, waste ground, roadsides, railway banks, hedges banks and ditches. A frequent garden weed with a preference for neutral, base-rich or calcareous soils, to an altitude of c. 790 m.

Pollination Insect- or self-pollinated. It is suggested that self-pollination is effected by the long stamens which mature at the same time as the stigma, while the shorter stamens open later and may effect cross-pollination.

Regeneration strategies Short overwintering stolons; feathery plumed seeds readily carried by wind.

Weed control Hand-weed young stolons or basal leaf rosettes. Carefully remove older plants, making sure to dig out roots and rhizomes as well, before the plants reach fruiting stage. Leaves and stems can be composted but do not compost roots and stolons – either incinerate or take to local garden waste facility.

Herbal, culinary, cultural and folklore None found.

1) Young leafing autumn stolons 2) seedling 3) open seed capsule, before seed release 4) open seed capsule 5) flower with four-lobed stigma

Hoary Willowherb, Lesser Hairy Willowherb *(Epilobium parviflorum)*

Native. Perennial. Stems 30-60 cm in height, sometimes up to 90 cm, erect, covered with short soft hairs, mixed with short glandular hairs at top of stems. In late autumn, at the base of the old flowering stem, almost stalkless shortly stoloniferous, basal rosettes of soft, shortly hairy leaves appear, from which normal leaves will develop the following year. Leaves without stalks, narrowly ovate, covered with fine soft downy hairs on both sides, leaf edges with shallow widely spaced teeth; stem leaves in opposite pairs, uppermost leaves not opposite. Flowers hermaphrodite, radially symmetric (6-9 mm diameter), single-stalked and grouped at top of stems. Four deeply-lobed, light mauvish-pink petals: eight stamens, four long, four short; stigma of pistil with four-curved lobes. Calyx with four downy-glandular haired sepals, c. half the length of the petals. Fruit capsule with four sections, long and thin (3.5-6.5 cm in length), with many plumed seeds. Flowering July-August. Distributed throughout the British Isles, but scarcer, and more localised, in northern Britain, Scotland and Shetland. A frequent plant of waste ground with a preference for damp sites: fenland, stream banks and marshes but also common on waste ground and in gardens. Found in altitudes of to c. 370 m.

Pollination Bees or self-pollinated.

Regeneration strategies Short overwintering stolons; feathery plumed seeds readily carried by wind.

Weed control Hand-weed young basal leaf rosettes. Carefully remove older plants, making sure to dig out roots and stolons as well, before the plants reach fruiting stage. Leaves and stems can be composted but do not compost roots or stolons – either incinerate or take to local garden waste facility.

Herbal, culinary, cultural and folklore None found.

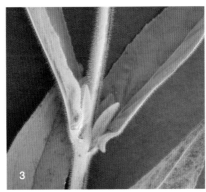

149

1) Young pre-flowering plant 2) seedling plant 3) softly hairy stems and leaves 4) flower and flower bud – note four-lobed stigma 5) seed capsules: oldest below, youngest top

Pale Willowherb, Small-flowered Willowherb *(Epilobium roseum)*

Native. Perennial. Stems 25-60 cm in height, sometimes up to 80 cm, stiffly erect, slender, lower stem smooth but upper stem covered with short hairs, many of them glandular and slightly sticky. In late autumn, at the base of the old flowering stem, almost stalkless, shortly stoloniferous, basal rosettes of smooth, slightly glossy leaves appear, from which normal leaves will develop the following year. Leaves smooth, narrowly ovate, lower leaf stalks 3-20 mm in length (often longer than in other common willowherb species), leaf margins finely and sharply toothed. Lower stem leaves in opposite pairs, uppermost leaves not opposite. Flowers hermaphrodite, radially symmetric (4-6 mm diameter) and single-stalked, grouped at top of stems. Four deeply lobed white petals, streaked rose-pink (unlike the other small-flowered common willowherbs with petals in the mauve-pink spectrum): eight stamens, four long, four short; stigma of pistil club-shaped. Calyx with four glandular-haired sepals, slightly shorter than the petals. Fruit capsule with four sections, long and thin (5-7 cm in length), covered with tiny glandular hairs and containing many plumed seeds. Flowering July-August. A local species scattered throughout the English and Welsh lowlands. Rare in Scotland and Ireland and absent from Orkney, Shetland and the Western Isles. A plant of waste ground, gardens, banks, damp woods, copses and hedgerows.

150

Additional notes A useful pointer in identifying this species, and the other common *Epilobium* with sticky glandular hairs – American Willowherb (*Epilobium ciliatum*) – is the presence of aphids (dead or alive) caught on the sticky upper stem hairs.

Pollination Self- and cross-pollinated.

Regeneration strategies Short stolons and feathery plumed seeds readily carried by wind.

Weed control Hand-weed young basal leaf rosettes. Carefully remove older plants, making sure to dig out roots and stolons as well, before the plants reach fruiting stage. Leaves and stems can be composted but do not compost roots or stolons – either incinerate or take to local garden waste facility.

Herbal, culinary, cultural and folklore None found.

1) Young overwintering plant 2) stem, habit and leaves 3) glandular hairs 4) flowers 5) open seed capsules

Square-stalked (or -stemmed) Willowherb
(*Epilobium tetragonum* subsp. *tetragonum*)

Native. Perennial. Stems 25-60 cm in height, sometimes up to 80 cm, stiffly erect, smooth, with four conspicuously raised lines ('wings'). Lower stem smooth, upper stem with short downy appressed hairs. In late autumn, at the base of the old flowering stem, almost stalkless, shortly stoloniferous, basal rosettes of smooth, glossy, elongate leaves appear, from which normal leaves will develop the following year. Leaves more or less stalkless, narrowly oblong, and smooth, leaf edges undulate with shallow widely spaced teeth; lower short-stalked stem leaves in opposite pairs, uppermost leaves not opposite. Flowers hermaphrodite, radially symmetric, 6-10 mm diameter, single-stalked and grouped at top of stems. Four deeply lobed, light pink or mauve-ish/pink petals: eight stamens, four long, four short; stigma of pistil club-shaped. Calyx with four downy sepals, c. half the length of the petals. Fruit capsule with four sections, downy, long and thin (7-9 cm in length, sometimes up to 11 cm), with many plumed seeds. Flowering July-August. Common throughout lowland England and Wales, extending north to Yorkshire, but almost absent from Scotland and Ireland. Occurs in hedges, banks, roadsides, ditches and stream banks, damp woodland, gardens, waste and cultivated ground.

151

Pollination Self-pollinated and cross-pollinated.

Regeneration strategies Short stolons and feathery plumed seeds readily carried by wind.

Weed control Hand-weed young basal leaf rosettes. Carefully remove older plants, making sure to dig out roots and stolons as well, before the plants reach fruiting stage. Leaves and stems can be composted but do not compost roots or stolons – either incinerate or take to local garden waste facility.

Herbal, culinary, cultural and folklore None found.

1) Young overwintering leafing stolon 2) young basal leaves 3) square stem and leaves 4) flower – note the club-shaped stigma 5) roots and young stolon nodules

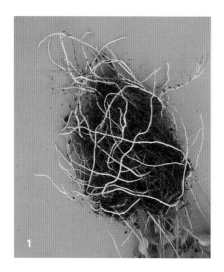

Enchanter's Nightshade *(Circaea lutetiana)*

Native. Perennial with slender, far-creeping rhizomes. Stems erect, 20-70 cm in height, with short, sparse glandular hairs. Short-stalked opposite leaves 4-10 cm long, ovate, wide-based with pointed tips, mid-to-deep green; leaf edges minutely and distantly toothed. Flower stems long and slender with sub-opposite, stalked, tiny hermaphrodite flowers comprising a pair of pale green, pink-tipped sepals at right angles to a pair of deeply lobed white petals of similar length (2-4 mm long); two stamens and a pistil with a two-lobed, often pale pink, stigma. Fruits c. 3 mm diameter, ovoid and densely covered with stiff, hooked white bristles. Flowering June-August. Widespread throughout the whole of the British Isles to Central Scotland, very rare in northern Scotland, and absent from Orkney, Shetland and the Outer Hebrides. Occurs in woods and shady places on moist, base-rich or calcareous soils to an altitude of 370 m. Very shade tolerant.

Pollination Probably by small flies.

Regeneration strategies Far-creeping rhizomes and hairy fruits that catch on fur or clothing.

Weed control Hand-weed young seedlings. Carefully remove older growth making sure to dig out roots and rhizomes as well, before the plants get too big, or reach fruiting stage. Leaves and stems can be composted but do not compost roots or rhizomes – either incinerate or take to local garden waste facility. Follow current best, preferably organic, practice for large invasions (see Bibliography and internet).

Herbal, culinary, cultural and folklore The Flemish botanist de l'Obel (1568-1616), who first gave this species a name, was trying to work out which plant Dioscorides referred to as "Kirkaia". Eventually he decided it must be the plant that would later be named *Circaea lutetiana* by Linnaeus. The genus name *Circaea* comes from the enchantress Circe of Greek mythology, and the species name *lutetiana* is from the Latin name for Paris which was, at one time, known as the 'Witch City'. Later, in Britain, it became locally known as Inchaunter's Nightshade, a name first recorded in print in the late 16th Century by the herbalist John Gerard. Enchanter's Nightshade is not related to Deadly Nightshade which belongs to the family Solanacaeae. Enchanter's Nightshade is a larval food plant for the Elephant Hawkmoth.

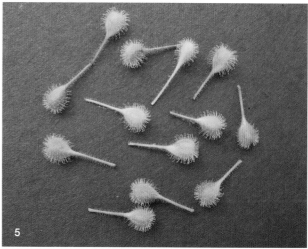

1) Young rhizomes, two and a half months growth 2) colony habit 3) flowering stem 4) seeding fruiting stems 5) fruits with hooked bristles

Common Evening Primrose *(Oenothera biennis)*

Introduced from the New World. It was being cultivated in Britain by 1629 and recorded in the wild by about 1650. Usually biennial, with stout tap root. Stems 50-100 cm in height, erect and robust, softly hairy. Leaves large (up to 20 cm long and 12 cm wide), narrowly ovate, mid-to-light green or olive green, slightly and softly hairy. In the first year a rosette of leaves develops, in the second year young stem leaves develop, these are arranged spirally at intervals on the lower part of the developing flower stem which continues to grow upwards throughout the flowering season. Flowers hermaphrodite, short-stalked, and radially symmetric, c. 4-6 cm diameter, sometimes as small as 3 or as large as 7 cm with four light lemon yellow, shallowly bi-lobed petals and eight stamens, stigma of pistil with four long lobes. When the flowers open in the early evening, the sepals bend back and point downwards; towards the middle of the next day the flowers wither. Calyx with four narrow green/pinkish sepals, turning pinker with age, c. same length as the petals. Fruit capsule long and cylindrical, with four valves containing numerous non-plumed seeds. Flowering June-September. Perhaps less common in southern England than previously, but with newer, scattered localities further north. Rare in Ireland. Occurs on waste ground, roadsides, railway banks and sand dunes.

Pollination Ultraviolet light reveals a bright nectar guide pattern in the petals to attract pollinators: mainly moths, butterflies and bees, including bumblebees. Small beetles and hoverflies also visit.

Regeneration strategies Very high number of large fruit capsules (seed pods), as many as 300 per adult plant, which split open when ripe to scatter small, copiously produced seeds (c. 90 to over 200 seeds per pod). These can remain dormant but viable in the ground for up to 40 years.

Weed control Hand-weed young seedlings, or dig out older plants before stems start to flower. Leaves and pre-flowering stems can be composted.

Herbal, culinary, cultural and folklore Evening Primrose Oil is extracted from the seeds and widely used in complementary medicine as a source of gamma linolenic acid (GLA), however, research over the last 20 years has largely discredited claims for the beneficial effects of taking Evening Primrose Oil. Traditionally a popular cottage garden plant, but less so now.

153

1) Young plant 2) flowering habit 3) flower – note four-lobed stigma and pollen on stamens in 'strings' 4) green fruit capsules 5) dry fruit capsule and seeds

OXALIDACEAE *(Wood-sorrel Family)*

Least Yellow-sorrel *(Oxalis exilis)*

Introduced from Australasia as a garden plant. Sometimes annual, often a short-lived perennial. Thread-like and inconspicuously hairy stoloniferous stems, often rooting at nodes, spreading from a slender tap root, to a length of up to 30 cm, sometimes as long as 35 cm. Leaf stalks 1-2.5 cm long, sometimes up to 7 cm. Leaves trifoliate, 0.7-1.0 cm diameter, sometimes up to 2 cm; leaflets heart-shaped, always light green, edges and undersides minutely hairy. Flowers hermaphrodite, radially symmetric, borne singly on erect stalks, 0.8-2.5 cm diameter, sometimes up to 3 cm. Flower diameter: 0.5-0.8 cm, sometimes up to 1 cm, with five light lemon yellow bluntly ovate petals; ten stamens, five short, five longer; pistil with a five-branched stigma. Calyx with five oblong sepals, c. 2 mm long and slightly hairy. Fruit capsule five-locular, conical to cylindrical (0.3-0.6 mm long, sometimes up to 0.7 mm), covered in short hairs. As the capsules ripen they burst open, ejecting the two to four seeds into the surrounding area. At the point of dispersal, the minute ovate, transversely ribbed, reddish-brown seeds are covered by a rapidly shed, translucent white membrane. Flowering June-October. A native of mountainous areas of New Zealand and Tasmania and probably introduced as pretty ground cover, especially as it seems to thrive best in shadier, cooler parts of the garden.

154

Pollination Self-pollination or insects.

Regeneration strategies Projectile seeds and stem runners.

Weed control Hand-weed young plants before capsules develop, or dig out overwintering plants before flowering begins. Leaves and pre-flowering plants can be composted.

Herbal, culinary, cultural and folklore Sometimes used in salads because of the pleasantly sharp flavour of the leaves, due to their oxalic acid content. For this reason anyone suffering from arthritis, rheumatism, kidney problems or hyperacidity should avoid including this plant in their diet.

Toxicity See comments above.

1) Seedlings 2) habit 3) flower 4) seed capsules 5) seed capsules, seeds and seed membranes

Procumbent Yellow-sorrel *(Oxalis corniculata)*

Introduced garden escape, origin obscure. Sometimes annual, often a short-lived perennial. Slightly hairy, thread-like stoloniferous stems extend from a slender tap root to a length of up to 35 cm, sometimes as long as 40 cm, often rooting at nodes. Leaf stalks 1.5-5 cm long, sometimes up to 8 cm. Leaves trifoliate, 1.5-2.5 cm diameter, leaflets heart-shaped, green or, in the case of *Oxalis corniculata* var. *atropurpurea*, reddish-purple, leaflet edges and undersides minutely hairy. Flowers hermaphrodite, radially symmetric, borne singly or in loose umbels of two to six on erect stalks, 3-4 cm long, sometimes up to 5 cm. Flower diameter: 1.0-1.5 cm, with five light or golden yellow bluntly ovate petals; ten stamens, five short, five longer; pistil with a five-branched stigma. Calyx with five oblong sepals (0.3-0.5 cm long), slightly hairy. Fruit capsule five-locular, conical to cylindrical (1.2-1.5 cm long), covered in short hairs. As the pods ripen they burst open, ejecting four to six, sometimes as many as eight seeds into the surrounding area. At the point of dispersal, the minute ovate, transversely ribbed, reddish-brown seeds are covered by a rapidly shed, translucent white membrane. Flowering June-September, sometimes as early as May or as late as October. An introduced species grown in gardens since the Middle Ages. It was first recorded as established in the wild before the end of the 16th Century. Although it occurs as a garden weed throughout much of England and Wales, it is most common in the south-west and the Channel Islands and rare in Scotland and Ireland. A garden opportunist, thriving in light moist shade but with a preference for a sunny spot. It is not unusual to find it sharing a pot at the local garden centre.

Pollination Self-pollinated.

Regeneration strategies Projectile seeds and stem runners.

Weed control Hand-weed young plants before capsules develop, or dig out overwintering plants before flowering begins. Leaves and pre-flowering plants can be composted.

Herbal, culinary, cultural and folklore Sometimes used in salads because of the pleasantly sharp flavour of the leaves, due to their oxalic acid content. For this reason anyone suffering from arthritis, rheumatism, kidney problems or hyperacidity should avoid including this plant in their diet. Flowers and plants sometimes used to produce dyes in the yellow-orange-brown spectrum.

Toxicity See comments above.

155

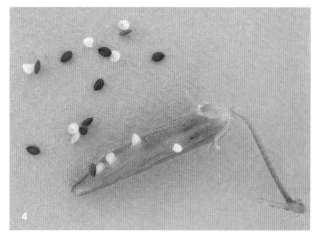

1) Young plant, bronze form 2) habit 3) seed capsules 4) seed capsules, seeds and seed membranes

Large-flowered Pink-sorrel *(Oxalis debilis/O. corymbosa)*

Introduced from tropical America as a garden plant. Perennial. Leafy plant, 10-30 cm in height, however, there is no above-ground stem other than the short axis of the loose-scaled subterranean bulb (1.5-3 cm long). On sprouting this bulb produces a ring of many 'adventitious' bulbils (3-6 mm long). One of these will become the main fleshy, whitish tap root, with numerous fine hairy roots; the scaly bulbs also produce roots and stalks. The parent bulb disintegrates at the end of the growing season, but is replaced by a new main bulb, which may draw on the old shrivelling tap root for resources. Leaves basal, mid-dull green, stalks 5-30 cm long, with long, sparse to moderately dense, spreading white hairs (more obvious with a hand lens); leaflet blades broadly heart-shaped with a shallow cleft, 1-4.5 cm long and 1.5-6 cm wide; margins of neighbouring leaflets touching. Flowers hermaphrodite, radially symmetric, eight to 15 borne singly on short stalks branching from the loosely erect stem (10-40 cm and higher); flower diameter: 3-4 cm; five petals with propeller-shaped tips, purplish pink with darker veins, 1.5-2 cm long; ten stamens, five short, five longer; pistil with five-branched stigma. Calyx shortly hairy with five oblong sepals (4-7 mm long). Fruits and seeds uncommon, capsules rarely formed. Flowering July-September. Distribution mainly south-east and central Britain, but also found sporadically elsewhere, notably in coastal Cornwall and Wales. It is usually found in gardens and allotments.

Pollination Self-pollination is frequent in *Oxalis* species, and this non-native species rarely sets seeds, but is strongly reliant on vegetative propagation.

Regeneration strategy Mostly vegetatively, via high production of bulbils.

Weed control Dig out carefully with a bucket or large sheet of plastic to hand to avoid the bulbils falling into the soil while collecting up the plants. It is advisable to take all parts of the plants to the local recycling facility for disposal.

Herbal, culinary, cultural and folklore An old cottage garden favourite, it is tolerated or encouraged in gardens, where it favours open sunny sites. There are two other introduced pink-flowered species of *Oxalis* that may be encountered, notably in south-west Britain: *O. articulata* (east temperate South America) and *O. latifolia* (West Indies, and central and equatorial South America). The three species are easily distinguished by their leaves: *O. debilis* has softly hairy leaves, and closely touching rounded heart-shaped leaflets, with a shallow cleft to each leaflet, while the other two species have smooth leaflets. *O. articulata* has heart-shaped leaflets that are less closely spaced, have a deeper cleft and little elongate yellow-orange glands around the leaflet margins. The leaflets of *O. latifolia* are not closely spaced, and have broadly triangular leaflets with a shallow cleft.

156

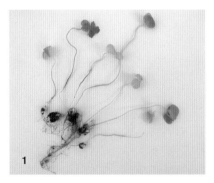
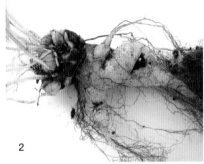

1) Young plantlets 2) corms and large tap root 3) young plant 4) flowers 5) habit

PAPAVERACEAE *(Poppy Family)*

Greater Celandine *(Chelidonium majus)*

Origin uncertain, arguably an early introduction, possibly an old 'herb garden' escape. Historically and currently strongly associated with human habitation. Perennial with short, branching rootstock. Stems 30-90 cm in height, brittle and light bluish-green. Leaves with slender, sparsely hairy stalks, comprising five to seven or more separate, smooth, broad-lobed leaflets, light green above, bluish-green below. Both stems and leaves exude deep yellow-orange latex if cut or damaged. Flowers hermaphrodite; the long stalked, radially symmetric flowers (2-2.5 cm diameter) are arranged in loose terminal groups of three to five, sometimes up to six. Four bright lemon yellow petals; stamens numerous, style very short with paired stigma lobes. Fruit is a cylindrical, smooth, pod-like capsule (3-5 cm long), containing numerous black shiny seeds (30-40). Each seed has a translucent white appendage, almost as large as the seed. Flowering May-August. Occurs throughout most of the British Isles, but scarce in northern Scotland, and scattered in Ireland. A frequent plant of hedgerows, banks, wall bases and roadsides.

Pollination Mainly bees and flies; however, in dull weather, when the flowers remain closed, the anthers may open in the bud and effect self-pollination.

Regeneration strategy Copiously produced seed, the white appendage of which is extremely attractive to ants, thus ensuring wider distribution.

Weed control Hand-weed young plants before flowers and pods develop, or dig out overwintering plants before flowering begins. Leaves and pre-flowering plants can be composted. Follow current best, preferably organic, practice for large invasions (see Bibliography and internet).

Herbal, culinary, cultural and folklore A confusing common name, as it is a member of the Poppy family, and not related to Celandine which is a member of the Buttercup family. Also known as Swallow-wort because it was observed long ago that it "… flowers when the Swallows come, and dies when they leave." It is also associated with Swallows because it was said that they cured the damaged eyes of their fledglings by putting this herb on them. In the Middle Ages the fresh yellow latex was used externally for eye ailments, warts and as a remedy against jaundice (possibly following the Doctrine of Signatures). It is, however, an extremely poisonous plant.

Toxicity The species is a vegetable irritant, causing nausea and dysentry and is a drastic purgative, previously used in rural areas as an emetic. The toxins are four alkaloids: chelidonine, homochelidonine, sanguinarine and chelerythrine. Animals avoid browsing the plant.

1) Young plant 2) adult habit 3) flowers 4) stem latex 5) fruit capsules and seeds with fleshy white appendage

Long-headed Poppy *(Papaver dubium)*

Native. Annual with narrow tap root. Flowering stems erect or almost, 20-60 cm in height, with flat-lying short hairs. Cut stems exude whitish latex. Leaves similar to the Field Poppy but with shorter, broader, more abruptly bristle-tipped segments and a smaller terminal segment. In bud the flower head droops and is covered by the calyx, which comprises a pair of large, green, ovate, hairy sepals that drop off as the flower opens. The flowers are hermaphrodite, radially symmetric, and held singly on each stem; the four petals are arranged in two pairs at right angles to each other. Overall flower diameter: 3-7 cm; petals light scarlet (occasionally with a dark spot). Stamens numerous and surround the large, smooth, greyish, slim goblet-shaped ovary (seed capsule); anthers dull purplish with yellow pollen; the pistil (which does not have a style) is the spoked wheel-like 'lid' of the seed capsule (more than twice as long as wide). After petals drop, the exposed seed capsule ripens and dries, and below the dried 'wheel' of the stigma a ring of small apertures opens the ovary segments to allow dispersal of the tiny, kidney-shaped seeds. Flowering June-July, sometimes as late as August. A lowland species, occurring in similar habitats to those of Field Poppy (sometimes both species can be found in close proximity), although often more common than Field Poppy in northern England. Scarcer and more localised in Wales, Scotland, and western Ireland. A weed of arable fields, especially where cereals are grown. Prefers light, well-drained soils on sands or chalk but avoids heavy clays.

Pollination Usually bees and hoverflies, but the flowers are also self-fertile.

Regeneration strategies Production of copious and long-viable seed; buried seed may remain dormant for more than 80 years, however, the seedlings generally germinate in autumn, resulting in higher seedling mortality than for Field Poppy with seeds that usually germinate in spring.

Weed control Harrow, hoe, pull out or dig in young green seedling plants before they produce flower buds, or follow current best, preferably organic, practice for large invasions (see Bibliography and internet).

Herbal, culinary, cultural and folklore Modest in comparison with its famous 'cousin', but sharing the culinary use of poppy seed in baking of bread or cakes. Fresh petals were sometimes used to produce a fine red colouring for syrups. It was also used in folk medicine for its narcotic qualities in the relief of pain. The generic name *Papaver* is thought to derive from *pappus*, the Latin name for breast, alluding to the milky latex produced by the stems. Many of the current uses of poppy seed are related to the Opium poppy (*Papaver somniferum*), rather than the 'Red Poppies'.

Toxicity The species is poisonous in all parts. The toxicity principally consists of the alkaloids morphine and rhoeadine, which have sedative and antitussive effects. Grazing animals are not attracted to them as they find the odour and taste unpleasant.

158

1) Flowering habit 2) leaves 3) flower 4) seed capsule and seeds

Field or Common Poppy *(Papaver rhoeas)*

Native. Annual (usually) with narrow tap root. Flowering stems erect or almost, 20-60 cm in height, slightly hairy or with stiff spreading hairs. Cut stems exude whitish latex. Leaves mid-green, stalked, stiffly hairy, and deeply segmented, segments with one, two or more shallow, bristle-tipped lobes. Upper leaves smaller, less lobed, without stalks. In bud the flower head droops and is covered by the calyx which comprises a pair of large, green, ovate, hairy sepals that drop off as the flower opens. The flowers are hermaphrodite, radially symmetric, and held singly on each stem; the four petals are arranged in two pairs at right angles to each other. Overall flower diameter: 7-10 cm; petals scarlet, in some populations with a dark spot at the base. Stamens numerous and surround the large, smooth, greyish, goblet-shaped ovary (seed capsule); anthers dull purplish with yellow pollen; the pistil (which does not have a style) is the spoked wheel-like 'lid' of the seed capsule (not more than twice as long as wide). After petals drop, the exposed capsule ripens and dries, and below the dried 'wheel' of the stigma, a ring of small apertures opens the ovary segments to allow dispersal of the tiny, kidney-shaped seeds. Flowering June-August, sometimes as late as September. A lowland species, common in England but scarcer and more localised in Wales, Scotland, and western Ireland. A weed of arable fields, especially where cereals are grown. It prefers light, well-drained soils on sands or chalk but avoids heavy clays.

Pollination The flowers are almost entirely self-sterile. Pollination is effected by a range of social and solitary bees or hoverflies.

Regeneration strategy Production of copious and long-viable seed; buried seed may remain dormant for more than 80 years. Seed normally germinates in spring, unlike Long-headed Poppy which has seed that normally germinates in autumn.

Weed control Harrow, hoe, pull out or dig in young green seedling plants before they produce flower buds, or follow current best, preferably organic, practice for large invasions (see Bibliography and internet).

Herbal, culinary, cultural and folklore In the late 19th Century this species gained iconic status through the writings of the *Daily Telegraph* drama critic of the time, Clement Scott. So captivated was Scott by the sight of endless poppies covering the clifftops in the, then fashionable, north-east Norfolk landscape, especially in the Cromer area, that he named it 'Poppy-land'. It became so popular for the well-to-do to visit this wonderful scarlet landscape in high summer that the local railway link was renamed 'The Poppy Line'. Tragically this species would later gain national iconic status following World War I, when disturbed seed from extensive digging for trench warfare caused poppies to regenerate and flower across the war-torn fields of northern France and Belgium. The poignant imagery of this species, in the hearts of so many, especially north-western Europeans, was triggered by a poem written in 1915 by the Canadian poet and military physician Colonel John McCrae: "In Flanders Fields the poppies blow between the crosses, row on row, ..." McCrae died from his war wounds in 1918. An American teacher, Moina Belle Michael, was so moved by the poem that she bought poppies and sold them to her friends and colleagues to raise funds for wounded US servicemen. In 1921 a French woman, Mme Guérin, took up the idea and visited various parts of the world affected by WWI, to suggest that artificial poppies should be made and sold to raise funds to help ex-servicemen and their families, devastated by the war. As a result the first Poppy Day in Britain was held on 11 November 1921. In the same year Field Marshall Earl Haigh became the founder President of the newly formed British Legion (Royal status was not conferred until 1971), to care for ex-servicemen, and to provide work for them and their families. The first British poppy factory was set up in 1922 in disused factory premises in east London. Demand was so high that, in 1926, production moved to a disused brewery premises in Richmond, west London, and houses were built for the workforce and their families on adjacent land. In the same year, on Lady Haigh's suggestion, a poppy factory was also established in Edinburgh. In 1932 the old Richmond Brewery was pulled down and a new factory was built on the site. In November 2014, as part of the memorial events to mark the Centenary of the outset of WWI, the artist Paul Cummins was commissioned to make 888,246 ceramic poppies (representing each soldier who died). These were 'planted' in waves of colour around the Tower of London.

Toxicity The species is poisonous in all parts. The toxicity principally consists of the alkaloids morphine and rhoeadine, which have sedative and antitussive effects. Grazing animals are not attracted to them as they find the odour and taste unpleasant.

159

1) Flower bud and leaves 2) petals with basal black spots 3) seed capsule and seeds

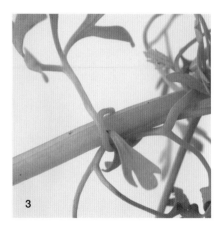

Common Fumitory *(Fumaria officinalis)*

Native. Annual with slender tap root. Stems smooth, tender, and rambling. Leaves long-stalked, smooth, very divided and slightly ferny in appearance. Leaf stems can twist around other stems to get a hold. Stems and leaves slightly greyish-green. Flowers hermaphrodite. The short-stalked bisymmetric flowers, (7-8 mm long, sometimes up to 9 mm) are arranged on long spikes of ten to 40 individual flowers; the lower part of the spike lacks flowers. There are four petals arranged in two differing, almost fused, pairs, both very elongate and highly modified: upper pair comprise two conjoined deep pink petals with a narrow greenish centre, and light rose-pink tube below, with a sac-like swollen base; these more or less conceal a much smaller, lower pair of very narrow conjoined petals which terminate in a spoon-like apex. The stamens comprise a fused filament 'sheath' with one central normal bi-lobed anther, flanked by a pair of one-lobed anthers (half-anthers), while the pistil (which does not have a style) is the tiny central area on the upper surface of the smooth, globose, grey-green ovary (c. 2-2.5 mm long). Calyx comprises a pair of small, elongate greenish sepals, with broad, semi-translucent, whitish, feathery margins, which fall early. After petal drop, the exposed ovary (fruit capsule) ripens and sheds one globose, slightly wrinkled brown seed. Flowering from June-October, sometimes as early as May. Distributed throughout the British Isles, particularly in central and eastern regions, scarcer in the west and in Ireland. Has a preference for well-drained conditions on either acidic or calcareous soils.

160

Pollination The flower self-pollinates and, although nectar is secreted in the base (sac) of the upper pair of petals, it is apparently not much visited by insects.

Regeneration strategy Locally, by seed. Also readily eaten by cows and sheep, with a resulting rich dung medium for later germination of seed.

Weed control Hand-weed young plants before flowers and pods develop, or dig out overwintering plants before flowering begins. Leaves and pre-flowering plants can be composted. Follow current best, preferably organic, practice for large invasions (see Bibliography and internet).

Herbal, culinary, cultural and folklore The botanical name comes from the Latin word for smoke, either because the juice was sometimes used to cure eye problems but made the eyes weep (like smoke), or because the greyish foliage of the freely rambling plants looked like smoke. Fumitory was said to have the power of expelling evil spirits. Contains fumaric acid which has been used as a food additive since 1946, notably in baking powder, or as a substitute for tartaric acid.

1) Young plant 2) adult habit 3) detail of stem tendril 4) flowering head 5) young green fruits

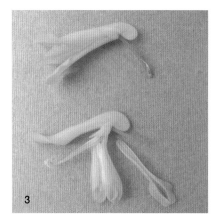

Yellow Corydalis *(Pseudofumaria lutea)*

Introduced. Native distribution southern foothills of the central and eastern Alps. Popular in the UK as a cottage garden plant and recorded as a garden escape in 1849 from Godalming (Surrey). Short-lived evergreen perennial, rhizomatous. Stems smooth, tender, spreading to upright, mound-forming, height and spread to 40 cm. Leaves 10-15 cm long, long-stalked, fern-like, soft light green, smooth, and finely divided into a number of small, broadly ovate leaflets, without tendrils or twining stalks. Stems and leaf stalks pinkish-green. Flowers hermaphrodite. The short-stalked, bisymmetric flowers (1-2 cm long) are arranged on smooth stems that continue to grow from the tip *(racemes)*, the flower stalks are attached all around the stem, but twist so that the flowers all face to one side. Racemes have from six to 16 individual flowers; the lower part of the stem is without flowers. There are four yellow petals: the large upper one curves up at the tip, and has a rounded, downward curving spur at the base; the lower petal is long and narrow with a spoon-like tip; the two central, elongate-ovoid, opposing petals are slightly shorter. The stamens comprise a fused filament 'sheath' with one central normal bi-lobed anther, flanked by a pair of one-lobed anthers (half-anthers); the pistil is at the tip of the developing seed pod (fruit). Calyx a pair of small, pale, elongate-ovate, translucent greenish-yellow sepals, with very slightly toothed margins, these fall early. After petals drop, the exposed seed pod ripens and releases four to eight dark brown (occasionally black) seeds with swollen white appendages *(elaiosomes)*. Flowering May-August. Generally favours cultivated places, especially in or near gardens and buildings; a great coloniser especially of old walls, dry banks where it is often encouraged or tolerated. Generally a lowland species but has been recorded at heights of 305 m in Great Hucklow, Derbyshire (it is possible that this may result from birds, who are attracted to the seed – see below).

161

Pollination Has an explosive pollen release system, triggered by insect visitors.

Regeneration strategy The white appendages on the seeds attract ants and birds, thereby effecting seed distribution.

Weed control Hand-weed young plants before flowers and pods develop, or dig out overwintering plants before flowering begins. Leaves and pre-flowering plants can be composted. Follow current best, preferably organic, practice for large invasions (see Bibliography and internet).

Herbal, culinary, cultural and folklore A well-established introduction and easy to pull up where it is not wanted. Often tolerated, even encouraged on old walls or in unsightly corners of the garden. As it is non-native there are no traditions or folk remedies associated with this species in the British Isles.

1) Adult habit 2) flower heads 3) flower (top) and dissection (bottom) 4) seed capsules 5) ripe seed capsules and seeds

PLANTAGINACEAE *(Plantain, Speedwell & Toadflax Family)*

Ribwort, Ribwort Plantain *(Plantago lanceolata)*

Native. Perennial with basal rosette of spreading and erect leaves, 10-15 cm in height, sometimes as short as 2 or as tall as 30 cm. Leaves lance-shaped, three- to five-ribbed and mid-green; leaf stalk usually about half as long as leaf. Flowers hermaphrodite, in a tightly packed elongate-ovoid inflorescence, 1-2 cm long, sometimes up to 5 cm, on long, slender, erect, ribbed flower stems 10-40 cm in height, sometimes up to 45 cm. Individual flowers radially symmetric, tiny (c. 2-3 mm long, sometimes up to 4 mm), with four membranous lobes (petals), four sepals, four long-filamented white stamens and a long thin pistil of which most of the length is the stigma. Each flower produces a lidded seed capsule enclosing one to two tiny light brown oval seeds. Flowering April-August. Common throughout the whole of the British Isles, both on the coast and inland; frequent on clifftops, dunes, meadows, pastures, grassy heaths, and other types of rough grassland, hedge banks and roadside verges. It is found growing on most soil types except acidic peat and uplands.

Pollination Highly adapted to wind-pollination with long-filamented stamens. Although wind-pollinated, insects also visit the flowers.

Regeneration strategy High seed production, with a germination rate of 60-90%, or as much as 100% from seed that has passed through birds. Seed longevity c. eight to ten years.

Weed control Hand-weed young plants before flowers and seed capsules develop, or dig out overwintering plants before flowering begins. Leaves and pre-flowering plants can be composted. Follow current best, preferably organic, practice for large invasions (see Bibliography and internet).

Herbal, culinary, cultural and folklore Previously valued as a way of preventing soil erosion, especially on thin soil overlying rocky substrata, thus maintaining fertility of otherwise barren land, notably in the Welsh mountains. Less tolerant of trampling than *Plantago major*, but is more palatable to sheep and cattle. Tolerant of mowing. Children like play-fighting with the long stemmed flower heads to 'knock the heads off the stalks' of each other's plantains.

1) Young plant 2) adult plants 3) habit 4) flowering head 5) seed heads 6) seed capsules closed (top), open (centre), released seeds (paired, with old placenta, bottom left & right)

Greater Plantain, Rat-tail Plantain *(Plantago major)*

Native. Perennial with basal rosette of spreading and erect leaves, 10-15 cm in height, sometimes up to 30 cm. Leaves ovate or elliptic, leaf margins may be slightly toothed and undulate, five- to nine-ribbed, mid-green. Flowers hermaphrodite, in a tightly packed elongate inflorescence, 10-15 cm long, sometimes as short as 1 or as long as 50 cm, usually one third to half entire length of the smooth flowering stems. Individual flowers radially symmetric, tiny, c. 3 mm overall, with four sepals, four greenish-brown membranous lobes (petals), and four purple stamens, which have much shorter filaments than the stamens of *P. lanceolata*, and a long thin pistil of which c. half of the length is the stigma. Each flower produces a lidded seed capsule which encloses eight to 16 tiny light brown oval seeds. Flowering May-September. Common throughout the whole of the British Isles, notably where turf or grassland is short, such as well-cropped pastures, and trackways where the herbage is kept short by trampling; can also be a nuisance on gravel paths. A troublesome weed of lawns, and highly tolerant of mowing. Occurs on almost all soil types, apart from acidic peat and mountain grassland, to an altitude of c. 625 m.

Pollination Wind, although self-pollination is also possible.

Regeneration strategy High seed production, with a germination rate of 60-90%. Seed longevity at least ten years; seeds as much as 40 years old have been germinated.

Weed control Hand-weed young plants before flower heads and seeds capsules develop, or dig out overwintering plants before flowering begins. Leaves and pre-flowering plants can be composted. Follow current best, preferably organic, practice for large invasions (see Bibliography and internet).

Herbal, culinary, cultural and folklore Rich in minerals, especially potassium, calcium and sulphur, and the blood clotting vitamin K; one of the most abundant, widespread and valuable of all temperate zone medicinal herbs. A favourite wound-healing herb, especially once among gypsies who used to peddle Plantain ointment as a general cure-all. In the Scottish Highlands it is called 'Slan-lus' meaning a healing plant. It is one of the Herbs of St. John, traditionally gathered in Britain for St. John's Night.

163

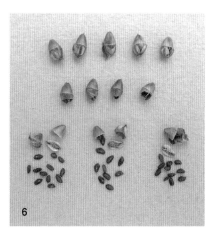

1) Young plants 2) young plant colony 3) flowering head 4) flowering and seeding heads 5) seed heads, green to ripe
6) seed capsules closed (top), open (centre), released seeds with old greyish placentas (bottom)

Foxglove *(Digitalis purpurea)*

Native. Biennial, rarely perennial. Erect flowering stems 50-150 cm in height, sometimes up to 200 cm. Ovate basal leaves arranged in a rosette. Upper stem leaves elongate-ovate, mid-green, with minutely wrinkled, softly hairy surface; leaf margins with very short rounded 'teeth', underside felty, pale greyish-green, narrowing into a winged (flanged) leaf stalk. Flowering stem with 20-80 flowers, with small, lance-shaped green bracts at base of flower stalks, these gradually diminish in size up the stem. Flowers hermaphrodite, bisymmetric. Flower a long, five-lobed, bell-shaped tube (3-4 cm, sometimes up to 5 cm long), exterior usually pinkish-purple; the upper two short lobes form the 'lip', the two side lobes are larger, and the basal lobe even larger. The interior of the flower is also usually pinkish-purple, the lower surface with deep pink spots on a white ground, and sometimes with sparse slender hairs projecting from the 'ceiling' of the flower tube. There are four paired stamens pressed against the upper 'ceiling' of the corolla, one pair with longer filaments than other pair; pistil long, curved over at its tip. Calyx distinct, much shorter than flower, with five light green, ovate-pointed sepals, one often slightly narrower than the other four. Fruit capsule with numerous, tiny, honey-comb-surfaced seeds. Flowering June-September. Occurs throughout the whole of the British Isles with the exception of Shetland. Scarce and localised in eastern counties of Cambridgeshire and Lincolnshire. A plant of woodland clearings, wood margins, hedge banks, footpaths, rocky hillsides to altitudes of c. 890 m with a preference for acidic or well-drained soils.

Pollination Bumblebees – an excellent example of floral adaptation to the body shape of the pollinator.

Regeneration strategy Copious seed production.

Weed control Remove young seedlings and plants immediately. Cut or pull up flowering plants before fruits mature. Compost only if there are no green or ripe seed pods, or take to local garden waste facility. Follow current best, preferably organic, practice for large invasions (see Bibliography and internet).

Herbal, culinary, cultural and folklore This wild species and its cultivars are widely grown in herbaceous borders. Its poisonous qualities have long been known, and its many common names include Dead Men's Bells and Dead Women's Thimbles. The 18th Century botanist William Withering carried out a clinical investigation of Foxglove chemistry (*Account of the Foxglove*) and demonstrated that it acts on the heart and was also a good diuretic. The association with foxes has never been satisfactorily resolved – it remains one of life's little mysteries.

Toxicity The whole plant is poisonous, but especially the seeds. It contains a number of glycosides, most notably digitoxin, that act on the muscles of the heart. The dried and powdered leaves are known to medicine as 'Digitalis'. Animals are not known to browse this species.

1) Seedling 2) young plant 3) flowering stem 4) inside flower 5) flower sectioned 6) seed heads and seeds

Purple Toadflax *(Linaria purpurea)*

Introduced mid-17th Century. A long established garden escape from the central Mediterranean. Perennial, with extensive system of vertical and creeping lateral roots that produce new shoots. Erect, slender, unbranched, smooth grey-green stems, 70 cm in height, sometimes as short as 45, sometimes as tall as 90 cm. Leaves linear, greyish-green, 2-6 cm long; lower leaves in whorls (rings), upper leaves alternate. Flowers hermaphrodite, bisymmetric, numerous, borne on long, slender, dense flowering stems. Flowers short-stalked with long strongly curved spurs, length of spur equals flower width: flowers 8-12 mm long with five mid-to-deep mauve, distinctly veined lobes. In form, the flower shape is usually described as resembling a little mouth: the throat (*palate*), an angled pair of ovoid swellings, a bi-lobed upper 'lip', and a tri-lobed lower lip; four stamens in two pairs; pistil long, slender, stigma small, un-lobed or with two small lobes. Five narrowly ovate sepals, joined only at base (1-4 cm long, sometimes up to 5 cm). Fruit a rounded ovate, two-locular capsule, opening by slits. Seeds numerous, like irregular segments of an orange, more or less three-sided, curved or straight outer margins with warty, wrinkly surface. Flowering June-August. Naturalised in a large number of places throughout the British Isles, but most commonly in the south, where it is often found growing on or near old walls, in dry hedge banks, or stony waste ground.

165

Pollination Bees, butterflies and moths, including the Toadflax Brocade Moth (*Calophasia lunula*).

Regeneration strategies Large amounts of seed shed locally to the parent plants and spreading by short rhizomes.

Weed control It will spread rapidly, if not discouraged. Remove young seedlings and plants immediately. Cut or pull up flowering plants before fruits mature and compost only if there are no green or ripe seed pods, or take to local garden waste facility. Follow current best, preferably organic, practice for large invasions (see Bibliography and internet).

Herbal, culinary, cultural and folklore A native of central and southern Italy and Sicily, this species and its cultivars are widely grown in herbaceous borders.

Toxicity Toxic to livestock.

 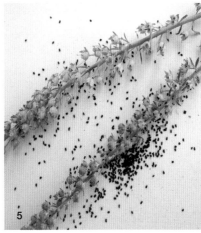 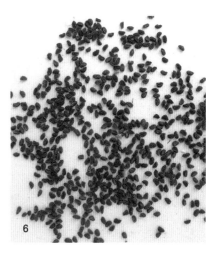

1) Young plants 2) habit 3) flowering stems 4) close-up of flowers 5) seed heads and seeds 6) seeds

Common or Yellow Toadflax *(Linaria vulgaris)*

Native. Perennial with extensive system of vertical and creeping lateral roots that produce new shoots. Erect, with numerous sturdy, unbranched, very shortly hairy light green stems, 30-70 cm in height, sometimes as short as 20 or as tall as 80 cm. Leaves narrowly linear, stalkless, mid-green or slightly greyish-green; leaf margins narrowly rolled under (*revolute*), 3-8 cm long; lower leaves opposite, upper leaves alternate. Flowers hermaphrodite, bisymmetric; many flowers closely grouped at the upper end of the long flowering stems. Flowers short-stalked with long spurs, in length more or less equal to width/depth of flower, 15-25 mm, sometimes up to 30 mm long, with four lobes. In form, the flower shape is usually described as being like a little mouth: a swollen orange throat (*palate*), a pale yellow, shallowly indented upper 'lip', and a large, pale yellow, bi-lobed lower lip. Four stamens in two pairs; pistil long, slender, stigma small, un-lobed or with two small lobes. Five ovate or elongate-ovate pointed sepals, joined only at base, width 1-2 cm, sometimes up to 5 cm. Fruit an ovoid two-loculed capsule, 5-10 mm long, sometimes up to 12 mm, opening by slits. Seeds numerous (c. 70 per capsule), warty, surrounded by a wide, thin, circular flange. Flowering July-October. Widely distributed throughout England, Wales and southern Scotland. Rare in northern and western Scotland and in Ireland, absent from Orkney and Shetland. A frequent plant of hedge banks, roadsides, waste places and rough grassland, usually on well-drained, dry, sandy or calcareous soils.

Pollination Long-tongued bees, notably bumblebees. Seed numbers are much higher when cross-pollinated, than when self-pollinated (as noted by Darwin, 1892).

Regeneration strategies Seed morphology suggests that wind dispersal might be a factor, at least sometimes.

Weed control It will spread rapidly, if not discouraged. Remove young seedlings and plants before flowering and compost only if there are no green or ripe seed pods. Follow current best, preferably organic, practice for large invasions (see Bibliography and internet).

Herbal, culinary, cultural and folklore Favourite common names are Eggs and Butter and Eggs and Bacon, in reference to the yellow and orange flowers. In Sussex the plant used to be called Gallwort, and was put in the water drunk by poultry, in order to cure them when 'drooping'. A yellow dye can be extracted from the flowers.

1) Habit 2) flowering plant and leaves 3) flower detail 4) fruits and seeds

Ivy-leaved Toadflax *(Cymbalaria muralis)*

Introduced early in 17th Century when William Coys, one of the best amateur gardeners of his time, grew it in his garden at North Ockenden in Essex. From its early introduction it seems to have spread fairly widely by the end of 17th Century, via keen gardeners. Perennial. Stems smooth, hairless, trailing or drooping, often purplish, 10-80 cm in height, rooting at intervals. Leaves 1-3 cm diameter, long-stalked, opposite at stem bases, otherwise alternate on either side of stem: broad, slightly fleshy, sometimes purplish beneath, with five, sometimes only three or as many as nine, rounded or broadly ovate lobes with pointed tips. Flowers hermaphrodite, bisymmetric; flower stalks c. 2 cm long; flowers 8-10 mm long, lilac, rarely white. The flower shape is usually described as being like a little mouth: a throat *(palate)* with paired white swellings each with a bright yellow blotch, an upper 'lip' with two small, narrow, lilac petals, usually streaked with purple, and a lower lip with three broad, larger, paler lilac petals. The outer base of the flower has a short, curved projection ('spur') about one third as long as the flower; there are four stamens and a single slender style. Five narrow, elongate, pale green sepals. The fruit is a globose capsule (4-5 mm long), containing c. 40 seeds (c. 0.6-0.8 mm long). The seeds are roundish with a rough, blocky, irregular surface. Flowering mostly May-September, but can often be found flowering somewhere at any time of the year. Common throughout most of the British Isles, with the exception of northern and north-east Scotland, Orkney, Shetland and the Outer Hebrides. Found on old walls in both rural and urban situations and occasionally on rocks, shingle and waste ground.

Pollination Self-pollinated and also visited by bees.

Regeneration strategy Strongly phototropic: the flowers are positively phototropic and grow towards light, while the seed heads are negatively phototropic and move towards dark, resulting in seed pods being directed toward cracks and crevices in walls, thus providing the ideal conditions the fertilised seed needs to germinate. Seed germination occurs in both spring and autumn.

Weed control Tends to favour loosely constructed stone walls. Often tolerated, but can cause appreciable damage to old stonework, especially in high or unreachable sites. Hand-weed before flowering, possibly repeating for a year or so, to be sure of clearance. Follow current best, preferably organic, practice for large invasions (see Bibliography and internet).

Herbal, culinary, cultural and folklore The leaves are sometimes eaten but can be mildly toxic and are best avoided. Its plentiful seed production is recorded in local names such as Hundreds-of-thousands and Mother-of-millions, while its mouth-like flowers give rise to Monkey-jaws and Rabbits' Mouths, and its boisterous spreading habit inspired Roving Sailor. Its abundance on Oxford college walls earned it the name of Oxford Weed.

167

1) Flowering habit 2) flower 3) long-stalked fruits 4) stages of ripening fruits 5) seeds

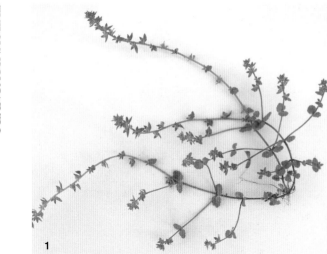

Wall Speedwell *(Veronica arvensis)*

Native. Annual. Stems erect or almost so, softly hairy, sometimes glandular, 3-25 cm in height. Leaves 1.5 cm long or less, arranged in opposite pairs, triangular-ovate and hairy, margins with coarse rounded teeth; only lower leaves stalked. Flowers hermaphrodite, bisymmetric, numerous from about 15 to 50 or more, closely associated in the axils of the bracts on the long terminal flowering stems (*racemes*). Bracts with short glandular hairs; upper bracts narrowly ovate, longer than flowers; lower bracts successively becoming more leaf-like. Flower stalks less than 1 mm long; flowers 2-3 mm across with four basally united, deep sky blue petals, each with slightly darker veining and a basal white eye: upper and lateral petals broadly ovate and of similar size, lower petal of similar length but slightly narrower; two stamens with thick filaments tapering to base, creamy white anthers and pollen; pistil with small rounded stigma and long thin style tapering to base. Four mid-green, narrowly ovate calyx lobes with pointed tips and stiff white glandular hairs alternating with, and c. twice the length of the petals. Fruit shorter than calyx, two-locular, flattened and broadly heart-shaped, 3-4 mm long, sometimes up to 5 mm. Seeds tiny, ellipsoid with rounded, ribbed margins and a central depression (*orifice*), about 18 per locule. Flowering March-October. Widespread throughout the whole of the British Isles. It is a common weed of arable crops and cultivated soils, banks and old walls, but also occurs less often on disturbed and open ground in grassland, commons and heaths on dry, acidic or calcareous soils.

168

Pollination Small insects or self-pollinated.

Regeneration strategy Plentiful seed, shed close to the parent plant. Dispersal via cattle dung is another probability.

Weed control It will spread rapidly, if not discouraged. Remove or dig in young seedlings, pull up older plants before flowering and compost. Follow current best, preferably organic, practice for large invasions (see Bibliography and internet).

Herbal, culinary, cultural and folklore None found.

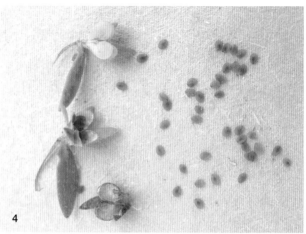

1) Plant habit 2) flowers and green seed capsules 3) fruiting stems, green to ripe 4) seed capsules and seeds

Slender Speedwell *(Veronica filiformis)*

Introduced. In cultivation in UK by 1808, but not widely grown until the 20th Century. First recorded in the wild in 1838, but not reported again until 1927. Perennial. Stems slender, often pinkish, shortly hairy, and spreading, rooting freely at nodes and producing extensive mats. Lowest stem leaves opposite, other stem leaves alternate; all leaves short-stalked, bright green, and rounded kidney-shaped with four or six broad shallow lobes and short, swollen-based hairs. Flowers hermaphrodite, bisymmetric, solitary in the leaf axils of the upper leaves. Flower stalks long (2-3 cm in length); flowers 10-12 mm across, sometimes up to 14 mm, with four basally united light blue petals, all with slightly darker veining and a basal white eye: upper and lateral petals broadly ovate and of similar size, but upper petal slightly deeper blue, lower petal narrower; two stamens with thick filaments tapering to base, deep blue anthers with creamy white pollen; pistil with small rounded stigma and long thin style tapering to base. Calyx with four light green, narrowly ovate sepals, one third to half the length of the petals. After flowers drop, the old calyx remains, but it does not enclose fruit, because this species does not set seed in the UK. Flowering April-July, sometimes as late as September. Occurs throughout the British Isles. Usually found in areas of low cut grass such as lawns, public parks, and sports fields; sometimes in meadows and on river banks.

Pollination In Britain this species does not self-pollinate or cross-pollinate effectively.

Regeneration strategies Stem-rooting. It rarely sets seed in Britain.

Weed control Although this species does not set seed the stems root with great efficiency. It will spread rapidly, if not discouraged, and because of this, it is often a problem in mown areas of grass. As viable seed is unlikely to be a problem, it is safe to leave it to flower and therefore easier to spot. For small areas hand-weed. Do not compost in case it roots, but dry and burn, or bag up and take to local garden waste facility. Follow current best, preferably organic, practice for large invasions (see Bibliography and internet).

Herbal, culinary, cultural and folklore Native to the mountains of Asia Minor and the Caucasus. Because of its pretty flowers that do not get lost in the leaves, it was first introduced to Britain as a rock garden plant in the early 19th Century. Since then it has spread throughout the British Isles.

169

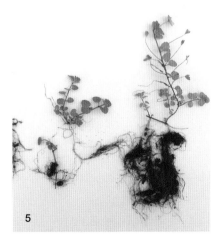

1) Flowering stems 2) habit 3) flowers 4) stem cuttings on 11 April 5) rooted stem cuttings on 2 June 6) barren calyces – no seed pods

Ivy-leaved Speedwell *(Veronica hederifolia)*

Native. Annual. Trailing stems 5-60 cm in length, with short, sparse, soft hairs. Leaves 2 cm long or less, short-stalked with straight bases (*truncate*), mid-to-deep green, with large upper lobe (broader than deep), and two to six smaller side lobes. Among the weedy species of *Veronica* described, these leaves are characteristic only for Ivy-leaved Speedwell. Flowers hermaphrodite, very slightly bisymmetric, solitary in the leaf axils. Flower stalks long, usually 3-4 times as long as calyx; flowers 6-8 mm across, sometimes as small as 5 or as large as 9 mm, with four basally united, sky blue petals with slightly darker veining, and a basal white eye, distinction between petals is slight; two stamens with thick filaments tapering to base, blue anthers with creamy white pollen; pistil with small rounded stigma, and short style. Calyx with four sepals, mid-green, narrowly ovate, recurved and pointed, with soft white hairs on margins, sometimes with reddish tips; sepals alternate with, and c. one third longer than petals. Fruit slightly shorter than calyx, broadly ovoid, two-locular, and 3-4 mm long, sometimes up to 5 mm diameter. Four seeds per locule, broadly ovate to orbicular, pale yellowish with rounded, ribbed margins and a central depression (*orifice*), with a small peg-like projection. Flowering late March-June, but flowers can often be found as late as August. Common in England south-east of a line from the Tyne to the Severn. Widespread in the rest of England, Wales and south-east Scotland but local elsewhere in Scotland, and in Ireland. A weed of cultivated soils and arable crops but perhaps most abundant in gardens. It is slightly shade tolerant.

Additional notes In Britain there are two subspecies of *Veronica hederifolia*: subsp. *hederifolia*, and *Veronica hederifolia* subsp. *lucorum*. They are not always easy to differentiate, even for botanists. Here subsp. *hederifolia* is described and illustrated.

Pollination Small insects or self-pollinated.

Regeneration strategy Plentiful seed, shed close to the parent plant.

Dispersal via cattle dung is another probability.

Weed control It will spread rapidly, if not discouraged. Remove or dig in young seedlings, pull up older plants before flowering and compost. Follow current best, preferably organic, practice for large invasions (see Bibliography and internet).

Herbal, culinary, cultural and folklore None found.

170

 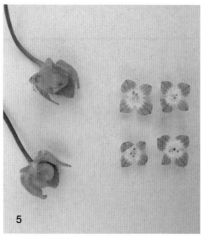 

1) Seedlings 2) trailing habit 3) colour variation between flowers 4) flowers and young fruit 5) details of flowers and young fruit 6) ripe four-seeded fruit

Common or Large Field-speedwell, Buxbaum's Speedwell *(Veronica persica)*

Introduced. First arrived in UK, Berkshire (Brimpton) c.1825, or slightly later. Annual. Stems hairy, often reddish, branched from base, spreading 10-40 cm. Leaves 1 3 cm long, mid-green, triangular ovate, short-stalked; leaf margins with coarse, rounded teeth (*crenate*); veins on leaf underside hairy. Flowers hermaphrodite, bisymmetric, solitary in the leaf axils. Flower stalks 15-40 mm long, flowers 8-12 mm across, with four basally united deep blue petals, all with darker blue veining and a basal white eye; upper petal bright blue, very slightly smaller than paler blue side petals, lower petal of similar length but narrower and white, or lightly tinged blue; two stamens with thick filaments tapering to base, deep blue anthers with creamy white pollen, pistil with small rounded stigma and long thin style tapering to base. Calyx with four light green ovate sepals alternating with the petals, and as long or slightly longer, slightly hairy at base only, enlarging and spreading in fruit. Fruit two-locular, flattened and broadly heart-shaped (3-4 mm long, sometimes as large as 5 mm). Seeds tiny, ellipsoid with rounded, ribbed margins and a central depression (*orifice*). Note that this is true for all six speedwells described. Flowering January-December. Completely naturalised throughout the whole of the British Isles, abundant in the south and east, but scarce in northern and western Scotland and in northern Ireland. It is a persistent weed of arable crops, cultivated land and gardens.

Pollination Small insects or self-pollinated.

Regeneration strategy Plentiful seed, shed close to the parent plant. One of a few very common weeds that can come into flower at any time of year, unaffected by day length.

Weed control It will spread rapidly, if not discouraged. Remove or dig in young seedlings, pull up older plants before flowering, and compost. Follow current best, preferably organic, practice for large invasions (see Bibliography and internet).

Herbal, culinary, cultural and folklore None found, but a traditional association with Speedwell should be mentioned, although associated with the beautiful Germander Speedwell (*Veronica chamaedrys*), rather than any of the more weedy species described. Speedwell means 'speed you well on your journey' and in Ireland pieces of Germander Speedwell (*Veronica chamaedrys*) were sewn into or onto clothing to protect the traveller from harm.

171

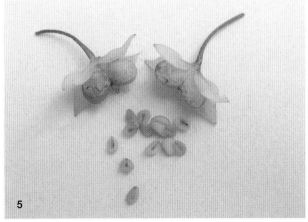

1) Seedlings 2) habit, young plant – note hairy stems 3) flower 4) young fruit capsule 5) ripe capsules and seeds

PLANTAGINACEAE

Grey Field-speedwell *(Veronica polita)*

Native. Annual. Branched at base with spreading, softly hairy, often pinkish stems, forming mats up to 30 cm in diameter, height up to c. 15 cm. Leaves 5-15 mm long, ovate, short-stalked, dull green, with short sparse hairs. Leaf margins with coarse, rounded or slightly pointed teeth (*crenate*). Veins on leaf undersides hairy. Flowers hermaphrodite, bisymmetric, solitary in the leaf axils. Flower stalks 6-15mm long; flowers very small, 2-3 mm across, with four basally united deep sapphire blue petals with darker blue veining, and a basal white eye, lower petal slightly smaller and narrower, than other three petals; two stamens with thick filaments tapering to base, creamy white anthers with creamy white pollen; pistil with small rounded stigma and long thin style tapering to base. Calyx with four mid-green ovate sepals, slightly longer than petals, enlarging and spreading in fruit, hairy at base only, alternating with, and about one third longer, than the petals. Fruit two-locular, flattened and heart-shaped (2.5-4 mm long). Seeds tiny, ellipsoid with rounded, ribbed margins and a central depression (*orifice*). Flowering January-December. Distributed throughout the British Isles as far north as the Tay. Common in the south but scattered and local further north and in Ireland. A weed of cultivated ground, arable crops, gardens and paths – usually on dry soils.

172

Pollination Self-pollinated.

Regeneration strategy Plentiful seed, shed close to the parent plant.

Weed control It will spread rapidly, if not discouraged. Remove or dig in young seedlings, pull up older plants before flowering and compost.

Follow current best, preferably organic, practice for large invasions (see Bibliography and internet).

Herbal, culinary, cultural and folklore None found.

1) Seedlings 2) young flowering plants 3) flowering plant habit 4) typical elongation of flowering stems 5) flower 6) dry seed heads

Thyme-leaved Speedwell *(Veronica serpyllifolia)*

Native. Perennial. Stems 10-15 cm in height, sometimes up to 30 cm, finely downy, creeping and rooting from underside, then often ascending. Leaves very small, light green with smooth surfaces (1-2 cm long), ovate or oblong, smooth-edged, round-tipped, almost stalkless, or with very short stalks. Flowers hermaphrodite, bisymmetric, closely associated in axils of bracts on long, terminal flowering stems (*racemes*) of up to 30 flowers; flower stalks shorter than the subtending bracts. Flowers 2 mm across, sometimes up to 3 mm, four-petalled, white with pale green eye at base; upper petal with strong purple veining, similar in size, or very slightly smaller than side petals which are more lightly veined with purple, lower petal quite small, often with no purple veining; two stamens with thick filaments tapering to base, greyish-purple anthers with creamy white pollen; pistil with small rounded, light magenta-coloured stigma and long thin style tapering to base. The four ovate sepals are slightly shorter than the petals, smooth and mid-green, not enlarging at fruiting stage. (Note that sepals of *Veronica persica* and *Veronica polita* do enlarge at fruiting stage.) Fruit two-locular, flattened and broadly heart-shaped (2.5-4 mm long), the dry ovate sepals close-pressed to the locule sides. Seeds tiny, ellipsoid with rounded, ribbed margins and a central depression (*orifice*). Flowering March-October. Widespread throughout the whole of the British Isles. It grows in short grassland, grass heath, on woodland rides and commons and as a garden weed on acidic, usually damp soils.

173

Pollination Pollinated by small flies.

Regeneration strategy Plentiful seed, shed close to the parent plant. Dispersed via cattle, horse and goat dung.

Weed control It will spread rapidly, if not discouraged. Remove or dig in young seedlings, pull up older plants before flowering and compost.

Follow current best, preferably organic, practice for large invasions (see Bibliography and internet).

Herbal, culinary, cultural and folklore None found.

1) Typical habit 2) typical elongation of flowering stems 3) flowers 4) ripe fruit pods 5) fruit pods and seeds

POLYGONACEAE *(Dock & Knotweed Family)*

Black-bindweed *(Fallopia convolvulus)*

Native. Annual. Herbaceous vine growing to 1-1.2 m length, sometimes as short as 0.30 or as long as 1.5 m. Slender, ribbed stems that readily twine clockwise around other plants. Leaves elongate-triangular, pointed at tips and bi-lobed-pointed at base, 1.5-6 cm long, 0.7-3 cm broad. Slender leaf stalk 0.6-1.5 cm (sometimes longer); base of leaf stalk and adjoining stem surrounded by a short, thin, tubular whitish papery sheath (*stipule*). Flowers hermaphrodite, almost radially symmetric, 3-4 mm diameter, sometimes up to 5 mm; short-stalked, greenish-pink or greenish-white, petals absent; clustered on short flowering stems comprising three whitish bracts with central green streak, and two white sepals; six stamens, pistil without style, tri-lobed stigma immediately above the ovary. Fruit (*achene*) light green and white, streaked with pink when young, dull blackish-brown when ripe, with three slightly concave sides, triangular with elliptic profile (c. 4 mm long). Flowering July-October. Common throughout the British Isles except for the north and west of Scotland and the Scottish Isles, where it is scarce. An autumn or spring germinating weed of arable land, roadsides, waste places and gardens.

174

Pollination There are nectar-secreting glands at the base of the stamens that attract insects.

Regeneration strategy Seed shed locally to the parent plant.

Weed control Small pre-flowering invasions are easily pulled up, or dug out, then composted or burned. Follow current best, preferably organic, practice for large invasions (see Bibliography and internet).

Herbal, culinary, cultural and folklore Like Fat Hen and Corn Spurrey, these seeds also formed part of the last meal of Tollund Man, recorded from the stomach contents (Denmark, early Celtic Iron Age – c. 400BC-200AD). Native throughout Europe, Asia and North Africa. Cultivated since the Neolithic Age and formerly a major seed contaminant. Closely related to buckwheat, it is one of many plant species where, in the past, the distinction between crop and weed was far from clear. Historically, writers have suggested that the seeds were as good as Buckwheat and produced more plentifully. Based on the leaf shape and twining habit, this species used to be considered as related to *Convolvulus*, hence its common name, however, not only is its flower and fruit structure very different, but its stems twine in the opposite direction to those of *Convolvulus*. It is a mildly tiresome British relative of two highly invasive foreign invaders.

1) Young plants 2) adult flowering plant 3) trailing habit 4) flower and fruits

Russian-vine *(Fallopia baldschuanica)*

Introduced in about 1894. First recorded in the wild in 1936. Deciduous woody perennial. A vine with climbing, clockwise-twining stems to at least 10 m in length. Young stems greenish-pink to light red. Lower stems become woody, easily making at least 4 m of growth in a year. Stalked leaves smooth, elongate ovate-triangular, mid-deep green, with straight margins, up to 10 cm long. Bases of leaf stalks, flowering stalks and adjoining stems surrounded by short, thin, tubular brownish papery sheaths (*stipules*). Flowers trumpet-shaped, hermaphrodite, in loose, spreading, terminal or lateral creamy white panicles, almost radially symmetric (8-10 mm diameter), comprising three whitish bracts with central green streak and two creamy white sepals, petals absent; six stamens, pistil without style, tri-lobed stigma immediately above the ovary. The three-winged fruits (*achenes*) often slightly pinkish when young, turning brown when ripe; the single central seed ripens to almost black. Flowering August-September. Very widespread, increasing in central and southern lowland England and gradually increasing in south-west. Favours open sites, usually near human habitation, especially hedgerows and old neglected buildings.

Pollination Bees visit for nectar but pollination and seed set rare in Britain. Probably self-incompatible.

Regeneration strategies British populations propagated vegetatively. Germinating seeds and seedlings are rare in the wild.

Weed control Think very carefully before planting, it is a rampant invader and clearing it will be hard work. Cut and burn if possible. Do not dump cuttings anywhere outside your own property, excepting the local garden waste facility. Russian-vine is still offered for sale by some garden centres and horticultural suppliers. Although not currently listed as an invasive weed, it is becoming a serious nuisance in many places, and may well be listed in the foreseeable future. Follow current best, preferably organic, practice for large invasions (see Bibliography and internet).

Herbal, culinary, cultural and folklore Fashionably and widely grown from mid-20th Century as cover for unsightly buildings etc. Now less popular but occasionally used for this purpose. Unfortunately some areas of the countryside, especially native hedgerows, are now seriously contaminated by this rampant scrambler.

175

1) Clambering habit 2) young fruits 3) flowers and young fruits 4) young fruits 5) ripe fruits

Japanese Knotweed *(Fallopia japonica)*

Introduced. First recorded wild in Maesteg, south Wales 1861-1886. Perennial. Robust, erect, smooth light green hollow stems with characteristic purple flecks and distinctive, slightly raised reddish joint rings (*nodes*). Growth height 2-4 m in a season (in places where stems have sprouted through cracks in concrete or paving the plants are typically shorter). Strong and extensive lateral rhizome system (4-5 m spread, sometimes up to 7 m and to a depth of 2-3 m); rhizomes thick and woody when old. Leaves short-stalked, broadly ovate, smooth-edged, with almost straight bases and pointed tips, dull green, 7-12 cm long, sometimes as short as 5 or as long as 14 cm, and 7-12 cm wide, sometimes slightly less, or more – up to 14 cm. Flowers functionally dioecious, densely clustered in more or less erect flowering branches (*racemes*), 6-9 cm long, sometimes as short as 5 or as long as 15 cm. Trumpet-shaped flowers almost radially symmetric (c. 5 mm diameter), comprising three whitish or pale green bracts and two white sepals, petals absent; six stamens, pistil with a short-styled, three-branched, fringed stigma on top of the ovary. Fruit a three-sided achene, diamond-shaped and dark glossy deep brown when ripe, however, no seed develops in the UK clone. Flowering August-October. Widely established throughout the British Isles, except for parts of Scotland and northern England. Grows along roadsides, on railway banks, in waste ground, rubbish tips and along river banks.

Pollination British populations have all regenerated from a single female clone. No pollen is produced but insects, including bees, wasps and flies visit for nectar.

176

Regeneration strategy Seed is not produced because there are no male plants in Britain to effect pollination. Nevertheless, it has spread to all parts of the British Isles from a single female clone (nicknamed 'the world's largest female'). British populations all result from root cuttings. The species is very resilient to being cut back and vigorously re-sprouts from the roots. Even small pieces of root rapidly regenerate, often reaching a depth of 3 m or more.

Weed control The World Conservation list describes it as "one of the world's worst weeds". It is a serious menace, especially in urban areas and, if not removed efficiently, can cause serious damage to buildings, drainage systems, and other water channels. Seek professional advice, and follow current best practice for any occurrences of this plant, whether on your own land or elsewhere (see Bibliography and internet). It is an offence (section 14.2) of the Wildlife and Countryside Act (1981): "… to plant or otherwise cause (*Fallopia japonica*) to grow in the wild." In the UK, it is classed as controlled waste, and needs a licence for its disposal.

Herbal, culinary, cultural and folklore In 1847 *Fallopia japonica* won a gold medal from the Agricultural and Horticultural Society of Utrecht as "the most interesting plant of the year"! Shoots are eaten as a vegetable, notably in Japan. It tastes "like sour rhubarb". Beekeepers value the flowers as an important source of nectar at a time when many other bee plants have stopped flowering. A mild-flavoured mono-floral honey called Bamboo Honey is produced in the north-eastern USA. A range of deep tan dye colours can be obtained from the leaves.

Toxicity Like other edible plants of this family, for example Rhubarb, Japanese Knotweed contains oxalic acids which if consumed may aggravate conditions such as rheumatism, gout or kidney stones.

1) Young stem and leaf growth 2) dense under-story population 3) young stem with typical red joint rings (nodes) 4) leaves and unopened flower clusters 5) open flowers

Equal-leaved Knotgrass *(Polygonum arenastrum)*

Native. Annual. Prostrate wiry stems, slightly ribbed, 10-30 cm long, growing out from the centre of plant and branching in very slightly zig-zag manner between stem nodes. Tap root up to c. 45 cm long in moist conditions, but usually shorter. Plants can form mats of up to 90-145 cm across. Leaves smooth, densely crowded, alternate, ovate oblong-blunt/round-tipped, greyish-green; branch and stem leaves all more or less equal-sized up to 20 mm long by 5 mm wide. The leaf stalk bases form a thin, tubular, greenish-white or brownish translucent papery sheath (*stipule*) which surrounds the main stem. Flowers hermaphrodite, and radially symmetric (c. 2-3 mm diameter), almost stalkless, from one to six in the angle between the stem and the leaf-stalk. Each flower comprises five white-tipped green sepals, or reddish in older, pollinated flowers, which are joined for half their length (petals absent); six stamens and a pistil with a short-styled, three-lobed stigma on top of the ovary. Fruit 1.5-2.5 mm long, enclosed by, or slightly longer than, the persistent sepals; dull or shiny on margins, striate and three-sided, all sides convex, but two sides are slightly larger than the third. Flowering July-October, sometimes as late as November. Widespread and locally common throughout the British Isles. It is very resistant to trampling and thrives in compacted ground and well-trodden conditions such as the sandy and gravelly soils of tracks, footpaths, roadsides and waste ground. It tolerates drier conditions than *P. aviculare*.

Pollination Usually self-pollinated.

Regeneration strategy Seed shed locally to parent plant. Knotgrasses have a marked capacity for regeneration if damaged during their growing season.

Weed control Small pre-flowering invasions are easily pulled up or dug out, then composted or burned. Follow current best, preferably organic, practice for large invasions (see Bibliography and internet).

Herbal, culinary, cultural and folklore The leaves are edible, but see note below.

Toxicity Like other edible plants of this family, for example Rhubarb, it contains oxalic acids which if consumed may aggravate conditions such as rheumatism, gout or kidney stones.

177

1) Typical spreading habit 2) flowers, and stems with equal-sized leaves 3) flowers, leaves and basal leaf sheaths

Knotgrass *(Polygonum aviculare)*

Native. Annual. Erect or semi-erect, slightly ribbed wiry stems (10-40 cm in height), branching from centre of tap rooted plant. Stem leaves smooth, almost stalkless, alternate, ovate-lanceolate, with finely rounded or tapering tips, greyish-green; stem leaves two to three times the length of those on flowering branches, 20-50 mm wide and 5-15 mm long. The tubular leaf stalk extensions (*stipules*) form a thin, greenish-white or pale brownish translucent papery sheath which surrounds the main stem, as well as the short leaf stalk. Flowers hermaphrodite, almost stalkless, from one to six in the angle between the stem and the leaf-stalk: radially symmetric (c. 2-3 mm diameter), comprising five white-tipped green sepals (deep pink in older pollinated flowers), which are joined for c. one third of their length; petals absent, six stamens and a pistil with a short-styled, three-lobed stigma on top of the ovary. Fruit dull or shiny on margins, three-sided with equal sides, striate (1.5-2.5 mm long), enclosed by, or slightly longer than, the persistent sepals. Flowering July-October, sometimes as early as June or as late as November. A common plant throughout the British Isles except for Orkney and Shetland where it is either very local or almost completely absent. A weed of waste and disturbed ground, roadsides, seashores, gardens and arable land.

Pollination Usually self-pollinated, although it attracts various insect visitors.

Regeneration strategy Seed shed locally to parent plant. Seeds of this Knotgrass have a viability of up to 60 years. Knotgrasses have a marked capacity for regeneration if damaged during their growing season.

Weed control Small pre-flowering invasions are easily pulled up or dug out, then composted or burned. Follow current best, preferably organic, practice for large invasions (see Bibliography and internet).

Herbal, culinary, cultural and folklore The fruits were traditionally used as an emetic and purgative. If fed to pigs it was "eaten greedily", and the celebrated 16th Century British herbalist John Gerard reported it being fed to sick pigs.

Toxicity Like other edible plants of this family, for example Rhubarb, Knotgrass contains oxalic acids which if consumed may aggravate conditions such as rheumatism, gout, or kidney stones.

178

1) Habit 2) stems showing large and small leaves 3) flowers, leaves and basal leaf sheaths

Pale Persicaria *(Persicaria lapathifolia)*

Native. Annual. Stems erect, or almost, 20-80 cm in height, sometimes up to 100 cm, usually light green, swollen above the leaf joints (*nodes*). The flowering stems are covered with very small, pale yellow glands. Leaves (c. 5-20 cm long), short-stalked, arranged alternately on stem, elongate-ovate with pointed tips and straight margins, sometimes with a darker blotch, and sometimes with dense, short soft hairs on underside. Thin, translucent, slightly fringed, tubular leaf extensions (*stipules*) encircle the bases of the leaf and flower stalks at stem junctions and, in upper part of stem, also the flower stalks. Flowers numerous, almost stalkless, on compact, short to elongate inflorescences (flower heads). Individual flowers hermaphrodite and radially symmetric (c. 2-3 mm diameter, sometimes up to 4 mm), comprising five greenish-white or pale pink sepals (petals absent); there are six stamens and a pistil with a shortly forked style and two hook-lobed stigmas above the ovoid ovary. Fruit shiny, flattened ovate, dark brownish-black, c. 2-3 mm long, sometimes as large as 4 mm. Flowering July-September, sometimes as early as June or as late as October. A very variable species. Common throughout most of Britain to an altitude of 365 m. Scarce or scattered in parts of northern England, Scotland and Ireland. It is found in similar places to *Persicaria maculosa* (Redshank), with which it sometimes grows. A weed of arable soils, waste ground, roadsides, gardens, rubbish tips, old habitations or beside ponds and rivers. Prefers nitrogen-rich soil, but not especially demanding. Can be a troublesome weed in fields.

Pollination Probably most often self-pollinated.

Regeneration strategy The seeds remain viable for decades. They can also pass intact through the digestive tracts of cattle and birds.

Weed control Small pre-flowering invasions are easily pulled up or dug out, then composted or burned. Follow current best, preferably organic, practice for large invasions (see Bibliography and internet).

Herbal, culinary, cultural and folklore See under Redshank (*Persicaria maculosa*).

Toxicity Like other edible plants of this family, for example Rhubarb, *Persicaria* species contain oxalic acids which if consumed may aggravate conditions such as rheumatism, gout or kidney stones.

179

1) Young plant 2) habit – leaves usually without dark spot 3) slightly spotted leaves 4) flowers and many-glanded stems

Redshank *(Persicaria maculosa)*

Native. Annual. Stems erect or almost so, 20-75 cm in height, sometimes up to 80 cm, usually light green, sometimes pinkish, swollen above the leaf joints (*nodes*). Flowering stems usually smooth, sometimes with scattered pale yellow glands. Leaves 5-10 cm, sometimes up to 15 cm long, short-stalked, arranged alternately on stem, elongate-ovate with pointed tips and straight margins, often with a dark blotch and sometimes with dense, short soft hairs on underside. Thin, translucent, tubular leaf extensions (*stipules*) with long slender hairs, encircle the bases of the leaf and flower stalks at stem junctions and, in upper part of stem, also the flower stalks. Flowers numerous, almost stalkless, on compact, short to elongate inflorescences (flower heads). Individual flowers hermaphrodite and radially symmetric (c. 2-3 mm diameter, sometimes up to 4 mm), comprising five whitish or greenish-pink to rose-pink sepals (petals absent); there are six stamens and a pistil with a shortly forked (or three-branched) style, and two, sometimes three, hook-shaped stigmas above the ovoid ovary. Fruit shiny, flattened ovate with pointed tip, dark brownish-black, c. 2-3 mm long, sometimes up to 4 mm. Flowering July-September, sometimes as early as June or as late as October. Widely distributed and common throughout the British Isles to an altitude of 430 m. It is found in similar places as *Persicaria lapathifolia* (Pale Persicaria), with which it sometimes grows. A troublesome weed of arable land, waste ground, roadsides, gardens, or beside ponds, streams and rivers. Most abundant on heavy non-calcareous soils, will also grow on black fen peat. Prefers nitrogen-rich soil, but not especially demanding.

180

Pollination Visited by a range of insects but probably most often self-pollinated.

Regeneration strategy The seeds remain viable for decades; they can also pass intact through the digestive tracts of cattle and birds.

Weed control Small pre-flowering invasions are easily pulled up or dug out, then composted or burned. Follow current best, preferably organic, practice for large invasions (see Bibliography and internet).

Herbal, culinary, cultural and folklore: The blotch on the leaves gave rise to an ancient legend that the plant grew under the cross on which Christ was crucified, and that drops of his blood fell on the leaves and stained them. In Gaelic this species is called 'Herb of the Crucifixion Tree'. In Shetland Redshank was used to provide a yellow dye. English tradition says that the Virgin Mary picked the leaves, but threw them away as useless as they were not as tasty (spicy) as those of the related Water Pepper (*Persicaria hydropiper*), but she left her thumbprint behind (forever!)

Toxicity Like other edible plants of this family, for example Rhubarb, *Persicaria* species contain oxalic acids which if consumed may aggravate conditions such as rheumatism, gout or kidney stones.

1) Habit on farmland 2) young plant with typical leaf spotting 3) typical pink flower heads 4) pale-flowered form – note sparse glands on flower stalk 5) one-seeded fruits

Common Sorrel *(Rumex acetosa)*

Native. Perennial. Stem hairless, finely ribbed, 60-80 cm in height, sometimes as short as 30 or as tall as 100 cm, with slender, tufted rootstock. A basal rosette of long-stalked, arrow-shaped leaves, 7-15 cm long and straight-edged. Upper leaves without stalks, the pointed bases clasping the stem. Short, often reddish, tubular leaf stalk extensions *(stipules)* at intervals up the stem. Flowering stems (inflorescences) up to 40 cm long but usually less, leafless, or nearly so, with whorls of radially symmetric reddish-green flowers. Male flowers and female flowers on separate plants *(dioecious)*. Male flowers on short slender stalks with two rings of three membranous, white-edged, green sepals; those of the outer ring smaller and more erect; each flower with six green, reddish or red stamens, with pale yellow pollen; open flowers 5-7 mm diameter, sometimes up to 8 mm. Female flowers also on short slender stalks, with three outer and three inner sepal-like segments; after flowering the three outer segments turn down round the flower stalk while the three inner segments enlarge and surround the young ovary (fruit), which has a three-branched feathery pistil. Fruit a three-winged achene. Seeds glossy brown, pointed, three-faced, ovate. Flowering May-June, sometimes as late as July. Common throughout the whole of the British Isles, it is a characteristic plant of grassland on neutral to mildly acidic soils, woodland rides and grassy clearings, meadows, roadside verges, river banks, stabilised coastal shingle and mountain ledges.

Pollination Wind-pollinated.

Regeneration strategy Plentiful seed dropped locally or spread by birds and animals.

Weed control Small pre-flowering invasions are easily pulled up or dug out, then composted or burned. Follow current best, preferably organic, practice for large invasions (see Bibliography and internet).

Herbal, culinary, cultural and folklore The leaves are pleasantly sour and edible, but see note below. The leaves are eaten by the larvae of several species of butterfly and moth.

Toxicity Like other edible plants of this family, for example Rhubarb, *Rumex* species contain oxalic acids which if consumed may aggravate conditions such as rheumatism, gout or kidney stones.

181

1) Stems and leaves 2) typical leaf shape 3) male flowering inflorescence 4) young fruiting stems 5) ripening fruits 6) ripe fruits

Curled Dock *(Rumex crispus)*

Native. Perennial. Stem 60-100 cm in height, sometimes as short as 30 cm or as tall as 150 cm, light green, sometimes pinkish, slightly ribbed. Has a very deep tap root to about 150 cm long and slender, spreading lateral roots to c. 125 cm long. Large basal rosette of long-stalked, smooth leaves. Stem leaves not stalked, elongate blades up to 30 cm long, tapering to a blunt point, slightly wavy to very wavy-edged. Leaf bases more or less irregular with wavy lobes. At the stem joints, short, tubular, pale brownish, papery, translucent leaf stalk extensions (*stipules*) encircle the bases of the leaf stalks and main stem; higher up, the stipules encircle the flower stalks. Main flowering stem with secondary branches ascending at a narrow angle. Flowers hermaphrodite, short-stalked and organised in discrete whorls (tiers) up the stem. Individual flowers radially symmetric (c. 3-4 mm diameter) with two rings of three membranous light green sepals, but no petals: sepals of the outer ring smaller, while those of the inner ring will develop to form the three-winged fruit valves. The sepals surround six stamens, with pale yellow pollen and a three-styled pistil. The fruit has three membranous winged fruit valves enclosing the seed. The valves are heart-shaped with straight margins (not toothed as in Broad-leaved Dock) and each valve has a swollen tubercle (which looks like a seed!). One tubercle is usually larger than the other two. Inside each small fruit is a single triangular-ovoid seed. Flowering June-October. Very common throughout the British Isles but less frequent in the north of Scotland. A common plant of waste ground, arable land, or disturbed ground, and waste places, roadsides, hedgerows, marshy areas, banks of lakes, ponds, marshy areas and waterways. Avoids the most acidic conditions and shady areas.

182

Pollination Usually wind.

Regeneration strategies The seeds remain encased in the winged fruit and when dry, the fruits are easily transported by wind or water. Adult plants with large forking tap roots. Seed dormancy/viability can be more than 50 years.

Weed control Leaves can be cut and composted, but any flowering, seeding parts, or the roots should be dealt with carefully. It is a serious agricultural pest, defined by DEFRA as one of the five most injurious weeds. Follow current official advice (see Bibliography for useful websites).

Herbal, culinary, cultural and folklore The leaves are edible (younger leaves best), but high in oxalic acid (see note below). One of the five most widely distributed plants in the world.

Toxicity Like other edible plants of this family, for example Rhubarb, *Rumex* species contain oxalic acids which if consumed may aggravate conditions such as rheumatism, gout or kidney stones.

1) Basal leaf clump 2) young adult stem leaf 3) young flowering stem 4) green fruits 5) ripe fruits

Broad-leaved Dock *(Rumex obtusifolius)*

Native. Long-lived perennial. Stems 80-100 cm in height, sometimes as short as 50 or as tall as 130 cm, green, ribbed, with a deep tap root up to about 100 cm and slender spreading lateral roots. Large basal rosette of long-stalked, smooth, ovate-oblong leaves with rounded tips and heart-shaped bases, twice as long as broad and up to 25 cm long. Stem leaves shorter-stalked, edges shallowly undulate/waved. Central leaf vein lighter green than leaves or reddish pink. At the stem joints short, tubular, pale brownish, papery, translucent leaf stalk extensions (*stipules*) encircle the bases of the leaf stalks and main stem. Higher up, the stipules encircle the flower stalks. Main flowering stem leafy in the lower part and with secondary branches ascending at a fairly narrow angle (less sharp than in Curled Dock). Flowers hermaphrodite, small, short-stalked and organised in discrete whorls (tiers) up the stem. Individual flowers radially symmetric (c. 5 mm diameter), with two rings of three membranous, light green sepals, but no petals: sepals of the outer ring smaller and narrower with lighter margins, those of the inner ring will develop to form the three-winged fruit valves. The sepals surround six stamens, with bright yellow pollen, and a three-styled pistil. The fruit has three membranous winged fruit valves enclosing the seed. The valves are elongate-triangular with three to five marginal 'teeth'. Only one valve has a swollen tubercle (which looks like a seed!), although there may be slight swelling on one or both of the other valves. Inside each small fruit is a single triangular-ovoid seed. Flowering June-October. Very common throughout the whole of the British Isles; a familiar plant of disturbed and trampled ground, farmyards, waste places, hedge banks, cultivated soils, and badly managed land, roadsides, banks of ponds, lakes and rivers, and partial shade. It will grow on any soil except acidic peat.

Pollination A wind-pollinated species.

Regeneration strategy The seeds remain encased in the winged fruit and, when dry, the fruits are easily transported by wind or water, and the teeth on the valves catch on clothing or fur. Adult plants have large forking tap roots and seed dormancy/viability can be more than 50 years.

Weed control Leaves can be cut and composted, but any flowering or seeding parts and the roots should be dealt with carefully. It is a serious agricultural pest, defined by DEFRA as one of the five most injurious weeds. Follow current official advice (see Bibliography for useful websites).

Herbal, culinary, cultural and folklore Boiled leaves were used as

183

pig food in northern England. The botanist William Withering (1741-1799) observed that Fallow Deer eat dock so greedily that it is rare to see a dock growing in a deer park. The leaves were valued by country folk for wrapping around butter or cheese, thus giving it one of its local names of Butter-dock. Children, especially, are pacified by being encouraged to rub dock leaves on nettle stings and conveniently, the two species are often found growing near to each other. Apparently, when powdered, it was also considered to make an excellent dentifrice. Formerly used by dyers – it produces a good yellow, notably for wool. The leaves are edible (younger leaves best), but high in oxalic acid (see note below).

Toxicity Like other edible plants of this family, for example Rhubarb, *Rumex* species contain oxalic acids which, if consumed, may aggravate conditions such as rheumatism, gout or kidney stones.

1) Seedling plants 2) young foliage 3) habit 4) flowering stem 5) seed heads 6) fruits

PRIMULACEAE *(Primrose Family)*

Scarlet Pimpernel, Poor-man's Weather-glass *(Anagallis arvensis)*

Native. Annual or short-lived perennial. Main stems rather lax, spreading, sending up many flowering branches. Stems pale green, smooth, square in section, gland-dotted, height/spread 5-30 cm. Leaves ovate or elongate-ovate, light-to-mid-green, stalkless, and dotted with black glands on underside. Flowers hermaphrodite, radially symmetric (up to 14 mm diameter), solitary, on slender stalks in leaf axils: five broadly ovate vermilion petals, fused together at their bases, petals longer than the sepals; five bright yellow stamens with feathery mauve filaments and a globose ovary with a long-styled pistil. Calyx with five light green pointed sepals. The seed capsule is globose with a dome-shaped 'lid' which retains the style. The lid pops off to release the 16-20 rounded-triangular seeds. Flowering June-August, sometimes as late as November. Widespread throughout the British Isles, north to Orkney, but becoming increasingly scarce and coastal in its distribution from County Durham northwards, and scattered throughout Ireland. A common weed of arable crops, gardens, paths and waste ground, in a wide range of conditions but with a marked preference for lighter well-drained soils.

Pollination Flowers open daily from c. 8am to 3pm. Pollinated by insects or self-pollinated.

Regeneration strategy Locally distributed seed. An average plant may produce about 900 seeds or more in a season.

Weed control Remove, dig in or green manure young plants before flowering occurs.

Herbal, culinary, cultural and folklore Blue, lilac, pink and white forms of this species also occur but the vermilion colour is genetically dominant. The tendency of the species to close its flowers with the approach of rain has provided this species with numerous local names, many associated with the shepherd, including Shepherds' Calendar/ Clock/Glass/Sundial/Warning/Watch. Like many other wild plants, it was used to cure or ease various common health problems. It was also used against melancholy and gave rise to a few delightful local names such as Laughter-Bringer, Shepherd's Delight and Shepherd's Joy. *The Scarlet Pimpernel* is also a famous novel set in the 'Reign of Terror' during the French Revolution and was published in 1905 by the London-based, Hungarian-born novelist Baroness Emma Orczy. The name refers to the hero's trademark: after every daring rescue he left a small card with a Scarlet Pimpernel depicted on it.

Toxicity Handling the leaves may cause dermatitis, but this is not commonly reported.

1) Seedling 2) over-ground trailing stems 3) habit, young plant 4) flower showing radial symmetry 5) green fruits 6) dry fruit capsules and seeds

RANUNCULACEAE *(Buttercup Family)*

Meadow Buttercup *(Ranunculus acris)*

Native. Perennial. Stems erect or slightly spreading, 15-60 cm in height, sometimes up to 100 cm, not ribbed, with short, soft hairs; lower stem hollow, roots without stolons. Basal leaves long-stalked, with slender, elongate lobes, which are further divided into three smaller, usually un-stalked lobes, central lobe longer, overall outline five-sided. Stem leaves shorter-stalked or without stalks, lobes often long and slender; leaves all softly hairy. Flowers hermaphrodite and radially symmetric (overall diameter 18-25 mm); flower stalks not ribbed. Five broadly rounded triangular petals, upper area of petal bright light, glossy yellow, lower section of petal slightly darker brownish-yellow, with petal venation more obvious, a nectar-secreting scale situated at the base of each petal; stamens numerous, surrounding the ovary. Calyx with five light green, narrowly ovate sepals, softly hairy on underside, c. half the length of the open petals and slightly cupped towards them. Fruit comprises a head of numerous carpels (divisions of the ovary), each with a pistil. The carpels mature into dry single-seeded fruits (*achenes*), irregular-ovoid, with pointed tips; achenes green when young and turning brown and dry when ripe. Flowering mostly May-August, but plants can be found flowering all year. Frequent in meadows and pastures throughout the British Isles. The most tolerant of the common buttercups for moist habitats, favouring damp meadows or pastures, especially those regularly cropped for hay, as well as pathways and roadsides. Favours heavy soils. It is the tallest of the three common Buttercups described.

Pollination Self-incompatible. In an individual flower the stigma of each carpel is receptive to fertilisation before the stamens are ready to release pollen. Thus, within an individual flower, over a period of a few days, the pollen is shed from the anthers, beginning with the outermost stamens and working towards the central stamens. Highly adapted to attract insects: cross-pollination is encouraged by the shiny petals and, consequently, the small nectar-secreting depressions in bases of the petals. Many different species of insects visit the flowers for pollen and nectar, these include various species of thrips, bugs, hoverflies, long-headed flies, robber flies, beetles, butterflies, bees, including honey bees, tiny chalcid wasps and short-tongued insects, including the Marsh Marigold Moth (*Micropterix calthella* – a small metallic moth). Some pollen also gets blown in the wind.

Regeneration strategy Efficient pollination and high seed production.

Seed dispersal by small rodents, farm animals, birds and readily carried on animal feet, shoes or vehicle wheels.

Weed control Remove, dig in or green manure young plants before flowering occurs. Follow current best, preferably organic, practice for large invasions (see Bibliography and internet).

Herbal, culinary, cultural and folklore The name Buttercup seems not to have come into common usage before the mid-18th Century. Prior to this time the commonly used name was Butter Flowers.

Toxicity Foliage poisonous to livestock because the sap contains protoanemonin, however, because the leaves have an acrid taste, grazing animals tend avoid them.

1) Stems and leaves 2) slender stem leaves 3) flowering habit 4) flower in natural habitat 5) flower from above and below

Bulbous Buttercup *(Ranunculus bulbosus)*

Native. Perennial. Stems erect or slightly spreading, 15-30 cm in height, sometimes up to 40 cm, ribbed, with short, soft hairs. Not stoloniferous, but forming a small, rounded or slightly oblate tuber at base of stem. Basal and lower stem leaves stalked, divided into three stalked lobes; the central lobe extends beyond the other two, giving the leaf an overall ovate outline; the main lobes further divided into usually two smaller lobes. Upper leaves without stalks and with narrow leaf segments; all leaves usually softly hairy. Flowers hermaphrodite and radially symmetric (overall diameter 2-3 cm); flower stalks ribbed. Five broadly rounded triangular petals, bright, glossy yellow, only slightly differentiated toward lower section; nectar-secreting scale situated at base of each petal; stamens numerous, surrounding the ovary. Calyx with five light yellowish-green sepals, softly hairy on underside, reflexed from the open petals. Fruit comprises a head of numerous carpels (divisions of the ovary), each with a pistil. Carpels mature into dry single-seeded fruits (*achenes*), irregular-ovoid, with pointed tips, green when young and turning brown and dry when ripe. Flowering May-June, the earliest flowering of the common buttercups. Occurs throughout the British Isles, particularly in the south and east, scarcer in the north and west, absent from Shetland. Characteristic of drier and better drained soils than either of the other two common species (Creeping Buttercup and Meadow Buttercup). It is particularly abundant in chalk and limestone grassland but is not a strict *calcicole* (calcium lover). It also occurs in calcareous dune turf. Its abundance in pastures is increased by grazing but it cannot compete with tall hay meadow vegetation. It is also intolerant of regular trampling and does not tolerate agricultural improvement of grassland. The most tolerant of dry conditions among the three common species.

Pollination Self-incompatible. In an individual flower the stigma of each carpel is receptive to fertilisation before the stamens are ready to release pollen. Thus, within an individual flower, over a period of a few days, the pollen is shed from the anthers, beginning with outermost stamens and working towards the central stamens. Highly adapted to attract insects: cross-pollination is encouraged by the shiny petals and, consequently, by the small nectar-secreting depressions in bases of the petals. It is pollinated by various insects, mainly flies, beetles and bees (especially honey bees), and also ichneumon wasps (including gall wasps).

Regeneration strategies Bulbous tubers/corms, efficient pollination and high seed production. Seeds readily carried on animal feet, and also by shoes and vehicle wheels.

Weed control Remove young plants before corms develop or flowering occurs. Follow current best, preferably organic, practice for large invasions (see Bibliography and internet).

Herbal, culinary, cultural and folklore Sometimes called St. Anthony's Turnip because of its bulbous rootstock. Buttercups contain the 'biting' chemical anemonol. The roots/tubers, especially of Bulbous Buttercup, were crushed with salt and applied to plague sores to raise blisters and draw out poisons from the inward parts. The herbalist Nicholas Culpeper says of the flowers that "Virgins in ancient time did use to make powder of them to strew bride-beds."

Toxicity Foliage poisonous to livestock because the sap contains protoanemonin, however, because the leaves have an acrid taste, grazing animals tend avoid them.

186

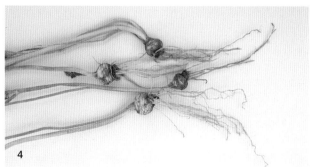

1) Stems and leaves 2) flower in natural habitat 3) flower from above and below – note reflexed sepals 4) rooted corms

Creeping Buttercup, Crowfoot *(Ranunculus repens)*

Native. Perennial with long stout roots. Stems erect or slightly spreading, 15-60 cm in height, with short soft hairs. Strong, leafy above-ground stolons that root at the nodes. Leaves mid-green; basal and lower stem leaves stalked, with groove on upper side, divided into three stalked lobes, often with a pale spot at the acute angles between lobes; central lobe is longer, stalked, extending beyond the other two lobes, giving the overall leaf an ovate-triangular outline. The main lobes further divided, usually into three-toothed segments. Upper leaves without stalks and with narrow leaf segments; all leaves softly hairy. Flowers hermaphrodite and radially symmetric (overall diameter 2-3 cm); flower stalks softly hairy and ribbed. Five broadly rounded, triangular, bright, glossy yolk-yellow petals, lower half of petal with radiating, linear brownish veining clearly demarcated; nectar-secreting scale situated at base of each petal; stamens numerous, surrounding the ovary. Calyx with five broadly ovate green sepals with longish soft hairs on underside, reflexed towards and c. two thirds the length of the open petals. Fruit comprises a head of numerous carpels (divisions of the ovary) each with a pistil. The carpels mature into dry single-seeded fruits (*achenes*), irregular-rounded ovoid, with pointed tips, green when young and turning brown and dry when ripe. Flowering May-August, sometimes as late as December, the longest main flowering period of the three common buttercups. Common throughout the British Isles, particularly on heavy wet soils, notably grassland or clay. It is most characteristic of damp grassland, marshes and fens, clearings and paths in woodland, and as an arable weed. Avoids well-drained grassland and the most acidic soils. Occurs more commonly in woodland than either of the other two common species. The most tolerant of moist conditions of the three common species.

Pollination Self-incompatible. In an individual flower the stigma of each carpel is receptive to fertilisation before the stamens are ready to release pollen. Thus, within an individual flower, over a period of a few days, the pollen is shed from the anthers, beginning with outermost stamens and working towards the central stamens. Highly adapted to attract insects: cross-pollination is encouraged by the shiny petals and, consequently, by small nectar-secreting depressions in bases of the petals. Pollinated mainly by flies, beetles and bees, including honey bees.

Regeneration strategies Long runners from the base of the plant: these runners develop young plants which root easily. Large quantities of seed are also produced.

Weed control Remove, dig in or green manure young plants before flowering occurs. Carefully dig out larger invasions, making sure that all the runners and young plants are removed, too. Follow current best, preferably organic, practice for large invasions (see Bibliography and internet).

Herbal, culinary, cultural and folklore Traditionally children play the game of taking a buttercup flower and holding it just below the chin of a willing participant to see 'if they like butter'. The shiny petals reflect on the chin and affirm a liking for butter.

Toxicity Foliage poisonous to livestock because the sap contains protoanemonin, however, because the leaves have an acrid taste, grazing animals tend avoid them.

187

1) Seedling plant 2) stoloniferous habit 3) a large colony 4) flower in natural habitat 5) flowers in comparison – Creeping Buttercup (*Ranunculus repens*) above and Meadow Buttercup (*Ranunculus acris*) below 6) young stoloniferous roots emerging

Lesser Celandine *(Ficaria verna* subsp. *fertilis* and subsp. *verna)*

Native. Perennial with numerous small, club- or spindle-shaped root-tubers (1-2.5 cm long). Stems smooth, slightly ribbed, erect or slightly spreading, 5-25 cm in height, sometimes up to 30 cm and branching. Leaves long-stalked, deep green, broadly ovate/heart-shaped, smooth, shiny, with slightly wavy margins; stem leaves alternate, similar to basal leaves but shorter-stalked. Flowers hermaphrodite and radially symmetric (overall diameter 2-3 cm), solitary, long-stalked in leaf axils; bright, glossy yolk-yellow petals, eight to 12, sometimes only seven, ovate, round-tipped and usually overlapping, with a nectar-secreting scale at base of each petal; numerous deep yellow-orange stamens, surrounding the ovary. Calyx with three broadly ovate, smooth, greenish-yellow sepals reflexed towards and c. half the length of the open petals. Fruit comprises a head of numerous carpels (divisions of the ovary), each with a pistil. The carpels often abort, if not they mature into dry, softly hairy single-seeded fruits (*achenes*) c. 2.5 mm long, irregular-ovoid, with pointed tips, green when young and turning brown and dry when ripe. Flowering March-May. Common throughout the British Isles. A characteristic plant of deciduous woodland, hedgerows, road verges, stream sides and damp pastures on seasonally wet or flooded soils. A species that occurs both in open and shaded conditions.

Additional notes In Britain there are two common subspecies of Celandine (*Ficaria verna*): subspecies *fertilis* – usually with broad overlapping petals and no bulbils in the axils of the leaves, growing in open or shaded conditions – and subspecies *verna* – narrow, non-overlapping petals, and small bulbils in the axils of the leaves, usually found in shade or disturbed ground.

Pollination Self-incompatible. In an individual flower the stigma of each carpel is receptive to fertilisation before the stamens are ready to release pollen. Thus, within an individual flower, over a period of a few days, the pollen is shed from the anthers, beginning with outermost stamens and working towards the central stamens. Highly adapted to attract insects: cross-pollination is encouraged by the shiny petals and, consequently, by small nectar-secreting depressions in the bases of the petals. Mainly visited by bumblebees, small flies (e.g. *Bibio johannis*) and small beetles; honey bees also visit, attracted by the seasonally early opening flowers.

Regeneration strategies Many of the seeds (achenes) abort before maturity, even those that do mature often do not have high fertility. Propagation is more often achieved vegetatively, by the numerous small finger-like tubers which separate easily and root, and from the bulbils in the leaf axils.

Weed control Hand-weed before flowering. Carefully dig out corms and young plants and destroy; this may need several successive attempts over time.

Herbal, culinary, cultural and folklore Also known as Pile-wort; due to the appearance of its root tubers, it was used as a remedy for piles (Doctrine of Signatures). In Germany, because the young leaves are rich in vitamin C, it was used to prevent or to cure scurvy. The leaves have also been used as salad leaves. In the Scottish Highlands and Islands the root tubers were thought to resemble cows' udders and dried tubers were hung in the cow byre as a charm to ensure high cream yield. Beloved of many poets and writers, including Wordsworth and D.H. Lawrence. Because it makes a small attractive border plant, this species and its cultivars are often grown in herbaceous beds, banks or shrubberies. Not to be confused with Greater Celandine (*Chelidonium major*), which is a member of the Poppy family (Papaveraceae).

188

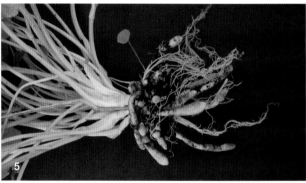

1) Young plant 2) leaves and closed flowers in natural habitat 3) flower 4) leaves and young fruiting heads 5) club-shaped root tubers

ROSACEAE *(Rose Family)*

Parsley-piert *(Aphanes arvensis)*

Native. Annual. Small, rather inconspicuous, 5-20 cm in height, sometimes as small as 2 cm. Stems usually much branched from the base, softly hairy (downy), pale greyish-green and leafy, stem branches spreading, often raised towards ends. Leaves 2-10 mm long, fan-shaped, short-stalked, divided into three segments, each segment divided into three to five smaller oblong lobes, alternate on stems. The junction between each leaf base and the main stem is surrounded by a two-paired, five- to seven-lobed leaf-like structure (*stipular cup*), the stalkless flower clusters are almost concealed within this cup. Flowers hermaphrodite and minute, radially symmetric; four light green sepals, no petals, one to two stamens. Fruits 2.2-2.6 mm long, oval, pointed and bottle-shaped. Flowering April-September, sometimes as late as October. Widely distributed throughout the British Isles, but seemingly scarce in parts of northern and western Scotland. A plant of bare ground and open patches of grassy heathland or commons. Occurs by roadsides, in waste and cultivated ground, and on dry well drained soils in both acidic and alkaline habitats. Intolerant of competition from more vigorous species.

189

Pollination Self-pollinated.

Regeneration strategy Locally shed seed.

Weed control Remove, dig in or green manure young plants early in the year, before flowering occurs. Alternatively dig out and bag up all growth and take to local recycling facility. Follow current best, preferably organic, practice for large invasions (see Bibliography and internet).

Herbal, culinary, cultural and folklore The herbalist Nicholas Culpeper suggested it as an addition to salads or for eating as a winter pickle. It was commonly considered to be useful in the relief of intestinal ailments, including kidney stones. The common name 'piert' is a corruption of the French for 'stone-piercer' and the genus name *Aphanes* from the Greek meaning unseen, unnoticed. Other local British names include Bowel-hive-grass, Colic-wort and Breakstone-Parsley.

1) Young plant 2) adult plant (Photos © Bayer CropSciences)

Wood Avens, Herb Bennet *(Geum urbanum)*

Native. Perennial with short, thick rhizome. Stems 20-60 cm, sometimes as high as 70 cm, more or less erect and softly hairy. Basal rosette leaves composite. Central leaf stalk with two to three pairs of unequally sized opposite leaflets, 0.5-1 cm, sometimes as long as 1.5 cm; the uppermost pair of leaflets slightly larger, the terminal leaflet large and sub-rounded (5-8 cm long); leaf margins scalloped (*crenulate*). Stem leaves stalked, alternately positioned on main stem. At the junction of each leaf or flower stalk with the main stem is a pair of semi-circular leafy *stipules* (modified leaf bases), more or less at right angles to main stem; like the leaves they have scalloped margins; all leaves slightly hairy on underside, with prominent veins. Flowers few, on long erect stalks, in the leaf axils. Individual flowers hermaphrodite and radially symmetric (c. 10-15 mm diameter, sometimes as large as 18 mm): five petals, broadly ovate, round-tipped, with narrow bases, clear lemon yellow, not glossy (5-9 mm long), with spaces between neighbouring petals so that the sepals behind and below are visible; numerous yellow stamens surrounding the ovary. Calyx with five ovate green sepals, slightly longer than petals, green with pointed tips, and softly hairy on reverse. As the flower matures, the sepals bend backwards, away from the petals. Below the sepals is an epicalyx with five narrow lobes. Fruit comprises a head of numerous carpels (divisions of the ovary), each single-seeded carpel (*achene*) has a long, hooked, persistent green style which turns purplish, then brown and dry; the carpels tend to stay together in fruit. Flowering June-August. Generally distributed throughout the whole of the British Isles, except for parts of central and northern Scotland. Common in woodlands, scrub, hedgerows, roadsides, and shaded habitats, especially in calcareous soils.

190

Pollination Usually self-pollinated, although insects such as small beetles do visit, attracted by the yellow flowers and a nectar-secreting ring at the base of the stamens.

Regeneration strategies Tough rhizomes. Seeds usually dispersed locally, but the hooked awns of the carpels can get caught in animal fur and help transport the seed further away from the parent plant.

Weed control Remove, dig in or green manure young plants before flowering occurs. Alternatively dig out and bag up all growth and take to local recycling facility. Follow current best, preferably organic, practice for large invasions (see Bibliography and internet).

Herbal, culinary, cultural and folklore Herbalists used extracts of the plant to calm fevers. The roots have a sweet, clove-like aroma and were used to impart flavour to ale. If chewed, they were said to overcome bad breath. The roots were also used to protect a house against the Devil, while dried roots were reputed to be a good moth repellent.

1) Young plant 2) pre-flowering leafy stems 3) flowering habit 4) flowers – note calyx lobes, and smaller epicalyx lobes 5) fruiting heads 6) dry dehisced seeds (achenes)

Silverweed *(Potentilla anserina)*

Native. Perennial. Short, thick rootstock with a rosette of leaves, from which long, ground-hugging, creeping, rooting stolons develop, up to c. 80 cm long. Basal leaves 5-25 cm long, composite, with a central spine/axis (*pinna*) and seven to 12, sometimes up to 15 pairs of unstalked main leaflets (1-6 cm long), alternating with tiny leaflets. Main leaflets narrowly ovate-oblong with deeply pointed-toothed margins; soft hairs give a silky feel and silvery white colour to both sides of the leaves, which tend to lie more or less horizontally. Flowers hermaphrodite, radially symmetric, solitary, on slender, light green or pinkish stalks, arising either from the rootstock or from the leaf axils of the runners. There are five slightly overlapping, broadly ovate and almost round petals, clear lemon yellow, not glossy (c. 8-9 mm long, sometimes up to 12 mm); numerous yellow stamens (c. 20) surround the ovary. The sepals of the calyx and the bracts of the epicalyx together number ten: they are shorter than the petals, have pointed tips, and are almost equal in size but in two distinct whorls. Fruit comprises a head of 12 to 50 carpels (divisions of the ovary): each single-seeded carpel (*achene*) has a slender style at the top. Flowering June-August. Widespread and common throughout the whole of the British Isles to an altitude of c. 430 m, except for parts of northern Scotland. An abundant plant of roadsides, farm tracks and field gateways, disturbed pastures, and fertile uncultivated arable soils or waste ground. A useful indicator of soil with poor drainage. Tolerant of trampling and soil compaction and also compacted sand dunes.

Pollination Usually self-pollinated but pollen fertility often low and variable. Studies suggest that it is possible this species places greater emphasis on vegetative reproduction. Various insect visitors, notably small flies. Nectar is secreted as a thin shiny film on the inner wall of the calyx tube, around the base of the stamens.

Regeneration strategies A coloniser via long, creeping, rooting stolons, and seeds distributed in mud, rain wash, or via birds who eat the seeds.

Weed control Remove, dig in or green manure small invasions before flowering time, or compost. Follow current best, preferably organic, practice for large invasions (see Bibliography and internet).

Herbal, culinary, cultural and folklore The rootstocks were an important source of food in the past and a marginal or famine food in upland Britain. In Scotland it is recorded that (under the name of Brisgein) it was cultivated for its rootstocks, which were boiled, roasted or eaten raw, or dried and ground into meal for bread and porridge. According to the 17th Century botanist John Ray, they taste like parsnip. Working people sometimes used the leaves to line out their shoes for comfort. Infusions of Silverweed leaves were used variously, for ulcers in the mouth, against piles, internal wounds, and wounds of the privy parts. The plant may have got its botanical name *anserina* (Latin *anser*: a goose) because it would have been a frequent weed of common grazing land, 'goose greens', where geese would have fed.

1) Leaves of young colonising plants 2) well-developed adult leaves 3) flower

Creeping Cinquefoil *(Potentilla reptans)*

Native. Perennial. Slender rootstock with a persistent rosette of leaves. Prostrate, rapidly rooting at nodes to form new plants (cf. Strawberry runners). Basal leaves long-stalked and mostly palmate, with five to seven ovate, toothed leaflets, c. 0.5-3 cm long, mid-green, smooth or softly hairy. Long, thin flowering stem runners 30-100 cm long or more. Flowers hermaphrodite, solitary, on slender, light green stalks, usually longer than the leaf stalks, and arising either from the rootstock or from the leaf axils of the runners. Five ovate, heart-shaped petals, clear lemon yellow, not glossy (c. 8-9 mm long, sometimes up to 12 mm), radially symmetric, arranged with spaces between each petal and its neighbours, so that the sepals behind and below are visible (flower diameter 1.7-2.5 cm); numerous yellow stamens (c. 20) surround the ovary. The five-pointed ovate sepals of the calyx are broader and longer than the five narrowly ovate bracts of the epicalyx immediately below. Fruit comprises a head of 60-120 carpels (divisions of the ovary): each single-seeded carpel (*achene*) has a slender style at the top. Flowering June-September. Common throughout the British Isles, north to the Clyde and the Firth of Forth, but rare further north and absent from Orkney and Shetland. A frequent plant of hedge banks, waste places, sometimes grassland, road verges, footpaths and tracks, mainly on fertile, mildly acidic, neutral or calcareous soils to altitudes of 430 m.

Pollination Self-fertile. The flowers close in dull weather and at night, but bees and flies visit, including long-headed flies (Dolichopodidae).

Regeneration strategies Via long, over-ground runners with rooting stolons that can colonise more than ten square metres in a season, or from seed distributed in mud, by rain wash, or via birds who eat the seeds.

Weed control Remove young plants and their runners before flowering occurs, compost or burn. Follow current best, preferably organic, practice for large invasions (see Bibliography and internet).

Herbal, culinary, cultural and folklore Rich in iron, calcium and magnesium, it is traditionally used as a nerve sedative and general astringent. An infusion made from it is used for sore throats or, applied to the skin to help clear pimples or soothe sunburn. The roots contain tannin, and have been used in the preparation of leather. Pliny the Elder records it as being used to purge, or bless a house against "naughtie spirits, or enchantments". Among the exquisite stone leaf carvings in the Church of Southwell Minster in Nottinghamshire are leaves of Creeping Cinquefoil.

1) Young plant 2) spreading habit 3) flowers 4) young fruit

Bramble, Blackberry *(Rubus fruticosus sensu lato)*

Native. Biennial with a perennial rootstock. Long, arching or scrambling sharply thorny, woody stems, sometimes smooth, rounded but often strongly ridged, frequently rooting where they touch the ground. Height/spread at least 3-6 m, sometimes up to 9 m. Leaves mid-to-deep green on upper surface, variably silvery-grey to softly hairy (felty) underneath, usually comprising three, sometimes five, rounded-ovate leaflets with toothed margins and midribs that are spiny on the underside of the leaf. Leaf stalks slender with a small, scale-like leaf stem appendage *(stipule)* at the junction with the main stem. Leaves and fruiting stems with soft, sometimes glandular, hairs, and small, thin, needle-like spines. Flowers hermaphrodite, radially symmetric, in clusters, on short stalks at the end of the branches. There are five broadly ovate, often slightly crinkly, white or light pink petals,10-12 mm long, sometimes as small as 8 or as large as 14 mm, and numerous stamens, some almost as long as the petals, surrounding the central cone-shaped receptacle (the expanded area at the top of the flower stalk that holds the numerous carpels). The calyx comprises five ovate-pointed, softly hairy, greyish-green sepals, which gradually bend backwards as the fruit develop. Each single-seeded carpel *(achene)* has a fleshy outer covering which turns black when ripe, at the tip of each achene is the slightly persistent pistil (like a tiny hair). The complete structure is a 'blackberry'. Flowering May-September. Common throughout the whole of the British Isles, except for parts of the Scottish Highlands and northern Scotland. Common in woodland, in scrub vegetation, on roadsides, on heaths and commons, hedgerows and cliffs.

Additional notes The Blackberry described is the well-known description of a botanically complex group of probably more than 300 British species and possibly as many as 2000 different species in Europe, most of them reproducing by seed produced without sexual fusion.

Pollination Much visited or pollinated by various insects: honey bees and bumblebees are frequent visitors, as well as many other species of bees and wasps, and some Lepidoptera, notably the Marsh Marigold Moth *(Micropterix calthella* – a small metallic moth). Various flies visit, but most importantly those of the Syrphidae; small beetles eat nectar, pollen and sometimes the petals too.

Regeneration strategies By seed. Every blackberry is a collection of tiny fruits, each one containing a single seed, and blackberries are greatly enjoyed by many birds and animals, including humans, making regeneration very efficient. Furthermore, the long arching

thorny stems have the ability to take root wherever they touch receptive ground.

Weed control Small invasions should be cut back and the rootstock and roots dug out, shredded, or chopped and burned. Follow current best, preferably organic, practice for large invasions (see Bibliography and internet).

193

Herbal, culinary, cultural and folklore Perhaps the most beloved of all British wild fruits and enjoyed since at least Neolithic times (c. 8000BC). Best eaten at its simplest straight from the hedgerow, or just stewed with local cooking apples and sugar, and then eaten, perhaps with cream, yoghurt or ice-cream. In the Scottish Highlands the roots provided an orange dye and the leaves were placed on burns and swellings. Various other shades of dye can be obtained from blackish purple to light mauves, and also greys, browns and greens.

1) Seedling 2) older overwintering stems 3) white flowers 4) pink flowers and Honey Bee (*Apis mellifera*) 5) leafy stems with young fruits in high summer 6) ripening fruits

RUBIACEAE *(Bedstraw & Goosegrass Family)*

Cleavers, Goosegrass, Sticky Willie *(Galium aparine)*

Native. Annual. Prostrate, scrambling-ascending, randomly spreading stems, 15-120 cm in height. Stems four-angled, the angles with rough, downward-pointing prickles that help the plant cling as it scrambles. Stem leaves mid-green (12-50 mm long) in whorls (rings) of six to eight at regular intervals along the main stems, narrowly ovate, with a large prickle at the leaf tip and covered with short, rough hairs. Leaf margins straight-edged, with very short stiff hairs aligned with the margin and pointing toward the leaf tip. Flowers hermaphrodite, radially symmetric (c. 2-4 mm diameter): white or greenish-white flowers, shortly tubular with four petals and four small stamens, arranged between the bases of the petal lobes; two pistils, one for each of the paired ovules, c. same height as stamens, with rounded stigmas. Calyx reduced to a minute ridge. The fruits are ovoid (2.5-3 mm diameter), paired and covered in hooked bristly hairs (burs); each fruit contains one seed. Flowering June-August. Common throughout the whole of the British Isles, except for parts of the Scottish Highlands. An abundant plant of hedgerows, ditches, scrubland, streams and riverbanks, limestone scree, shingle beaches, and waste ground, usually favouring fertile soils.

194

Pollination Self-pollination or small flies, including long-headed flies (Dolichopodidae) and small beetles.

Regeneration strategy The burred fruits cling to fur or feathers (and clothing) and effect natural transport very easily; viable seed also often present in manure.

Weed control Remove young plants as soon as noticed as it is easy at this stage, if left it becomes really problematic. Try to wear gloves and non-catching outer clothing (e.g. plastic rainwear or overalls) that the plant and its seeds cannot adhere to. Roll up all the pulled runners and bag up, take to local garden waste facility, do not put in compost – the following year watch out for the young plants, and deal with the

problem earlier. Follow current best, preferably organic, practice for large invasions (see Bibliography and internet).

Herbal, culinary, cultural and folklore As the name suggests, geese are fond of this plant, and it was often fed to them or pre-chopped for young goslings. In the time of Dioscorides the stems were made into filters for straining milk. Linnaeus also mentions this use of Goosegrass in Sweden in his writings; apparently it was still used for this purpose in some areas of Britain, into the early 20th Century. A red dye can be obtained from the roots. It is also rich in minerals, especially calcium, sodium and silica, and considered good for hair and teeth if taken as an infusion in hot water or milk. Children enjoy sticking it to the clothing of other children.

 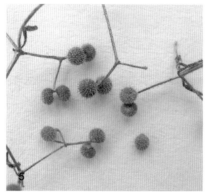 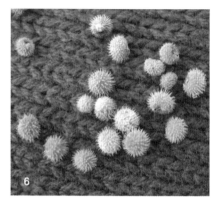

1) Young plants 2) scrambling, ascending stems 3) flowers 4) scrambling stems 5) dry fruits 6) dry fruits caught on clothing

Field Madder *(Sherardia arvensis)*

Native. Annual. Stems more or less prostrate, spreading from 5-40 cm, or to a maximum height of c. 4-7 cm. Stems four-angled, more or less smooth, but angles with rough, downward-pointing prickles. Lower leaves four in a whorl (ring), ovate with pointed tips, soon withering; upper leaves 5-18 mm long, in whorls (rings) of five to six at regular intervals along the main stems, narrowly ovate, with a large prickle at the leaf tip; upper surface with sparse hairs. Leaf margins straight-edged, with very short stiff hairs closely aligned with the leaf margin, and pointing toward the leaf tip. Flowers hermaphrodite or *gynodioecious* (female only) and radially symmetric (c. 3-4 mm diameter, sometimes up to 5 mm), in a cluster of four to eight at the end of a stem; clusters surrounded below by a calyx-like structure (*involucre*) of eight to ten ovate-pointed leaf-like bracts. Flowers pale lilac, funnel-shaped, with long slender tube c. twice the length of petals; four small stamens are arranged between the bases of the petal lobes: there are two pistils with rounded stigmas, one for each of the paired ovules; they are about the same height as the stamens. The actual calyx, at the top of the paired ovoid fruits (ovules), is shortly four-, five- or six-lobed. Each fruit c. 3-4 mm long with a single seed; the outer convex faces of the fruit are covered with short bristles. Flowering May-October. Widely distributed throughout the British Isles but becoming scarcer northwards. Rare and almost completely coastal north of a line from Solway to the Firth of Forth. It is a common plant of arable fields, path sides and waste ground, on dry, well-drained calcareous soils to an altitude of c. 365 m.

195

Pollination: Automatic self-pollination frequent in hermaphrodite flowers; nectar is secreted in a fleshy disk at the base of the style. The flowers are visited by flies.

Regeneration strategy Outer faces of the fruits shortly bristly, allowing fruits to cling to fur or feathers (and clothing) and to effect natural transport very easily.

Weed control Probably not as difficult to remove as Cleavers, but best to remove young plants when noticed, as it will spread quickly if left to flower and seed. Try to wear gloves and non-catching outer clothing (e.g. plastic rainwear or overalls) that the plant and its seeds cannot adhere to. Gather up all the pulled plants and runners, bag up, and take to local garden waste facility. Do not put in compost. The following year watch out for the young plants, and deal with the problem earlier. Follow current best, preferably organic, practice for large invasions (see Bibliography and internet).

Herbal, culinary, cultural and folklore Madders were used for dying clothes, and although both Field Madder (*Sherardia arvensis*) and Wild Madder (*Rubia peregrina*) were occasionally used in the Middle Ages, it was the central Asian plant *Rubia tinctorum* (known simply as Madder) which was imported for this purpose. The roots were the source of the dye. *Sherardia arvensis* can yield a rose-pink dye.

1) Young seedling plants 2) habit 3) close-up of flowers – note white leaf margins with upward pointing hairs 4) green fruit 5) fruiting head and individual fruits

SCROPHULARIACEAE *(Buddleia & Verbascum Family)*

Butterfly Bush, Buddleia *(Buddleja davidii)*

Introduced to horticulture from China 1896, a garden escape, and colonizing waste ground by 1930s. Perennial. A variable, fast-growing woody deciduous shrub with long, arching shoots; height and spread c. 5 m tall and 5 m wide. Leaves mid-green to grey-green, softly hairy (felty), especially the undersides, 10-25 cm long, narrowly ovate with pointed tips. Leaf margins with small shallow teeth. The hermaphrodite flowers are densely packed on sausage-like panicles which narrow towards tip, 10-30 cm long. Flowers fragrant: individual flowers minute (4-6 mm diameter, sometimes less), four-petalled and radially symmetric, tubular (c. 4-7 mm long), light-to-mid-mauve with an orange throat; four stamens. Fruit capsule pod-like and woody. Seeds minute, winged like miniature two-bladed propellers. Flowering June-October. Now thoroughly naturalised throughout southern England, as well as in a number of scattered localities in Scotland, Wales and Ireland. Favours railway and roadside embankments, derelict or waste ground, and cliffs, often close to the sea.

196

Pollination The heavy pungent scent of the flowers make this species a favourite haunt for many species of butterflies and bees, possibly helping to maintain some native British butterfly populations, or even species.

Regeneration strategy Tiny, light, propeller-like seeds are produced in huge quantities, easily carried along by the wind; it is not at all unusual to see *Buddleja* plants growing out of the higher elevations of, usually neglected, tall buildings.

Weed control Spreads by minute winged seeds. Seedlings are easy to recognise and easily to pull up when young. Older woody growth can be cut back, cut up, shredded and composted, or dried and burned. For large colonies follow current best, preferably organic, practice (see Bibliography and internet).

Herbal, culinary, cultural and folklore There are numerous cultivars of this species. Much of its original popularity is due to the scent of its flowers – a slightly curious fruity smell. It was rapidly realised that butterflies couldn't get enough of it and that it is seemingly more attractive to British butterflies than any native species; thus it gained its popular name, and was a 'must' for any British garden. The common name Buddleia (with an 'i') is a variant spelling of the botanical name *Buddleja* (with a 'j').

1) Seedling 2) invasive growth 3) spreading in waste land 4) part of inflorescence 5) seed heads 6) seed capsules and winged seeds

SOLANACEAE *(Nightshade Family)*

Thorn-apple, Jimson Weed *(Datura stramonium)*

Introduced somewhere between the Roman occupation of Britain, and the discovery of North America. It was being cultivated in Britain by 1597; first recorded in the wild in 1777. Annual. Stems pale green, smooth, freely branching from the base to c. 1.5 m in height. Green plant is described as "foul-smelling". Short-stemmed leaves smooth, upper surface dark green, underside lighter greyish-green, broad and long, with coarse jaggedly indented margins. Flowers hermaphrodite, radially symmetric, produced singly on short stalks, either in the axils of the leaves or where the branches fork; trumpet-shaped, white, creamy or violet (6-9 cm long); the upper margin with five shallow, pointed teeth. There are five stamens with long filaments and a slightly longer pistil, with a round, flattish stigma. During the day the flower folds (like a furled umbrella), at night it unfolds to a five-pointed (occasionally six-pointed) trumpet, releasing a pleasant fragrance that attracts nocturnal moths to visit and effect pollination. Calyx pale green, long, tubular, swollen at the base and sharply angled. Fruit capsule four-locular and spiny, c. 5 cm in diameter, splitting lengthwise when ripe. Seeds kidney-shaped, brown and pitted when mature. Flowering July-October. An infrequent lowland plant, mainly of southern and eastern England, occurring erratically as a casual on waste ground and cultivated soils. It is usually a garden escape, or a contaminant of bird seed. Plants of this species can reappear after unusually long periods of seed dormancy (see below).

197

Pollination Moths, including hawkmoths, are its main visitors but it may also self-fertilise.

Regeneration strategy The seeds maintain their viability for many years. In an experiment undertaken for his PhD dissertation, the biologist J.W.T. Duvel selected weed seeds from a number of different plant families and buried them at three different depths. The results, published in 1946, showed that the greater the depth, the greater the longevity of the seed. Thorn-apple was among the species selected for testing. After 39 years at the greatest depth (42 inches/1.07 m) 91% of the buried Thorn-apple seed was still viable. A similar result was obtained for Black Nightshade, another member of family Solanaceae, included in the experiment.

Weed control For small invasions weed out young, pre-flowering plants. These can be composted, as the toxins will break down

naturally. If plants have set seed they should be burned, or taken to the local garden waste facility. Follow current best, preferably organic, practice for large invasions (see Bibliography and internet). Always wear gloves or thoroughly wash hands after handling this plant.

Herbal, culinary, cultural and folklore Chemical extracts used in medicine, including treatment of brain tumours, to ease asthma symptoms, and as an analgesic during surgery. It is also a powerful hallucinogen and deliriant, which has been used spiritually to induce intense visions.

Toxicity All parts of the plant are poisonous, especially the seeds, whose toxic compounds are a mixture of the alkaloids: atropine, scopolamine and hyoscyamine. Its disagreeable odour and taste make it unpalatable to most livestock.

1) Young plant 2) young adult plant 3) flower 4) fruit

Bittersweet, Woody Nightshade *(Solanum dulcamara)*

Native. Perennial. A rhizomatous, semi-woody, sprawling herbaceous vine, reaching 1-2 m in height, sometimes 4 m, by climbing through shrubby vegetation. Stems very slightly hairy; young stems purplish, older stems brown and woody. Leaves 4-12 cm long, short-stalked, alternate on stems, mid-green, greyish and felty on undersides, ovate with pointed tips or, in older or larger leaves, often shaped like an arrow-head. Leaf margins straight, upper surface smooth, or with short scattered hairs 'lying' on the surface. Damaged stems or leaves give off a rank, bitter smell. Flowers hermaphrodite, radially symmetric (c. 0.8-1 cm diameter), long-stalked, in loose clusters of six to 12 (sometimes only three or as many as 20). Five elongate-ovate, pointed purple petals with paired whitish-green dots at their bases. The petals open to slightly less than horizontal to reveal a central column of five long, bright yellow, closely-united stamens – or rather, it is the elongate porate anthers of the stamens that are seen; the stamen filaments are very short; the long narrow pistil is concealed in the stamen column, its tip (stigma) more or less level with the tips of the stamens. Calyx small, green, purple or brownish, with five short, slightly hairy rounded lobes that persist to fruiting stage. As the flower ages following pollination, the petals bend backwards towards the flower stem. The fruit is a broadly ovoid berry, 10 mm long, sometimes up to 15 mm, mid-green turning scarlet when ripe. Each two-loculed berry contains about 30 ovoid, flattish pale yellow seeds. Flowering June-September. A widespread and common plant throughout England and Wales, excepting parts of central Wales, becoming scarce northwards and rare or absent from central and northern Scotland; local and scattered throughout Ireland. It grows near ponds and lakes, in hedgerows, woodland margins and scrub, also occurring in reed beds and fen carr on rich alluvial soils or calcareous peats. There is a prostrate form that colonises shingle beaches.

Pollination The poricidal anthers of the stamens are a highly specialised evolutionary adaptation to 'buzz-pollination'. The flowers are freely visited by bees, who release the pollen with rapid vibrations of their wings as they hang beneath the stamen column. Bee visitors include bumblebees, for example *Bombus lucorum*. The species also self-pollinates.

Regeneration strategies If vegetative shoots are injured, more root shoots are freely produced. Small pieces of rhizome can generate new plants. Red fruits attractive to various birds, for example Thrushes, Blackbirds, Robins, Wood Pigeons and Blackcaps, who are not affected by the toxins.

Weed control For small invasions, protect hands with gloves and pull out young pre-flowering vines. These can be composted, as the toxins will break down naturally. If plants have set seed they should be burned or taken to the local garden waste facility. Follow current best, preferably organic, practice for large invasions (see Bibliography and internet).

Herbal, culinary, cultural and folklore The botanical epithet *dulcamara* means bittersweet – early tasters of the plant said that the root tasted first bitter then sweet. This species is sometimes confused with the much less common Deadly Nightshade (*Atropa belladonna*), a favourite poison of old 'who-dunnits', which has large bell-shaped pale mauve flowers and large black berries (1.2-1.5 cm) with large sepals.

Toxicity The alkaloid solanine occurs in the stems, leaves and the red berries. The plant is poisonous to humans and livestock, although cases of ingestion by either are rare, however, the ripe berries are potentially attractive to young children.

1) Flowers 2) ripe and green fruits

Black Nightshade *(Solanum nigrum* subsp. *nigrum)*

Native. Annual or biennial. Much-branched bushy habit, height 30-60 cm, sometimes as low as 20 or as high as 80 cm. Stems erect or almost so, smooth or slightly hairy, often flushed deep purple, or slightly purplish, sometimes green. Leaves broad-based ovate, narrower towards tip, margins straight or irregularly lobed or indented, 4-12 cm long, short-stalked, alternate on stems, mid-green. Flowers hermaphrodite, radially symmetric (c. 0.6-1.5 cm diameter), long-stalked, in loose clusters of three to eight, sometimes up to ten. Five elongate-ovate, pointed petals, white, or purple speckled, opening to slightly less than horizontal to reveal a central column of five long stamens, closely-arranged, but not united – or rather, it is the elongate porate yellow anthers of the stamens that are seen; the stamen filaments are short; the long narrow pistil is concealed in the stamen column, its tip (stigma) more or less level with the tips of the stamens. Calyx small, green, purple or brownish, with five short, slightly hairy rounded lobes that persist to fruiting stage. As the flower ages following pollination, the petals bend backwards towards the flower stem. The fruit is a globose berry, 0.5-1 cm diameter, mid-green, turning dull black when ripe. Each two-loculed berry contains about 40 ovoid, flattish, pale yellow seeds. Flowering July-September. Widespread in England, south and east of a line from the Humber to the Severn, but scarce in Wales and the south-west and absent from Ireland and Scotland. A frequent and troublesome weed of arable crops on fertile soils in southern England; it also occurs in gardens, market gardens, farmyards, around manure heaps and on organically-rich waste ground.

Pollination The poricidal anthers of the stamens are a highly specialised evolutionary adaptation to 'buzz-pollination'. The flowers are freely visited by bees, who release the pollen with rapid vibrations of their wings as they hang beneath the stamen column. Bee visitors include bumblebees, for example *Bombus lucorum*. The species also self-pollinates.

Regeneration strategy Fruits eaten by birds. The seeds maintain their viability for many years. In an experiment undertaken for his PhD dissertation, the biologist J.W.T. Duvel selected weed seeds from a number of different plant families which were buried at three different depths. The results, published in 1946, showed that the greater the depth, the greater the longevity of the seed. After 39 years at the greatest depth (42 inches/1.07 m) 91% of the buried Black Nightshade was still viable. A similar result was obtained for Thorn-apple, another member of family Solanaceae included in the experiment.

Weed control For small invasions, protect hands with gloves and pull out young pre-flowering plants. These can be composted, as the toxins will break down naturally. If plants have set seed they should be burned, or taken to the local garden waste facility. Follow current best, preferably organic, practice for large invasions (see Bibliography and internet).

Herbal, culinary, cultural and folklore A globally widespread weedy species, with little British or European folklore attached to it.

Toxicity The plant has an unpleasant odour. The alkaloid solanine occurs mainly in the black berries and, to a lesser extent, in the stems and leaves. It is poisonous to humans and livestock, although cases of ingestion by either are rare.

1) Young plant 2) adult plant 3) flowers 4) ripe and green fruits

URTICACEAE *(Nettle Family)*

Helxine, Mind-your-own-business *(Soleirolia soleirolii)*

Introduced from west Mediterranean islands, date of introduction uncertain, but probably mid-late 19th Century. Short-lived perennial. Stems prostrate, slightly translucent, very pale green or pinkish, generally mat-forming, 2-30 cm across. Leaves tiny, 3-5 mm long, sometimes up to 8 mm, bright green, shiny, alternate, more or less round to rounded-ovate, often with sparse non-stinging hairs. Flowers radially symmetric, very small (2-3 mm diameter), monoecious: subtended by four shortly hairy, reddish winged bracts. Female flowers with a pale whitish or light pink starry/feathery pistil; male flowers with four sepals and four stamens with longish filaments and white anthers. Fruit *(achenes)* 1.2-1.5 mm long, four-winged, red, hairy. Seeds 0.6-0.8 mm long, sometimes up to 0.9 mm, ovoid, light brown and shiny. Flowering May-October. Prefers damp shady places, usually in gardens, sometimes by streams.

Pollination Many species in family Urticaceae, including nettles, are wind-pollinated, however, Helxine does not appear to have any features suggesting that cross-fertilisation is achieved in this way. The close proximity of male and female flowers suggests that either (or both) foraging flies and self-pollination are involved. Closed, the four young stamens look like minute red pumpkins, while the filaments of the adult stamens are long and thick, and strongly exerted in the form of a cross – it is possible that the filaments unfurl rapidly, flinging pollen from the anthers onto the neighbouring feathery stigmas of female flowers with facility.

Regeneration strategy Once established, it can be very invasive in damp places, as the prostrate stems produce masses of tiny roots which facilitate rapid anchorage and spread.

Weed control A difficult weed to eradicate, especially in lawns. Lightly scarify at beginning and end of mowing season, aerate and feed the lawn regularly to encourage turf vigour and density. In planted areas try burying it deeply with mulch; in paths or damp places try pouring kettles of boiling water on to it or, where the ground dries out at certain times of year, rake or hoe dried patches as often as practicable and remove and destroy the rakings.

Herbal, culinary, cultural and folklore Named for Joseph François Soleirol (1796-1863), a French infantry captain who collected plants in Corsica during the early 19th Century. Very popular as a conservatory or parlour plant during the late 19th and early 20th Centuries. It is currently enjoying renewed novelty as a pretty green covering plant in fashionable gardens. Its growth form has also earned it another common name: Irish Moss, but it is a flowering plant, not a moss.

Toxicity May cause an allergic skin reaction in some individuals, but this is not common.

1) Leaves and overall appearance 2) habit – runners 3) rooting runners 4) male flowers (c. 3 mm wide) with four long-filamented white stamens
5) feathery star-like stigmas (c. 1 mm wide) of female pistils 6) small urn-shaped red fruits

Common Nettle, Stinging Nettle *(Urtica dioica)*

Native. Perennial. Stems usually unbranched, hairy, square in section, green or reddish, 30-150 cm in height, with tough yellow rhizomes that creep and root at nodes. Leaves opposite on stems, mid-dark green, 4-8 cm long, with basal leaf extensions (*stipules*). Blades of lower leaves short-stalked and ovate, leaf apex pointed, with regular simple-toothed margins and secondary leaf ribs widely angled from central rib. Stems and leaves covered with stinging and non-stinging hairs (stinging hairs usually longer). Flowers minute, radially symmetric, with tepals only, dioecious (on separate plants), borne on tassle-like flowering stalks. Flowers of the 'staminate' male plants have four stamens with pale creamy yellow anthers, while flowers of the 'pistillate' female plants have a pale whitish starry/feathery pistil above an ovary. Fruit c. 2 mm long, flat, elliptic with a single-seed (*achene*). Flowering June-August, sometimes as late as September, abundant and widespread, especially in waste ground, farmyards, or other nutrient-rich habitats.

Additional notes The stinging hairs: each long slender hair has a fine tube stiffened with calcified calcium carbonate at its base and with silicified silica at its tip. On contact the silicified tip breaks off and the fine point pierces the skin. Pressure frees the fluid calcium carbonate from the hair into the skin (and the itch is born!).

Pollination Wind.

Regeneration strategies Extensive underground rhizomes and copious seed production.

Weed control Attend to minor invasions sooner rather than later. Wear protective gloves, cut back top growth, chop up the cut nettles, and add rainwater to make nitrogen-rich fertiliser. Dig out rhizomes, dry and burn, or take to local garden waste facility. Follow current best, preferably organic, practice for large invasions (see Bibliography and internet).

Herbal, culinary, cultural and folklore Nettle fibre can be spun as fine as linen and was, and still is, used for clothing (see Introduction for more detail on the economic resources of this species). A simple and delicious soup is made from the young leaf tips. The roots are said to produce a good yellow dye, and the leaves a range of greens and browns. The outer rind of the British cheese Cornish Yarg is coated with Stinging Nettle leaves to attract naturally occurring moulds. The expression "to get nettled" has its origins in beating with nettles; arthritic joints were traditionally treated by whipping with a branch of stinging nettles, and various modern studies endorse the likely effectiveness of this treatment. Nettles also provide larval food for a range of butterflies, notably Peacock, Red Admiral and Small Tortoiseshell.

201

1) Young seedling plant 2) young colony of overwintered plants 3) leaf, upper and lower faces 4) male flowering habit 5) male flowers with stamens 6) female flowering habit

Small Nettle, Annual Nettle *(Urtica urens)*

Native. Annual. Stems hairy, 10-60 cm in height, ribbed, green, easily uprooted. Leaves 1.4-4 cm long, sometimes up to 5 cm, mid-green, with small basal leaf extensions (*stipules*). Upper leaves short-stalked, but blades of lower leaves shorter than stalks. Leaf apex ovate-rounded, with regular deeply toothed margins; main teeth usually with one to two secondary teeth. Leaf venation notably more linear than in *Urtica dioica*. Stems and leaves covered with stinging (more than *Urtica dioica*) and non-stinging hairs (stinging hairs usually longer – see Stinging Nettle (*Urtica dioica*) for explanation of stinging hairs). Flowers minute with tepals only, monoecious (on the same plant), borne in clusters in the leaf axils. Flowers of the 'staminate' male plants have four stamens with pale creamy yellow anthers, while flowers of the 'pistillate' female plants have a pale whitish starry/feathery pistil above an ovary. Fruit c. 2 mm long, flat, elliptic, with a single seed (*achene*). Flowering June-August, sometimes as late as September. A nitrate lover, distributed throughout the British Isles, common in the east, more localised in the west. A plant of gardens, arable and waste ground, on calcareous to mildly acidic, light, well-drained sandy soils, and other nitrate-rich habitats.

202

Pollination Wind.

Regeneration strategy Copiously produced seed shed locally.

Weed control Attend to minor invasions before flowering time. Wear protective gloves – providing the plants have not started flowering, being rich in nitrogen, they can make a valuable addition to the compost heap. Flowering or seeding plants should be dried and burned, or taken to local garden waste facility. Follow current best, preferably organic, practice for large invasions (see Bibliography and internet).

Herbal, culinary, cultural and folklore Nothing specific found. Stinging Nettle is the main source for almost all notable material, although many sayings and remedies are associated with both species, including nettles being kept in a room to protect the occupants, enhancing male fertility and finally, keeping nettles in the pocket to protect the wearer and bestow courage. (See Stinging Nettle for explanation of what causes the sting.)

1) Young seedling plant 2) habit 3) leaves from above 4) leaves, upper and lower faces 5) male flowers (stamens), female fruits less obvious 6) female fruits

VIOLACEAE *(Violet Family)*

Field Pansy *(Viola arvensis)*

Native. Annual. Height 3-45 cm. Stems pale green, slightly ridged. Leaves short-stalked, soft, mid-green, spirally arranged on stem, ovate with wavy margins. Basal stipules large, crowded, deeply incised (feathery). Flowers hermaphrodite, bisymmetric and solitary on long smooth, ribbed stems. Five petals: two pale creamy white upper pairs, the uppermost pair often slightly smaller and unmarked, the lower pair with (usually) two basal purple streaks and a large, spurred, lower central petal, which may also be creamy white, but is often slightly darker cream or pale yellow, with five purple streaks radiating from the centre base. Sometimes there is a pale violet tinge to the upper petals: there are five stamens, and a short pistil. Five light green, elongate-pointed, hairless sepals with short basal extensions. Fruit a capsule in three segments, containing around 75 seeds in total, tiny, shiny mid-soft brown and droplet-shaped. Flowering April-October, mainly on calcareous and neutral soils. Common throughout the British Isles but scarce or local in west and north-west Scotland, occurring up to c. 580 m. An annual weed of arable fields and, less frequently, waste ground.

203

Pollination A variety of insect visitors, but more frequently self-pollinated; cleistogamous flowers also occur.

Regeneration strategy The ripe fruits split with some force ejecting the seeds, often a considerable distance (as much as 2 m), from the parent plant. Long seed viability of more than four years. Also dispersed via cattle dung.

Weed control Hand-weeding and hoeing or turning young pre-flowering plants back into soil as green manure.

Herbal, culinary, cultural and folklore Pansies are associated with thoughtfulness and remembrance. The common name is derived from the French *pensée* meaning thought or sentiment. In folklore it is widely associated with love.

1) Seedlings 2) habit 3) flower 4) seeds

FLOWERING PLANTS
Monocotyledons

AMARYLLIDACEAE *(Onion & Daffodil Family)*

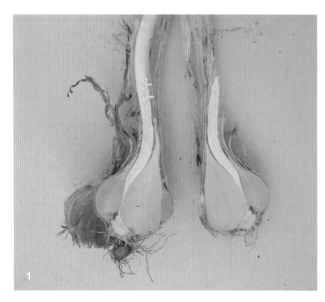 

Crow Garlic, Wild Onion *(Allium vineale)*

Native. Bulbous perennial smelling of onions. Height of flowering/fruiting stem 30-80 cm. Leaves long, deep grey-green and tubular. Flower heads often lack the hermaphrodite flowers (bell-shaped with six pink or greenish-white tepals and six stamens). The ovary is three-celled, and each ovary comprises two ovules. The ovules usually germinate while still in place at the top of the fruiting stem, giving rise to the curious grassy heads more frequently encountered than the flower heads. Flowering June-July. Occurs on fields, roadsides and grassy banks (where leaves often mistaken for grass – until crushed!). Generally widespread, but much less common in Ireland.

Pollination Various insects.

Regeneration strategies Both by seed and vegetatively. Although it can produce seed, it also produces heads of numerous, rapidly germinating bulbils, and this is the most frequent regeneration strategy.

Weed control Dig up young plants and bulbs before the bulbil and/or flower heads ripen. Thoroughly chop up/shred bulbs and compost, or take to local garden waste facility.

Herbal, culinary, cultural and folklore Has been used as a flavouring but only *in extremis* it would seem. Crow Garlic has been notorious among farmers since at least Anglo Saxon times because cattle grazing on it produced unpleasantly tainted milk.

1) Section through bulb 2) young, grass-like leaves 3) fruiting heads in grassy bank 4) fruiting and germinating seed heads

Ramsons, Wood Garlic *(Allium ursinum)*

Native. Bulbous perennial. Leaves elongate, broadly ovate and glossy. Strong odour of onion/garlic. Height of flower stem 10-45 cm. Flower heads with many small, starry, white, six-tepaled, hermaphrodite flowers, each with six stamens. Ovary three-celled, each ovary comprises two ovules. Flowering April-June, sometimes as early as March. Occurs in damp woods and shady places, widely distributed.

Pollination Various insects.

Regeneration strategy High seed production.

Weed control Dig up young plants and their bulbs, preferably before flowering but definitely before seed ripens. Thoroughly chop up/shred bulbs and compost, or take to local garden waste facility. Follow current best practice for large invasions (see Bibliography and internet).

Herbal, culinary, cultural and folklore: The 16th Century herbalist John Gerard recorded that in the Low Countries, the leaves were crushed and used with butter as a fish sauce.

207

1) Young leaves in early spring 2) bulbs 3) flowers 4) dry seed heads 5) seeds, c. 0.8-1 mm long

ARACEAE *(Wild Arum Family)*

Lords and Ladies, Wild Arum, Cuckoo Pint *(Arum maculatum)*

Native. Tuberous perennial. Height 30-50 cm. Large ovate leaves, deeply lobed at base, mid-green, often with few to many purple blotches. A large pale green *spathe*, 15-25 cm long, encloses the unusual monoecious floral structure: an elongate purple, pale brownish-purple or light yellow *spadix* (10-15 cm long, sometimes up to 25 cm), with a basal stem (c. 4-7 cm long, sometimes up to 8 cm). At the base of the spadix is a band of untidy, slightly fleshy bristles. Below the bristles, a ring of brownish male flowers (each with one stamen), and below the male flowers, a broader ring of creamy female flowers (ovary with one carpel). When the flowers are mature, the spadix emits an odour that attracts flies into the spathe to effect pollination (see below). Fruits shiny, green at first then turning deep orange to vermilion. Flowering March-April, sometimes as late as May. Widely distributed throughout the British Isles in woodlands and hedges, especially on base-rich soils, to a height of c. 400 m.

Pollination Notably Owl Midges (*Psychoda phalaenoides*). The female flowers become receptive during the afternoon and the odour from the spadix attracts the midges into the spathe. To reach the female flowers the midges must pass through the ring of bristles, and below the immature ring of male flowers. Once entrapped, the midges, dusted with pollen from another spadix with mature male flowers, unwittingly 'brush' the pollen onto the receptive female flowers. This triggers the stamens to ripen, dusting the flies with pollen as they make their escape through the wilted ring of bristles.

Regeneration strategies Spreads by corms and by seed from the berries. The berries, although deadly to humans, are reported to be consumed by pheasants and blackbirds.

Weed control Dig out corms (indicated by small leaf spathes sprouting up) and destroy or, later in the season, remove and destroy fruiting stems. Follow current best practice for large invasions (see Bibliography and internet).

Herbal, culinary, cultural and folklore The spadix of Arum has given rise to an unprecedented volume of local names (over 100) alluding to the male sexual organ (human and canine mainly) and human sexual activity in general, much to the delight of children (and adults!) venturing into the potentially arid realms of learning botanical names. The Rev. Gilbert White (*The Natural History of Selbourne*) records Thrushes scratching the corms/tubers out of the ground and eating them in harsh winters. Among other common names for this species are Adder's (or Toad's) Meal, and Adder's (or Toad's) Meat, though whether these names refer to the berries or the corms is uncertain. In the past, the tubers were made into a starchy food called 'salep' (from the Arabic *tha'leb* meaning Fox orchid). This 'Portland Sago' (large quantities were shipped from the Isle of Portland to London) became popular as a substitute for arrowroot.

Toxicity The fruits are extremely poisonous to humans, and the plants are not readily eaten by livestock, although pigs are known to root out the corms.

1) reproductive spathe 2) reproductive structure – hairs, stamens and carpels 3) ripe fruits (berries)

ASPARAGACEAE *(Asparagus & Bluebell Family)*

Hybrid Bluebell *(Hyacinthoides* x *massartiana)*

Part-introduced neophyte: first record of this hybrid between the native British Bluebell (*Hyacinthoides non-scripta*) and the introduced Spanish Bluebell (*Hyacinthoides hispanica*), is from Banffshire in 1963. Bulbous perennial. Leaves broad, 10-30 mm wide, 20-50 cm long, strap-shaped, mid-green. Flowering stem may slightly droop or nod, height 20-50 cm, stem generally thicker than that of either parent. Florets bell-shaped, hermaphrodite, moderately spreading: six free tepals slightly recurved at tips, either light blue, white or pink; six stamens sometimes slightly bluish, but usually cream, especially in white or pink flowers; pollen cream. Fruit a three-celled capsule with brown shiny seeds. Flowering April-June. Its distribution as a widespread garden nuisance is made worse by it being dumped in banks and wayside places where it may proliferate. While attempts to eradicate the spread of the Hybrid Bluebell continue, confusion and misidentification of the hybrids as the Spanish Bluebell also continues. Occurrences of the smaller true Spanish Bluebell, *Hyacinthoides hispanica*, are comparatively rare, compared with the much larger Hybrid Bluebell.

Pollination Uncertain – probably similar to English and Spanish Bluebells.

Regeneration strategies Unfortunately the hybrid produces viable seed. It also spreads from bulbs like its parents.

Weed control Produces viable seeds and deeply buried bulbs: remove seed heads while young and green, or dig out bulbs and destroy by burning. Home compost (if efficient system in operation), otherwise take to local authority green waste facility.

Herbal, culinary, cultural and folklore Often tolerated in gardens where it is frequently referred to (incorrectly) as the Spanish Bluebell.

1) Flowering group – note upright flower heads and broad leaves 2) flowers are many per stem with cream stamens
3) white or pink forms also occur in the hybrid

Bluebell *(Hyacinthoides non-scripta)*

Native – not a weed but one parent of *Hyacinthoides* x *massartiana*. Bulbous perennial. Leaf length 20-45 cm, usually narrow (c. 7-15 mm wide), strap-like, mid-green and glossy. Height of flowering stem 30-45 cm. Flowering head one-sided, curving towards apex, but straightening at fruiting stage. Flowers hermaphrodite, elongate, pendulous, appearing tubular: six free tepals distinctly recurved at tips, mid-to-deep blue/purplish, six stamens with cream pollen. Fruit a three-celled capsule with ovoid, dark brown shiny seeds. Flowers April-June. A widely distributed species throughout the British Isles with the exception of Orkney and Shetland. Bluebell woods are among the most distinctly British of all plant communities; the species is tolerant of many soil types although it is most typical of acidic sandy loams. It is also found in abundance on heavier, and/or calcareous soils and grows and flowers freely in light shade.

Pollination Hoverflies, notably the Syrphidae (*Rhingia* species) which have longer mouth parts, for feeding from tubular flowers, however, the flowers are not strictly tubular and bumblebees and honey bees are able to insert their tongues between the basal margins of the petals to obtain nectar.

Regeneration strategies Seeds and bulbs.

Herbal, culinary, cultural and folklore One of our most loved wild flowers. Preferring open woodland, it is in general not an invader of cultivated land unless encouraged.

210

1) Bluebells in natural habitat – note curving flower heads and narrow leaves
2) note the elongated flower shape 3) flowers have cream stamens

Spanish Bluebell *(Hyacinthoides hispanica)*

Introduced neophyte c. 1683. First record from non-cultivated ground in 1875, south-east Yorkshire. Bulbous perennial. Leaves 20-50 cm long, 10-35 mm wide, broad, strap-shaped, mid-green and glossy. Height of flowering stem 20-50 cm. Flowering head more or less erect, not one-sided. Flowers hermaphrodite, six free tepals spreading at tips, not recurved (more *Scilla*-like), light blue to pale mauve-ish blue; stamens blue, pollen cream or bluish. Fruit a three-celled capsule with brown shiny seeds. Flowering from late April to June. This non-native species is often confused with the Hybrid Bluebell *Hyacinthoides* x *massartiana*, which is frequently referred to as the Spanish Bluebell. This is incorrect – the prolific Hybrid Bluebell is the unfortunate ugly duckling offspring of two very lovely native species: *H. hispanica*, from south-west Europe and *H. non-scripta*, from north-west Europe.

Pollination Early emerging small dark *Halictus* bees, working in early spring.

Regeneration strategies Seeds and bulbs.

Weed control None usually required. Follow advice for Hybrid Bluebell if necessary.

Herbal, culinary, cultural and folklore A lovely species – less frequently cultivated now.

Flowers are few per stem with blue stamens

Field Wood-rush, Easter Grass *(Luzula campestris)*

Native. Perennial. Short rootstock and shortly creeping stolons. Flowering stems c. 15 cm long, sometimes up to 25 cm. Grass-like leaves 2-4 mm wide, arising from the base and from the flowering stems, with distinctive long whitish hairs along the margins. Flowering heads of three to many flower clusters. Flowers hermaphrodite, with six chestnut-brown petal-like structures, lance-shaped and longer than seed capsules; six yellow stamens with long anthers (two to six times as long as the stamen filaments), yellow stigma of the pistil divided into three long 'fingers'. Seed capsules rounded, 2.5-3 mm long, seeds almost globular with a large white basal appendage. Flowering March-May. Very common throughout the British Isles. One of the earliest grass-like flowering plants to appear in spring, especially common in pastures, lawns, churchyards and on grassy banks. It will grow to 1000 m above sea level.

212

Pollination Generally wind, however, insect visitors include the hoverfly *Platycheirus albomanus*.

Regeneration strategies Locally dropped seed and short creeping stolons.

Weed control Hand-weeding is difficult as it almost always occurs in grass. Sulphate of iron, when applied as a moss control product or as a constituent of *lawn sand*, is reported to work well. Apply twice, six weeks apart.

Herbal, culinary, cultural and folklore In west Yorkshire its flowering was an indication that it was time to put the cattle out to pasture. Also known as Good Friday Grass, or Sweeps' Brooms.

1) Habit 2) leaves and leaf hairs 3) stamens and stigmas 4) young fruit

CYPERACEAE *(Sedge Family)*

Pendulous Sedge *(Carex pendula)*

Native. Perennial. Short rhizomes. Distinctive reddish-brown sheaths at base of leaf shoots; forms large stout clumps. Overall plant height 60-150 cm, sometimes up to 180 cm. Leaves mid-green, erect or curving, strap-like, 1.5-2 cm wide with central midrib. The flowering stem is triangular in cross section, with long, drooping flower spikes of monoecious flowers. Often the uppermost spike is exclusively male (6-10 cm long) and comprises a thick mass of tiny flowers, each flower with three light yellow stamens. Although predominantly female, one or several of the other upper spikes may also have male flowers at their tips, while the lower spikes (7-16 cm long) are exclusively female. Each female flower comprises a single-seeded ovary with a three-branched pistil, the ovary is subtended by a green bract. The ripe seeds are dark brown. Flowering May-June. Predominantly a lowland species in the south and east of England, scattered in Wales and Ireland. Much rarer in the north of England, and mainly coastal in Scotland. A preference for base-rich, heavy clay soils, especially in damp woods and on shady stream banks, or where there is a constant water supply.

Pollination Wind, but also visited by Marsh Marigold Moths (*Micropterix calthella* – a small metallic moth) who feed on the pollen.

Regeneration strategy Copious seed production and moist shady conditions encourage rapid colonisation.

Weed control Remove young plants before flowering stage and compost, or follow current best, preferably organic, practice for large invasions (see Bibliography and internet).

Herbal, culinary, cultural and folklore Often enjoyed or tolerated by gardeners, especially in larger gardens with wild woodland areas.

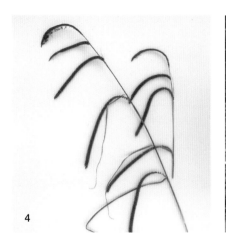

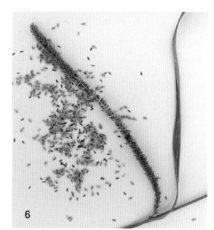

1) Young plant 2) rootstock and basal leaves show typical red-brown colouration 3) adult plant habit
4) fruiting stem – old male flowers (top) and female fronds of young fruits 5) male flowering frond (top) and at the tips of two female fronds below 6) ripe seeds and female frond

POACEAE *(Grass Family)*

Common Couch-grass, Couch-grass, Twitch *(Elymus repens)*

Native. Perennial. Stem (*culm*) green or grey green, usually stiffly erect or almost so, jointed (*noded*), height up to 110 cm, sometimes up to 160 cm. Extensively creeping and branching rhizomes, forming loose tufts or patches. Stems and stem joints (*internodes*) smooth. Leaves green or grey-green, finely ribbed, slightly rough to the touch on upper surface and along the edges. The flower head (*panicle*) is more or less straight, stiff, and elongate, 7.5-13.5 cm long, sometimes as small as 4.5 or as large as 21.5 cm. The individual flower units (*spikelets*) are long and narrow (12-18 mm long, sometimes as short as 10 or as long as 22 mm), and alternate on either side of the central zig-zag flower stalk. Each spikelet has two rigid, lance-shaped basal scales (the lower and upper *glumes*), sometimes with a short spine (*awn*), smaller than 4 mm in length. Above the glumes are four to seven, sometimes up to nine, closely arranged hermaphrodite flowers (*florets*). The florets have two basal scales a lower scale (*lemma*) and an upper scale (*palea*). The lemma sometimes with short point, or a short bristle-like projection (*awn*) c. twice the length of the lemma. Otherwise the floret comprises mostly reproductive parts: a shortly hairy ovary, with usually two very small, paired *lodicules* (probably vestigial petals/sepals) at the base, two short white feathery stigmas which spread and project laterally on either side of the open floret, and three stamens with long anthers and short filaments. The fruit (a *caryopsis* – typical of grasses) is droplet-shaped, slightly flattened, hairy at the top, and with a groove on one side. It is shed with its outer covering, the *pericarp* (the outer persistent casing of the ovary wall) still firmly attached. Flowering late June-early August, sometimes as late as September. Common throughout the British Isles, in fields and waste places. Particularly abundant in areas of arable farming in the lowlands. It becomes rarer in upland areas, especially in parts of north-west Scotland. Occurring on a wide range of cultivated and waste ground, including road verges, rough grassland and railway embankments. An especially problematic weed of agricultural land, gardens, allotments and orchards. It is sometimes used as a binding agent for sand dunes. It is also common on cliffs, shingle, sea walls and saltmarshes (especially in the north), river margins, hedgerows and rubbish heaps. Excepting acidic peat, it occurs on a wide range of soil types and is particularly associated with fertile arable clay. In the north-west of England it has been recorded as high as 845 m above sea level.

Pollination Wind.

Regeneration strategies Notably the extensive rhizomes. Self-incompatible with low seed production.

Weed control Hand-weed, using a fork to carefully dig out and remove all underground roots and rhizomes, before the plants get too big, or reach seeding stage. Leaves and stems can be composted but do not compost rhizomes or seed heads – either incinerate or take to local garden waste facility. Follow current best, preferably organic, practice for large invasions (see Bibliography and internet).

Herbal, culinary, cultural and folklore Its rhizomes are nutritious, during WWI the rhizomes were sometimes used to make ersatz coffee, and also dried and ground into flour. A British weed introduced to North America by immigrants. It is widely considered to be the most medicinal of all quick (living) grasses. A rich source of potassium and other minerals. It is considered to make a good tonic to purify the blood and reduce kidney stones. Horses and cattle are very fond of the underground stems, and it is one of the main grasses that dogs and cats seek out to chew when they need to vomit to clear their stomachs. In Italy and France the roots are traditionally harvested and sold in the markets.

214

1) Leaves and flower heads (panicles) 2) close-up of panicles and spikelets 3) roots and runners, six months growth

Black-grass, Black Twitch *(Alopecurus myosuroides)*

Introduced, first record in UK 1597 in Paddington, London. Annual. Stem (*culm*) green or grey-green, usually stiffly erect, few joints (*nodes*), height 20-80 cm, sometimes up to 90 cm. Stem enclosed by smooth, hairless, green or purplish-green leaf sheaths. Leaves green, flat, 3-16 cm long and 2-8 mm wide, rough on both sides or smooth underneath. The flower head (*panicle*) stiff, spike-like, cylindrical and elongate, 5.5-11 cm in length (sometimes as short as 4 or as long as 12.5 cm) and 6.5 mm in width (sometimes as narrow as 3.5 or as wide as 7.5 mm). The flower units (*spikelets*) on the tightly packed flower head are one-flowered, ovate-oblong, 5.2-6.6 mm long, sometimes up to 7 mm. The spikelets have conjoined pairs of lance-shaped basal scales (*glumes*). Above the glumes are four to seven, sometimes up to nine closely arranged hermaphrodite flowers (*florets*). The florets have only one basal scale, the *lemma*. The upper scale (*palea*) is absent. The lemma has a long slender bristle-like projection (*awn*) c. twice the length of the lemma. Otherwise the floret comprises mostly reproductive parts: a shortly hairy ovary with usually two very small paired *lodicules* (probably vestigial petals/sepals) at the base, two long, rather upright, white feathery stigmas which spread and project laterally on either side of the open floret, and three stamens with long orange-brown anthers, and filaments of similar length. The fruit (a *caryopsis* – typical of grasses) is droplet-shaped, slightly flattened, hairy at the top, and with a groove on one side. It is shed with its outer covering, the *pericarp* (the outer persistent casing of the ovary wall) still firmly attached. Flowering and fruiting June-August, sometimes as early as May or as late as September. Very common in England south of the divide marked by the Humber-Severn Estuary. Scattered or casual elsewhere: south-west England, Wales, northern England and Scotland, though rare in Ireland. Almost entirely associated with arable land and neighbouring habitats such as field headlands and waste ground. Its biology pre-adapts it perfectly to the conditions found in winter-sown crops. Thrives best on heavy soils of poor structure or limited drainage, subject to winter wet.

Pollination Wind and self-fertilisation.

Regeneration strategy By seed dropped locally or carried by birds and other animals, including humans.

Weed control Highly invasive once it gets hold, however, it is an annual and small pre-flowering invasions are easily pulled up, composted, or burned. Follow current best, preferably organic, practice for large invasions (see Bibliography and internet).

Herbal, culinary, cultural and folklore The earliest record for this species in Britain is late 16th Century, but it is possible that it may have been earlier. Outside of Britain it used to be cultivated as birdseed and apparently pheasants devour it with relish. It is reputed to be one of the world's worst weeds, and some strains have developed resistance to herbicides.

1) Typical growth habit 2) young flower heads (panicles) with purplish basal spikelet scales (glumes) 3) stamens of flowering spikelets, only the stamens are conspicuous 4) post-flowering – note straight awns and remains of old stamens

Soft-brome, Lop-grass *(Bromus hordeaceus)*

Native. Annual. Stem (*culm*) green or grey-green, slender erect or almost so, jointed (*noded*). Height 90-100 cm, sometimes up to 125 cm. Stems enclosed by leaf sheaths, the lower sheaths densely and softly hairy, upper sheaths less so, or even smooth, sometimes smooth throughout. Leaves long (up to 20 cm), flat, 2-7 mm wide, greyish-green, softly hairy. The flower head (*panicle*) at first erect and loose, to very loose, somewhat denser and more nodding at maturity, 2-12.5 cm long, sometimes up to 18 cm. Main branches softly hairy, the longest with up to five individual flower units (*spikelets*) which, excluding *awns* (bristle-like projections), are narrowly ovate-oblong, 11-2 mm in length, sometimes as short as 9 or as long as 24 mm. A spikelet has a basal pair of scales (*glumes*). Lower glume ovate to oblong, 5-9 mm long, sometimes as short as 4 or as long as 10 mm. Upper glume elliptic, 9.5 mm in length, sometimes as short as 5.5 or as long as 11 mm. Both glumes usually softly hairy, sometimes smooth. Above the glumes, within a spikelet, are five to 13 closely arranged hermaphrodite flowers (*florets*). A floret has two basal scales: a lower scale (the *lemma*) and an upper scale (the *palea*). The lemma (but not the palea) has a slender bristle-like projection (*awn*), 3-7 mm long. Otherwise the floret comprises mostly reproductive parts: an ovary with usually two very small paired *lodicules* at the base (probably vestigial petals/sepals), two short white feathery stigmas which spread and project laterally either side of the open floret, and three small stamens with filaments c. twice the anther length. The fruit (a *caryopsis* – typical of grasses) is droplet-shaped, slightly flattened, hairy at the top, and with a groove on one side. It is shed with its outer covering, the *pericarp* (the outer persistent casing of the ovary wall) still firmly attached. Flowering May-August. Widespread throughout the British Isles and very common in most of lowland Britain, especially England and Wales. Rare or absent in central and northern parts of mainland Scotland, somewhat scattered in central Ireland but common elsewhere. Occurs in grassy open habitats including hay meadows, lawns and road verges and in more disturbed habitats such as arable fields and headlands, waste ground, dockland and spoil tips. Also coastal cliffs, shingle beaches, sandy places near the sea. Most of the habitats are associated with human activity and tend to have moderately fertile, neutral soils.

Pollination Highly self-fertilising but occasional cycles of outbreeding may occur through wind.

Regeneration strategy Seed, shed locally, or carried by animals on feet or fur.

Weed control Small pre-flowering invasions are easily pulled up, composted, or burned. Follow current best, preferably organic, practice for large invasions (see Bibliography and internet).

Herbal, culinary, cultural and folklore None found.

1) Typical growth habit 2) young flowering stems 3) close-up of spikelets

Barren Brome *(Bromus sterilis, Anisantha sterilis)*

Native, or an early introduction. Annual. Stem (*culm*) green or grey-green, usually erect or almost so, jointed (*noded*), height 80-120 cm. Leaves green or slightly purplish, softly hairy, downy-edged, tending to curve downwards. Leaf sheaths tubular, soon splitting. Leaf blades flat, pointed, 2-7 mm wide and 5-25 cm long. The slender, ascending branches of the flower head (*panicle*) later become lax and open, or rather drooping, 11-2 cm in length, sometimes as short as 8 or as long as 26 cm. Usually smooth, slightly rough or softly hairy, with 12-16 (sometimes only six or as many as 18) individual oblong flower units (*spikelets*). Excluding *awns* (bristle-like projections) the spikelets open out and become wedge-shaped in outline at maturity, 24-36 mm in length, sometimes as short as 20 or as long as 43 mm. Each spikelet has four to ten, sometimes up to 12 flowers (*florets*), of which the apical two to four florets are sterile. At the base of the spikelet there is a pair of scales (*glumes*). The lower glume narrow, spear-shaped, 9-13 mm in length, sometimes as short as 7 or as long as 15 mm. The upper glume also spear-shaped, 12.5-19.5 mm in length, sometimes as short as 11 or as long as 22 mm. Above the glumes, within each spikelet, are five to 12, sometimes only four, or as many as 13 closely arranged hermaphrodite flowers (*florets*). The florets have two basal scales: a lower scale (the *lemma*) and an upper scale (the *palea*). The lemma has a long slender bristle-like projection (*awn*), 15-22 mm in length, sometimes as short as 13 or as long as 35 mm. Otherwise the floret comprises mostly reproductive parts: an ovary with usually two very small paired *lodicules* at the base (probably vestigial petals/sepals), two short, white feathery stigmas which spread and project laterally on either side of the open floret, and three stamens with filaments and elongate anthers of similar length. The fruit (a *caryopsis* – typical of grasses) is droplet-shaped, slightly flattened, hairy at the top, and with a groove on one side; it is shed with its outer covering, the *pericarp* (the outer persistent casing of the ovary wall) still firmly attached. Flowering May-August. Widespread and abundant throughout lowland Britain. Largely confined to the east of Scotland and the south-east of Ireland. Occurring near and in hedgerows, and a wide variety of disturbed habitats such as roadsides, waste ground, field margins, railway embankments, building sites, and rough open grassland. Most frequent on moderately fertile, well-drained soils. Although principally a lowland species, it has been recorded at 365 m above sea level in Derbyshire.

217

Pollination Largely self-pollinated but also by wind.

Regeneration strategy Seed, shed locally, or carried by animals on feet or fur, or by humans on shoes, clothing, or vehicle tyres.

Weed control Small pre-flowering invasions are easily pulled up, or dug out, then composted, or burned. Follow current best, preferably organic, practice for large invasions (see Bibliography and internet).

Herbal, culinary, cultural and folklore The 'barren' in the common name refers to its negative agricultural productivity, rather than its reproductive capability.

1) Hedgerow population 2) flowering stems (panicles) of spikelets 3) spikelets on long slender stalks 4) young flower spikelets

Cock's-foot *(Dactylis glomerata)*

Native. Perennial with fibrous, prominently clustered roots to a depth of 50 cm, and compressed vegetative shoots. Stem (*culm*) erect, or ascending, jointed (*noded*), strong and sturdy, green or greyish-green, up to 120-140 cm in height, sometimes as short as 15 or as tall as 145 cm. Leaves long, folded at first, sharply pointed (2-14 mm wide and 10-45 cm long). Lower leaf sheaths and upper leaves keeled, with pronounced central dorsal ridge (*rib*). The flower heads (*panicles*) one-sided to erect, oblong-ovate, 3-25 cm long, sometimes up to 30 cm from top to lower branches, and green, purplish or light yellowish. Upper flowering branches closer together than lower branches, somewhat denser and more nodding at maturity, 2-12.5 cm long, sometimes up to 18 cm. Branches erect, spreading or sometimes deflexed. Individual flower spikelets oblong or wedge-shaped, 4.5-7.5 long, sometimes up to 9.5 mm. Spikelets have a basal pair of membranous scales (*glumes*). Glumes slightly bristly on central 'keel', lanceolate-ovate, finely pointed. Lower glume 3-6 mm long, upper glume 3.5-7 mm long. Above the glumes, within a spikelet, are two to five closely arranged hermaphrodite flowers (*florets*). A floret has two basal scales: a lower scale (the *lemma*) and an upper scale (the *palea*). The lanceolate lemma has a short bristle-like projection (*awn*). Otherwise the floret comprises mostly reproductive parts: an ovary with two very small paired *lodicules* at the base (probably vestigial petals/sepals), two long white feathery stigmas which spread and project laterally on either side of the open floret, and three stamens with anthers three times the length of the filaments and, unusually, either creamy or purple-coloured, the latter giving a striking appearance to the flowering stems. The fruit (a *caryopsis* – typical of grasses) is droplet-shaped, slightly flattened, hairy at the top, with a groove on one side. It is shed with its outer covering, the *pericarp* (the outer persistent casing of the ovary wall) still firmly attached. Flowering June-September, sometimes as early as January or as late as December. Occurs throughout the British Isles and, except for parts of the Scottish highlands, is common, often abundant, in a range of habitats, including meadows, pastures, down-land, rough grassland, hedgerows, woodland, riverbanks, coastal cliffs, and fixed dunes. It is also common in more man-made environments such as paths, roadsides, quarries, spoil tips, or manure heaps. Prefers neutral to basic soil (pH 5.0-8.0). Although a native species, it is a very variable grass, affected by a long history of cultivation, introduction and selection by plant-breeders, often from indigenous populations. The species can form huge tussocks in unmanaged sites.

Pollination Wind.

Regeneration strategy Almost exclusively by seed, which germinates in spring. The seed does not have great longevity (two to three years).

Weed control Small pre-flowering invasions of young plants can be pulled up, or dug out if roots too well established, then composted, or burned. Follow current best, preferably organic, practice for large invasions (see Bibliography and internet).

Herbal, culinary, cultural and folklore The common name Cock's-foot clearly alludes to the resemblance of the flower heads to a cockerel's foot.

218

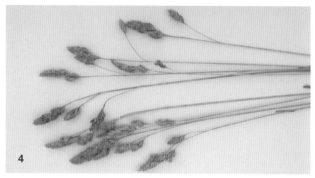

1) Typical growth and habitat 2) flowering head (panicle) with showy mauve stamens 3) panicle with yellow stamens 4) old, dead panicles

Yorkshire-fog *(Holcus lanatus)*

Native. Perennial. Loosely clustered stems (*culms*) slender to somewhat stout, often ascending from bent basal stem joints (*nodes*). Stems and leaves green or greyish, 20-80 cm in height (sometimes up to 120 cm), usually softly hairy, rarely almost smooth. Lower sheaths usually with soft reflexed hairs. Leaves 4-20 cm long, flat, 3-10 mm wide. Overall outline of flower head (*panicle*) ovate-to-lance-shaped and 3-20 cm long and 1-8 cm wide, dense to rather loose, erect or nodding. Very soft, whitish, pale green, or softly tinged with pink or mauve. Flower head branches slender and very divided. Individual flower spikelets short-stalked (1-4 mm long), spikelets oblong to elliptic, 4-6 mm long, and two-flowered. Each spikelet has a basal pair of scales (*glumes*) which are either equal or with the upper glume longer, broader, and as long as the spikelet. Glumes papery and finely rough or hairy. Lower glume narrowly ovate or oblong, upper glume ovate-elliptic and usually tipped with a short spike (*awn*), c. 1 mm long. Above the glumes, within each spikelet, are two closely arranged flowers (*florets*) which have two basal scales: a broadly ovate lower scale (the *lemma*) and an oblong upper scale (the *palea*). The lower floret, with an awnless lemma, is hermaphrodite with two very small paired *lodicules* at the base (probably vestigial petals/sepals), three stamens and a feathery, two branched stigma. The upper floret is usually male, with three short-filamented stamens and an awned lemma. The fruit (a *caryopsis* – typical of grasses) is droplet-shaped, slightly flattened, hairy at the top, and with a groove on one side. It is shed with its outer covering, the *pericarp* (the outer persistent casing of the ovary wall) still firmly attached. Flowering June-August. The most widespread grass in the British Isles, occurring almost everywhere. It is found in all types of grassland: hay meadows, rough pasture, chalk and limestone grassland, moorland, open woodland and scrub, hedgerows, stream sides, arable land, lawns, waste ground, and other man-made habits such as paths, rubbish heaps and by walls. Tolerant of a high range of soil types, although most abundant on moderately fertile soils (pH 5.0-6.0) which hold water reasonably well. From sea-level to 650 m (Cumberland) or, exceptionally, to 845 m (Westmorland).

Pollination Wind.

Regeneration strategy Prolific seed output with rapid germination but also with long viability for buried seed.

Weed control Small pre-flowering invasions of young plants can be pulled up, or dug out if roots are too well established, then composted, or burned. Follow current best, preferably organic, practice for large invasions (see Bibliography and internet).

Herbal, culinary, cultural and folklore Has value as a grazing grass, especially on poor soils unsuitable for more desirable grasses.

1) Young flower heads (panicles) 2) flowering group 3) flower panicles

Wall Barley *(Hordeum murinum* subsp. *murinum)*

Native. Annual. Stem (*culm*) light-to-mid-green, smooth, solitary, usually erect or slightly angled by bending at stem joints (*nodes* or *internodes*), height up to 50-70 cm. Lower stem sheaths densely and softly hairy, upper sheaths less so, or smooth. Leaves long, pointed, 2-20 cm, flat, 2.5-6.5 mm wide, light-to-mid-green, smooth or thinly hairy. The flower head (*panicle*) erect or slightly inclined, dense and laterally compressed, 4-8.5 cm long, sometimes up to 10.5 cm. Spikelets all about equal in size, the upper central spikelet more or less stalkless. Every spikelet has a basal pair of scales (*glumes*), these are bristle-like, long-awned (6-27 mm in length, sometimes as short as 15 or as long as 30 mm), and slightly flattened, with short, rough-haired margins. Spikelets have three flowers (*florets*), each with two basal scales: a lower scale (the *lemma*) and an upper scale (the *palea*). Both lemma and palea are narrowly lanceolate, graduating into long, stiff, finely bristled awns (25-62 mm long). Otherwise a floret comprises mostly reproductive parts: an ovary with two very small paired *lodicules* at the base (probably vestigial petals/sepals), two short, white feathery stigmas which spread and project laterally on either side of the open floret, and three long-filamented stamens. The fruit (a *caryopsis* – typical of grasses) is droplet-shaped, slightly flattened, hairy at the top, and with a groove on one side. It is shed with its outer covering, the *pericarp* (the outer persistent casing of the ovary wall) still firmly attached. It is more nutritive in seed than in flower, unlike all other annual grasses. Flowering late May-August, sometimes as late as October. Common and widespread throughout lowland England and Wales, including the Isles of Scilly and the Channel Islands. It extends along the east coast of Scotland as far north as East Ross but is absent from the west, as well as most of the British uplands (although, exceptionally, it has been recorded at 450 m above sea level in Westmorland), also absent from most of Ireland, excepting Dublin where it is increasing. It is almost exclusively associated with man-made, and/or urban environments: bases of buildings, building sites, demolition sites, roadsides, farmyards, pavements and footpaths. An example of a weed that takes advantage of additional light and inhospitable conditions presented by walkways and roads, to reduce competition from other weeds.

Pollination A self-pollinating winter annual.

Regeneration strategy Seed, shed locally or carried by animals on feet or fur, or by humans on shoes, clothing, or vehicle tyres. Seed germinating from mid-August, sometimes continuing into December.

Weed control Small pre-flowering invasions are easily pulled up, or dug out, then composted, or burned. Follow current best, preferably organic, practice for large invasions (see Bibliography and internet).

Herbal, culinary, cultural and folklore The botanical name *murinum*, is a reference to an old common name Mouse Barley: the Latin *murinus* means 'of mice and rats', and often used to include larger animals such as Martens, Stoats etc. – *not* derived from wall (Latin – *muralis*). The long bristly awns make them a source of school children's pranks, especially by getting the seed heads under another child's clothing to cause minor misery, or throwing the heads as darts.

1) Typical opportunistic habitat 2) young flower heads (panicles) of spikelets 3) close-up of young panicle

Perennial Rye-grass, Ray-grass *(Lolium perenne)*

Native. Perennial. Loosely to densely clustered vegetative shoots ('tufted'), without rhizomes. Stem *(culm)* smooth, jointed *(noded)*, green, erect or almost so, 70-90 cm in height. Leaves green, hairless, lower leaf sheaths smooth. Stem bases usually pinkish when young. Upper leaf blades pointed or blunt, folded when young, 3-20 cm long, 2-6 mm wide, with small narrow basal projections *(auricles)*. The flower head *(panicle)* straight, or slightly curved, stiff, slender, flattened, 10-20 cm in length, sometimes as short as 4 or as long as 30 cm. The central flower stem *(floral axis)* is regularly wavy to accommodate the stalkless flowering units *(spikelets)* alternately arranged on either side of the stem; the spikelets are oblong-ovate and 7-20 mm long. Each spikelet has one basal scale, an upper *glume*. Apart from the topmost spikelet, which has both a lower and an 'upper' glume (the two glumes are very similar), the upper glume is usually shorter than the spikelet and narrowly ovate to oblong-ovate, blunt-tipped, curved, and smooth. Above the glumes, within each spikelet, are four to 13, sometimes up to 14 closely arranged hermaphrodite flowers *(florets)*. Each floret has two basal scales: a lower scale (the *lemma*) and an upper scale (the *palea*). The lemma is awn-less. Otherwise a floret comprises mostly reproductive parts: an ovary with two very small, paired *lodicules* at the base (probably vestigial petals/sepals), two short, white feathery stigmas which spread and project laterally on either side of the open floret, and three stamens with short filaments and long anthers. The fruit (a *caryopsis* – typical of grasses) is droplet-shaped, slightly flattened, with a groove on one side. It is shed with its outer covering, the *pericarp* (the outer persistent casing of the ovary wall) still firmly attached. Flowering May-August. An extremely common tough grass found throughout the British Isles in a wide range of grassy habitats. Abundant, often dominant in agriculturally improved lowland pasture, short-term meadowland and sports fields. Common in old meadows, on down land, water meadows, road verges and waste ground. Thrives best, with longer lived populations, in heavy, fertile, neutral soils, but will grow in slightly acidic or basic soils. Frequently sown with Red or White Clovers.

Pollination Wind.

Regeneration strategy Seed.

Weed control Small pre-flowering invasions are easily pulled up, or dug out, then composted, or burned. Follow current best, preferably organic, practice for large invasions (see Bibliography and internet).

Herbal, culinary, cultural and folklore Cultivated since at least the 17th Century, probably earlier.

1) Habit 2) young flower heads (panicles) with feathery pistils just showing in some flowers within the spikelets
3) panicles of open flowers showing stamens

Annual Meadow-grass, Annual Poa *(Poa annua)*

Native. Annual or short-lived perennial. Stems smooth, erect, spreading or prostrate, 3-35 cm in height, sometimes up to 45 cm. Sometimes with a spreading base and rooting at the *nodes* (stem joints), unbranched, or only near base. Basal leaf sheaths slightly flattened. Leaves green (in dry conditions may be slightly purplish), hairless, abruptly pointed or blunt, with a central *dorsal ridge* (rib), folded or opening out, 1-5 mm wide, often crinkled when young. Flower head (*panicle*) pale to light green, occasionally reddish tinged, outline ovate or triangular, open and loose, or rarely lightly contracted, 1-8.5 cm long, sometimes up to 13 cm, branches solitary or paired, rarely three together, spreading or slightly drooping at maturity. Flower branches short, smooth, in pairs or solitary, rarely three together, spreading or slightly drooping. Individual flower units (*spikelets*) ovate or oblong, 3-8 mm long, sometimes up to 10 mm. Each spikelet has a basal pair of scales (*glumes*): lower glume narrowly ovate (1.5-2.5 cm long, sometimes up to 3.5 mm), upper glume more broadly ovate (1.7-3.5 mm long, sometimes up to 4.7 mm), glumes more or less smooth. Above the glumes, within each spikelet, are three to eight, sometimes only two or as many as ten, closely arranged hermaphrodite flowers (*florets*). Each floret has two ovate basal scales: a lower scale (the *lemma*) and a slightly shorter upper scale (the *palea*). Otherwise the floret comprises mostly reproductive parts: an ovary with two very small paired *lodicules* at the base (probably vestigial petals/sepals), two short, white feathery stigmas which spread and project laterally on either side of the open floret, and three small, long-filamented stamens. The fruit (a *caryopsis* – typical of grasses) is droplet-shaped, slightly flattened, with a groove on one side. It is shed with its outer covering, the *pericarp* (the outer persistent casing of the ovary wall) still firmly attached. Flowering all year. Distributed throughout the British Isles but most common on cultivated land and in gardens, pathways or on waste land; a common constituent of grassland that is heavily grazed, mown or trampled. Will thrive in damp or dry places, in lightly or semi-shaded situations. Occurring on a wide range of basic to neutral soils, from coarse sands to heavy clay, avoiding only very acidic conditions. It is also found from near sea level to high, mountainous elevations.

Pollination Mainly self-pollination (c. 85%) or wind.

Regeneration strategy One of a few very common weeds that can come into flower at any time of year, unaffected by day length. It seeds throughout the year, and continuously replaces dying plants with new ones; flowering and setting seed occurs within six weeks of germination. Seed transported by animals, on vehicle tyres and soles of boots and shoes, or by rain-wash.

Weed control Small invasions are easily pulled up, or dug out; however, as it is nearly always flowering and seeding, bagging and taking to local garden waste recycling facility might be worthwhile. Follow current best, preferably organic, practice for large invasions (see Bibliography and internet).

Herbal, culinary, cultural and folklore Little found, except that one of its local names is Causeway Grass, reflecting the frequent occurrence of this species on pathways.

222

1) Typical habit 2) short, shallow roots 3) flowering stems (panicles) – old panicle to the left

Rough or Rough-stalked Meadow-grass *(Poa trivialis)*

Native. Perennial. 75-90 cm in height, sometimes as short as 20 or as tall as 100 cm. Densely clustered, tufted vegetative shoots, outer stems often ascending from a spreading base, rooting at the joints (*nodes*) to produce short creeping stolons. Lower leaf sheaths usually slightly rough, but sometimes smooth. Leaves green, sometimes purplish, smooth, abruptly pointed, 3-20 cm long, flat or folded and 2-4.5 mm, sometimes up to 6 mm wide. Flower head (*panicle*) erect or nodding, open and very loose, or contracted and rather dense, 6-20 cm long, sometimes as short as 3 cm. Flower head ovate or oblong in outline, up to 15 cm wide and green, reddish or purplish. Flower branches rough, in clusters of three to six or seven to nine on lowest branches. Individual flower units (*spikelets*) ovate to elliptic, 3-4.5 mm long, sometimes up to 6 mm. Each spikelet has a basal pair of scales (*glumes*): lower glume narrowly ovate, 2-3 mm long, sometimes as short as 1.7 mm. Upper glume more broadly ovate, 2.2-3.5 mm long. Glumes slightly rough, with sharp-pointed tips. Above the glumes, within each spikelet, are two to four closely arranged hermaphrodite flowers (*florets*). Each floret has two ovate basal scales: a lower scale (the *lemma*) and a slightly shorter upper scale (the *palea*), both awn-less. Otherwise the floret comprises mostly reproductive parts: an ovary with two very small, paired *lodicules* at the base (probably vestigial petals/sepals), two white feathery stigmas which spread and project laterally on either side of the open floret, and three stamens with filaments and anthers of similar length. The fruit (a *caryopsis* – typical of grasses) is droplet-shaped, slightly flattened, with a groove on one side. It is shed with its outer covering, the *pericarp* (the outer persistent casing of the ovary wall) still firmly attached. Flowering May-July. Widely distributed throughout the British Isles, in a wide range of habitats. Very common in meadows and pastures, especially in moist fertile lowland habitats including marshes, edges of ponds and streams, sometimes appearing to be semi-aquatic, but always well-rooted in the bankside. A frequent coloniser of both waste and cultivated land, and a weed of cereal crops, and cultivated grassland. It also occurs in woodland margins, hedgerows and scrub, in all but driest, least fertile, or very acidic soils. From sea level to 1065 m (Inverness).

Pollination A flexible breeding system, normally cross-pollinating (wind), but also self-pollinates.

Regeneration strategy Produces huge numbers of seed, germinating in spring or in autumn. Seed transported by animals, on vehicle tyres and soles of boots and shoes or by rain-wash.

Weed control Small invasions of young or pre-flowering plants are fairly easily pulled up, or dug out, however, to avoid the risk of introducing seed into the composter, bagging and taking to local garden waste recycling facility should be considered. Follow current best, preferably organic, practice for large invasions (see Bibliography and internet).

Herbal, culinary, cultural and folklore None found.

223

1) Stem bases and root system 2) flowering heads (panicles) 3) flower spikelets

APPENDICES

APPENDIX
Summary descriptions of the plant families

See main illustrations and descriptions for more information on the British weed species referred to below. Data follow Angiosperm Phylogeny Group 2009 (and later modifications), Stace 2010 (Third Edition), and Mabberley 2009 (Third Edition).

NON-FLOWERING PLANTS

1. **EQUISETACEAE** (HORSETAIL FAMILY) *page 34*
An early evolving, non-flowering, group of plants, the Horsetails, represented by a single genus of 15, almost cosmopolitan, species including Field Horsetail (*Equisetum arvense*).

2. **DENNSTAEDTIACEAE** (BRACKEN FAMILY) *page 35*
A small cosmopolitan family of ten genera and c. 230 species worldwide; of these only one species, the globally widespread and invasive Bracken (*Pteridium aquilinum*), is represented in the British flora.

DICOTYLEDONS

3. **ADOXACEAE** (VIBURNUM FAMILY) *page 38*
A small family of four genera and c. 225 species worldwide; occurring in temperate to warm climates and tropical mountains. Life forms: perennial herbaceous, shrubs and small trees. Only a few species in three of the four genera: *Adoxa*, *Sambucus* and *Viburnum* are represented in the British Flora, including Elder or Bourtree (*Sambucus nigra*), a widespread invasive, short-lived shrub.

4. **AMARANTHACEAE** (GOOSE-FOOT FAMILY) *page 39*
A moderately sized family of 175 genera and c. 2000 species, with a worldwide distribution, mainly in the tropics or warm temperate zones. Life forms: mostly herbaceous, but some are climbers, shrubs or, rarely, trees. About 58 cool temperate zone species occur naturally in the British Isles, only a few are considered weedy. A further 17 alien species of genus *Amaranthus* arrived in the UK at various times, via raw wool, or in birdseed, or soya bean waste, including one well-established weed, Common Amaranth (*Amaranthus retroflexus*).

5. **APIACEAE** (CARROT FAMILY) *page 44*
A large cosmopolitan family of c. 428 genera and c. 3500 species, mostly occurring in northern temperate areas and tropical mountains. Life forms: mainly herbaceous, but there are some shrubs and trees. In the British native flora there are c. 50 genera and about 70 species, of these only five species are widespread weeds, including one alien species Giant Hogweed (*Heracleum mantegazzianum*).

6. **ARALIACEAE** (IVY FAMILY) *page 50*
A moderate-sized, mainly tropical family, of 39 genera and c. 1425 species. Most species are tropical, notably in Indo-Malaysia and tropical America, although a small number of species occur in temperate regions. Life forms: herbaceous, lianes, woody epiphytes, shrubs and trees. In the British flora there are two species with climbing stems: Common Ivy (*Hedera helix*) and Irish Ivy (*Hedera hibernica*).

7. **ASTERACEAE** (DAISY FAMILY – previously Compositae) *page 51*
The largest of all the flowering plant families worldwide, with about 1600 genera and c. 23,600 species. Different species occupy a wide range of habitats, and exhibit a remarkable range of life forms: herbaceous, climbers, shrubs, and trees. In the British flora there are just over 100 almost entirely herbaceous genera, and about 700 native, or introduced, species; by far the largest native genus in Britain is *Hieraceum*, with over 400 species. Among the British members of this well-represented family there are about 30 widespread weedy species.

8. **BALSAMINIACEAE** (BALSAM FAMILY) *page 82*
A moderate-sized family of two genera (*Impatiens* and *Hydrocera*) and c. 1000 almost entirely herbaceous species; mainly Old World tropical, but with a few temperate species. The British flora includes three species of Balsam (*Impatiens*), all three are non-native but only *Impatiens glandulifera* (Indian Balsam) causes major problems.

9. **BORAGINACEAE** (BORAGE FAMILY) *page 83*
A moderate to large almost cosmopolitan family with 142 genera and 2450 species. Life forms: many herbaceous species, as well as shrubs, and trees. The British flora has 19 genera and just over 50 species, all are herbaceous. Of these species only a few are generally considered to be frequent weeds.

10. **BRASSICACEAE** (CABBAGE FAMILY – previously Cruciferae) *page 87*
A large family of c. 320 genera and over 3,400 species, especially widespread in temperate zones, notably in the Mediterranean, central Asia, and western North America. Life forms: mostly herbaceous, less frequently lianes, shrubs or small trees. The British flora has 52 genera and c. 135 species, all are herbaceous, and a notable number of these are introduced (non-native); about 15 species are considered to be widespread weeds.

11. **CANNABACEAE** (HEMP FAMILY) *page 102*
A small family of ten genera and 80 species which occur in either temperate or tropical regions. Life forms: herbaceous, lianes and trees. The British flora includes two species: *Cannabis sativa* (Cannabis – an introduced casual exploited for its tough fibres, birdseed and illicitly, on a small scale, as a drug) and *Humulus lupulus* (Hops) which is native to Britain, and has been used in the brewing industry since the 15th Century. The scrambling stems ('bines') of Hops are a common site in British hedgerows.

12. **CARYOPHYLLACEAE** (CAMPION & PINK FAMILY) *page 103*
A large cosmopolitan family of 85 genera and 2630 species, mostly occurring in the temperate and warm regions of the northern hemisphere. Life forms: the majority of species are herbaceous, more rarely shrubs, lianes, or even small trees. The British flora has c. 99 herbaceous species, in 24 genera, of which about one third are introduced (non-native); there about eight widespread weedy species.

13. **CONVOLVULACEAE** (BINDWEED FAMILY) *page 111*
A moderately sized cosmopolitan family of around 52 genera and 1650 species, mainly occurring in warm temperate to tropical areas. Life forms include many herbaceous climbers (always twining to the right), as well as lianes, herbs, shrubs and, rarely, trees. The British flora includes 11 species in four genera; of these two are widespread native weeds.

14. **CUCURBITACEAE** (BRYONY & CUCUMBER FAMILY) *page 113*
A small family of c. 122 genera and 940 species, mainly occurring in tropical, subtropical, or warm temperate regions, but with a few cool temperate species. Life forms: most members of the family are juicy-stemmed climbers or trailers often with coiled tendrils or, rarely, somewhat woody or tree-like. The family is well-known throughout the world for species with often large, edible fruits, including melons, squashes, pumpkins, cucumbers, courgettes, and gourds as well as loofahs – the fibrous fruit 'skeletons' of *Luffa cylindrica*. In the British Isles there are six introduced species, but only one native species, *Bryonia dioica*, which bears berries, not gourd-like fruits. In some regions it is a troublesome hedgerow weed.

15. **ERICACEAE** (HEATHER FAMILY) *page 114*
A large cosmopolitan family (excluding deserts), usually montane in tropical regions; there are c. 117 genera and 3850 species. Life forms: most species are shrubs or trees, less often lianes or sub-herbaceous, many species are acid-lovers. There are 42 species in the British flora of which c. 50% are native. Only one species is a widespread and seriously troublesome weed: Rhododendron (*Rhododendron ponticum*).

16. **EUPHORBIACEAE** (SPURGE FAMILY) *page 116*
A large cosmopolitan family of c. 229 genera and 6500 species. Many life forms including herbaceous, lianes, shrubs, trees, and some succulents; stems and leaves often with milky latex. In the British flora there are only about 21 species in three genera: *Euphorbia* (most), *Mecurialis* and the shrubby *Ricinus* (Castor-oil-plant), an introduced species of Asian origin. Of these, five *Euphorbia* species are widespread weeds.

17. **FABACEAE** (PEA FAMILY – previously Leguminosae) *page 121*
A very large cosmopolitan family of 720 genera and about 19,500 species, the third largest flowering plant family in the world, and one of the most important of all food plant families (peas, lentils and pulses), second only to the grasses. Many life forms including trees, shrubs, lianes and herbaceous; sometimes thorny, often with root nodules containing nitrogen-fixing bacteria. The family is well-represented in the British flora with c. 152 species, including both native and introduced species. About eight species are widespread weeds.

18. **GERANIACEAE** (GERANIUM FAMILY) *page 129*
A small family of five genera and 650 species, some are subtropical but most occur in the temperate regions. Life forms: herbaceous or shrubs (some with swollen stems). Many species and their numerous cultivars are highly valued in horticulture; geranium oil (notably from the South African *Pelargonium graveolens*) is much prized. The highly popular and colourful horticultural bedding 'geraniums' are bred from *Pelargonium* species, not botanical *Geranium* species. The British flora includes 41 species (25 are non-native) in three genera: *Erodium*, *Geranium* and *Monsonia*; of these only four species of *Geranium* are widespread weeds.

19. **HYPERICACEAE** (ST. JOHN'S-WORT FAMILY) *page 133*
A small cosmopolitan family of eight genera and 480 species. Life forms: some trees, but mostly shrubs and herbs. The British flora includes about 20 species all in the genus *Hypericum*; 12 of these species are native and eight have been introduced, of these only two native species are widespread weeds.

20. **LAMIACEAE** (DEAD-NETTLE FAMILY – previously Labiatae) *page 136*
A large cosmopolitan family, excluding high altitudes and latitudes, comprising 238 genera and 6500 species. Life forms: usually trees, shrubs or herbaceous, rarely lianes. Many species highly valued for their aromatic oils, e.g. mints, thymes and basils, or for their horticultural merit, notably salvias, with more than 800 species. The British flora includes 84 species (of which c. one third are non-native) in 27 genera; of these, seven species are recognised as widespread weeds.

21. **MALVACEAE** (MALLOW FAMILY) *page 143*
A large cosmopolitan family, especially in the tropics, of 113 genera and 5000 species. Life forms: trees (often with fibrous bark) including the well-known swollen trunked baobabs (*Adansonia* species), shrubs, including cotton (the fluffy-seeded *Gossypiums*), and many herbaceous species. Genera (and their species or cultivars) well-known to horticulture include *Abutilon*, *Alcea* (hollyhocks), *Lavatera*(s), *Hibiscus*, *Malva* (mallows) and *Sidalcea*. The British flora includes 27 species (in nine genera); of these only nine species are native, the remainder have been introduced, largely reflecting their popularity as garden introductions. Two species of *Malva* are recognised as widespread weeds.

22. **ONAGRACEAE** (WILLOWHERB FAMILY) *page 145*
A small cosmopolitan family, notably in the temperate-to-warm Americas, comprising 22 genera and 656 species. Life forms: mainly herbaceous or shrubs, rarely trees (e.g. *Fuchsia excorticata* – New Zealand *Fuchsia* 'Kotukutuku' which grows up to 15 m high). Many species cultivars well-known in horticulture, especially in the genera *Fuchsia*, *Oenothera* (Evening Primrose), *Clarkia* and the (now illegal to bring into UK) highly invasive Water Primrose *Ludwigia hexapetala* (= *L. grandiflora*). The British flora includes c. 29 species (in seven genera). Nine species are recognised as widespread weeds.

23. **OXALIDACEAE** (WOOD-SORREL FAMILY) *page 154*
A small, mainly tropical and subtropical family, with a few temperate species, comprising five genera and 565 species; distributed in Asia, Africa, and tropical America. Life forms: mainly herbaceous with bulbs or tubers, but also shrubs and small trees. Numerous species and cultivars of *Oxalis* are well-known to horticulture, an intriguing genus because of the ability of the leaflets to fold downward at night or in cold weather. The British flora includes one genus, *Oxalis*, and 15 species, the only native species is the exquisite Wood-sorrel

– *Oxalis acetosella*. All other species are introduced, including a number of local nuisance weeds, as well as the three most widespread: *Oxalis exilis*, *O. corniculata* and *O. debilis*.

24. **PAPAVERACEAE** (POPPY FAMILY) *page 157*
A small family comprising 43 genera and 820 species; predominantly northern temperate but, notably, there are also species in Australia, mountainous tropical Africa, South Africa and South America. Life forms: predominantly herbaceous, scramblers, sub-shrubs or low-growing swollen-trunked (*pachycaul*) trees. A family best known to horticulture for many colourful species of *Papaver* (poppies), including Opium Poppies, harvested for their alkaloid (notably morphine) rich latex, and also for their non-opiate seeds which are used in baking. The British flora includes 12 genera and 32 species, of which c. 20 species are native, or very old introductions. Five widespread weedy species are recognised.

25. **PLANTAGINACEAE** (PLANTAIN, SPEEDWELL & TOADFLAX FAMILY) *page 162*
A moderate-to-large cosmopolitan family of 101 genera and c. 1900 species. Life forms: usually herbaceous, less often shrubs, or aquatics. There are many well-known horticultural cultivars of genera such as *Hebe*, *Digitalis* (foxgloves), *Bacopa*, *Penstemon*, *Linaria*, *Veronica* and *Antirrhinum*. The British flora includes 11 genera and c. 64 species, about half of which are native. Twelve widespread weedy species are recognised, including six species of *Veronica*.

26. **POLYGONACEAE** (DOCK & KNOTWEED FAMILY) *page 174*
A moderately sized family of 46 genera and c. 1200 species; more or less cosmopolitan, especially in the temperate northern hemisphere. Life forms: herbaceous, lianes, shrubs and trees; stipules of leaves often conspicuous, and united as a thin, dry sheath (*ocrea*) around the stem. Well-known examples include the knotweeds – notably the invasive Japanese Knotweed (*Fallopia japonica*), Russian-vine (*Fallopia baldschuanica*) and Docks. The British flora includes nine genera and c. 64 species, about half of which are native. Ten widespread weedy species are recognised.

27. **PRIMULACEAE** (PRIMROSE FAMILY) *page 184*
A large family of 60 genera and c. 2575 species with a sub-cosmopolitan distribution, especially in the tropics and northern hemisphere. Life forms: herbs, sub-shrubs, and evergreen trees with strikingly swollen trunks in some species. A number of species are well-known to horticulture including many species, and cultivars, of *Primula*, *Dodecatheon* and *Cyclamen*. The British flora includes nine genera and c. 30 species, of which about 50% are native. One much loved but widespread weed, Scarlet Pimpernel, is recognised.

28. **RANUNCULACEAE** (BUTTERCUP FAMILY) *page 185*
A moderately sized family of 56 genera and 2100 species, mainly northern temperate and boreal. Life forms: herbaceous, sometimes aquatic, lianes (for example some *Clematis* species), and small shrubs. A number of genera include species well-known to horticulture, such as *Helleborus*, *Aconitum*, *Anemone*, globe flowers (*Trollius*), Love-in-a-mist (*Nigella*), and *Aquilegia*. The British flora includes 65 species in 18 genera of which c. 45 species are native. Four widespread weedy species are recognised.

29. **ROSACEAE** (ROSE FAMILY) *page 189*
A large family of 85 genera and 3000 species (unusually, including many species produced asexually). A sub-cosmopolitan distribution, especially in the temperate and warm northern hemisphere. Life forms: herbaceous, climbing/rambling, shrubs and trees. Many genera well known in horticulture including *Malus* (apples), *Pyrus* (pears), *Rosa*, *Spiraea*, *Pyracantha*, *Kerria*, *Fragraria* (strawberries), *Alchemilla* and *Cydonia* (quinces). The British flora includes 36 genera and c. 290 species (excluding the Bramble/Blackberry complex). Less than half the species are native. Four or five widespread weedy species are recognised.

30. **RUBIACEAE** (BEDSTRAW & GOOSEGRASS FAMILY) *page 194*
A very large family of 563 genera and 10,900 species with a cosmopolitan distribution, especially in warm and tropical regions. Life forms: herbaceous, lianes, some epiphytes, shrubs and trees and, rarely, aquatic. Well-known genera and species include *Gardenia*, *Coffea* (coffee) and *Rubus tinctoria* (Madder). The British flora includes 24 species in eight genera, the majority are native, the most well represented genus is *Galium* and includes Lady's Bedstraw (*Galium verum*) and Sweet Woodruff (*Galium odoratum*). Two widespread weedy species are recognised.

31. SCROPHULARIACEAE (BUDDLEIA & VERBASCUM FAMILY) *page 196*
A moderately sized family of 54 genera and c. 1800 species distributed in warm to tropical regions, especially South Africa, and some temperate species. Life forms: herbaceous, shrubs (rarely epiphytic), small trees and the mainly mud-loving to aquatic genus *Limosella*. Well-known horticultural genera include Buddleia or Butterfly Bush (*Buddleja*), *Diascia*, *Nemesia*, *Verbascum* and *Phygelius*. The British flora includes 31 species in six genera; some are native to Britain, but many have been introduced. Only one widespread weedy species, the Butterfly Bush (*Buddleja davidii*) is recognised.

32. SOLANACEAE (NIGHTSHADE FAMILY) *page 197*
A large sub-cosmopolitan family of 91 genera and 2,450 species, especially well-represented in tropical America. More than half the species in the family are in the genus *Solanum*. Life forms: herbaceous, lianes, shrubs and trees. An economically important family which includes tomatoes (*Lycopersicon esculentum*), potatoes (*Solanum tuberosum*) the fourth most important food crop worldwide, capsicums and chillies (various species of genus *Capsicum*), aubergines (*Solanum melongena*), husk tomatoes (*Physalis pubescens*), the once very popular flower arrangers' Chinese Lantern Plant (*Physalis alkekengi*), and tobacco (*Nicotiana tabacum*). The British flora includes 31 species in 11 genera; almost all are introduced. Three widespread weeds are recognised.

33. URTICACEAE (NETTLE FAMILY) *page 200*
A moderately sized family of 55 genera and 1650 species, mainly tropical, but a few in the temperate zones. Unusually, this is a family with predominantly dioecious, less frequently monoecious, flowers in inflorescences that have (usually) evolved for wind-pollination. The male flowers of many species have stamens which spring back as the flower opens to shed their pollen explosively. More than half the species are in the two very large genera *Elatostema* (c. 300 species) and *Pilea* (c. 650 species). Life forms: herbaceous, lianes, shrubs, and a few tree species (some with swollen trunks). The stem fibres of some species have economic importance, notably *Urtica dioica* (Stinging Nettle), and *Boemeria nivea* (ramie, or China Grass). The British flora includes five species in three genera; three species are recognised as widespread weeds.

34. VIOLACEAE (VIOLET FAMILY) *page 203*
A small almost cosmopolitan family of 24 genera and 700 species, although in the tropics many species tend to be restricted to higher mountainous areas; the major exception is the large genus *Viola* (c. 400 species) which only occurs in the temperate zones. Life forms: mainly herbaceous or shrubs, a few climbers, and trees. Many species of *Viola* (pansies and violets) are much valued by horticulturalists and gardeners, and there are innumerable cultivars. The African Violet (*Saintpaulia ionantha*) is not related, and in another family – Gesneriaceae. The British flora includes 15 species of *Viola* and, with the exception of one introduction: the delicately long-petalled, pale mauve *Viola cornuta*, a native of the Pyrenees, and the hybrid garden pansy *Viola* x *wittrockiana*, which has innumerable variants, the remaining 13 species are native. A slight exception is *Viola arvensis*, introduced to Britain before 1500AD (an archaeophyte), a species which is a widespread field weed.

35. AMARYLLIDACEAE (ONION & DAFFODIL FAMILY) *page 206*
A small family of 60 genera and 900 species, mainly warm temperate and subtropical, notably South Africa and the Andes, and warmer regions of Europe. Life forms: perennial herbs with bulbs, rarely rhizomes, e.g. *Clivia*. Leaves smooth, usually flat, fleshy and sheathing at base. Many genera have species much prized in horticulture, notably the bulb industry, e.g. *Narcissus*, *Hymenocallis*, *Clivia*, *Amaryllis*, *Hippeastrum*, *Crinum*, *Nerine*, and *Galanthus* (snowdrops). The British flora includes 63 species in 13 genera, the great majority are introduced, except for seven of the 21 species of *Allium*, one species of *Lecojum* and one species of *Narcissus* are native. Two of the native species of *Allium* are widespread weeds.

228

36. ARACEAE (WILD ARUM FAMILY) *page 208*
A large family of 105 genera and 3250 species, mostly tropical and subtropical, with a few temperate species. Life forms: herbaceous – often enormous, with corms or tubers, climbers with aerial roots, or scrambling shrubs, rarely true epiphytes or free-floating aquatics. A number of species are well-known to horticulture including *Monstera deliciosa* (which also has an edible spadix), and Arum Lilies (*Zantedeschia aethiopica*) which have long been prized for their pure white spadices; species of *Colocasia*, *Xanthosoma*, *Alocasia*, *Amorphophallus* and *Cyrtosperma* are grown throughout the tropics for their starchy swollen tuberous corms as subsistence food. The British flora includes seven species, including *Zantedeschia*, in six genera; all these species are introduced with exception of Lords and Ladies (*Arum maculatum*), which is also a widespread weed.

37. ASPARAGACEAE (ASPARAGUS & BLUEBELL FAMILY) *page 209*
A large sub-cosmopolitan family of 103 genera and 2250 species, occupying a range of habitats including arid regions. Life forms: herbaceous, some with rhizomes, corms or bulbs, some very poisonous, lianes, swollen-stemmed shrubby forms, for example some *Dracaena* species, very large thick ovate leaves in rosettes, often with very spiny margins (e.g. *Agave*). In British horticulture some species of *Yucca*, *Agave*, *Hosta*, *Muscari* and *Scilla* are often cultivated, and *Asparagus* shoots are a perennial table delicacy during early summer; *Aspidistra* – beloved of Victorians for their parlours, is also a member of this family. The British flora includes 38 species in 13 genera, of which about one third are native. The only widespread weed, is the Hybrid Bluebell (*Hyacinthoides* x *massartiana*).

38. JUNCACEAE (RUSH FAMILY) *page 212*
A small family of 7 genera and 430 species; worldwide but mainly cool temperate regions, and cool zones of tropical mountains in damp habitats. Life forms: herbaceous, leaves usually glabrous but hairy in *Luzula*; rhizomatous, with erect stems, leaves either cylindrical or flat and grass-like. The British flora includes 39 species in two genera: *Luzula* and *Juncus*; almost all are native. One species of *Luzula* is considered to be a widespread weed.

39. CYPERACEAE (SEDGE FAMILY) *page 213*
A large cosmopolitan family of 92 genera and 4450 species, mainly in the temperate zones. Life forms: usually herbaceous rhizomatous perennials, rarely annuals, liana-like, or swollen-stemmed shrubby forms (Dracaena-like). Many economically valuable species including: *Cyperus papyrus* (used since ancient times for paper-making), *Elaeocharis tuberosa* (Chinese Water-chestnut), and Galingale (*Cyperus longus*) with sweet-scented rhizomes used in perfumery (not to be confused with Galangal, a member of the ginger family used in Asian cuisine). The British flora includes 113 native species of *Carex* and one introduced species: *Carex vulpinoidea*. Only one species, *Carex pendula*, is considered a widespread weed.

40. POACEAE (GRASS FAMILY – previously Gramineae) *page 214*
A very large cosmopolitan family of 715 genera and 10,550 species, ranging from the Polar Circle to the Equator. Across the vast range of grass species, there are species adapted to survive and thrive in almost any ecological and/or climatic conditions; it is the most widely distributed and ecologically most dominant family in the world. Life forms: usually perennial, with fibrous root systems, often rhizomatous, or branching, often at ground level, to form rosettes or tussocks, that help such species to survive trampling and grazing. Grass species range from small annuals, e.g. Annual Meadow-grass (*Poa annua*) to huge Bamboos up to 40 m (130 ft). Economically, worldwide, it is the most valuable of all plant families – it provides all the cereal crops, including three of the four most important food crops in the world: wheat (*Tricitum aestivum*), maize (*Zea mays*), and rice (*Oryza sativa*); it also provides most of the world's sugar (*Saccharum officinarum*). Bamboo (*Bambusa*) species are traditionally used as building material in many parts of the world, and various grasses are used for thatch and matting or paper making. Grass is prized for lawns and playing fields, and is the major component species of pastureland. The British flora includes c. 265 species in 100 genera; almost half the species are introduced either via imported raw wool, seed (including bird seed) or as garden ornamentals, including Bamboo. Although there are a number of weedy species only about ten are nationally widespread.

GLOSSARY

Definitions are for words and abbreviations used in the text of the book or within the explanations in the Glossary

Achene – a small dry thin-walled fruit, not splitting when ripe and containing a single seed. In some species, notably of the Daisy family (Asteraceae), the elongate achene has a bristly or feathery parachute-like structure to encourage wind dispersal of the seed. (See also **beak**, **pappus**.)

Actinomorphic – with radially symmetric flowers (e.g. buttercups, Herb Robert, mallows), or inflorescences (e.g. daisies). (See also **bilateral symmetry**, **radial symmetry**, **zygomorphic**.)

ADAS – Agricultural Development and Advisory Service. (See also **DEFRA**, **MAFF**.)

Adventitious – describing organs that arise in unexpected positions, such as stem buds growing on a root.

Agamospermy – production of viable seed without fertilisation having taken place. (See also **apomict**.)

Androecium – collective term for the stamens (the male reproductive organs) within a flower. (See also **gynoecium**, **stamens**.)

Angiosperms – flowering plants which almost all produce seeds enclosed within carpels. Ranging from weedy annuals, perennials, bulbous plants, climbers, shrubs to large trees, they are unique in the plant kingdom in undergoing a double fertilisation event. The degree of relationship between species of flowering plants has traditionally been mainly based on anatomical characters. Modern DNA sequencing has allowed greater understanding of relationships. Although the data often support accepted views on the closeness, or otherwise, of plant species, many relationships in the taxonomic hierarchy have been re-aligned following DNA analysis. (See also **gymnosperms**, **taxonomy** and **Bibliography: Angiosperm Phylogeny Group** website.)

Annual – the life cycle of the plant completed within 12 months from seed germination to death of plant.

Anther – apical portion of stamen, usually comprising four pollen sacs (locules), which produce the pollen grains. (See also **filament**, **locules**.)

Apomict/apomictic/apomixy/apomixis – an identified/named species (taxon) that reproduces either by agamospermy (the production of embryos and seeds without fertilisation) or asexually by vegetative reproduction for example bulbils, plantlets from stolons, leaves or fragmentation. (See also **agamospermy**, **bulbil**, **stolon**.)

Archaeophytes – plants arriving and becoming naturalised in the UK before 1500AD.

Aril – a fleshy or hairy outgrowth of a seed or ovule, commonly derived from the funiculus or hilum. It only becomes conspicuous following fertilisation. The most well-known example is 'mace', the aril surrounding a nutmeg (the seed). (See also **integument**.)

Autogamy/autogamous – self-pollination: most hermaphrodite flowers are able to self-pollinate if there are no insect visitors, however, self-fertilisation does not necessarily follow. There are many examples in Brassicaceae. (See also **chasmogamous**, **chasmogamy**.)

Axil (axillary) – the point/junction between (usually) the stem and a leaf (or other organ) that develops from a stem. (See also **runner**.)

Beak – the stalk-like structure associated with the achene pappus, notably in some species of family Asteraceae. (See also **achene**, **pappus**, **stalk**.)

Biennial – a plant completing its life cycle in two years: vegetative growth (leaves etc.) in first year, flowers, fruits and seeds in second year, before dying. (See also **annual**, **perennial**.)

Bilateral symmetry/bisymmetric/zygomorphic – flowers that have only one plane of symmetry, either side of an imaginary central line. Typical within families Fabaceae, Lamiaceae, Scrophulariaceae, and Violaceae. (See also **actinomorphic**.)

Bine – the flexible stem (UK) of a scrambling plant used to help it scramble or climb, e.g. Bindweeds and Hops. (See also **liane**.)

Bisexual – a flower with both male (stamens) and female (pistil and ovary) organs. (See also **hermaphrodite**, **perfect flower**.)

Bract – a leaf-like organ subtending an inflorescence. (See also **spathe**.)

Bulb – an underground storage organ; the bud(s) enclosed by fleshy scale leaves and/or leaf bases; for example, among the weeds: Ramsons (*Allium ursinum*), the Hybrid Bluebell (*Hyacinthus x massartiana*), and its parents, the English and Spanish Bluebells (*Hyacinthus non-scripta* and *H. hispanica*).

Bulbil – a small bulb, often in the axil of a leaf stem, sometimes on old flower heads, e.g. Crow Garlic (*Allium vineale*).

Calcicole – plants only growing on soils with lime. (See also **calcifuge**.)

Calcifuge – lime intolerant plants. (See also **calcicole**.)

Calyx – the sepals collectively. (See also **bract**, **epicalyx**, **involucre**.)

Capsule – a dry fruit composed of more than one carpel that opens to shed its seeds.

Carpel – the structure that holds and encloses the ovules in flowering plants – a single carpel is synonymous with a 'pistil' or an 'apocarpous gynoecium'. A group of carpels is termed a 'syncarpous gynoecium'.

Caryopsis – the small dry thin-walled fruit of grasses (Poaceae) comprising a single seed fused to the pericarp (the thin wall of the ripe ovary).

Casuals – species which are recent arrivals to the UK and have not, or may not, naturalise.

Chasmogamy/chasmogamous – the ability of a plant with open non-cleistogamous flowers to self-fertilise if no insect vectors are available to cross-pollinate, for example many species of Brassicaceae. However, seed set does not necessarily follow. (See also **autogamy**, **cleistogamous**, **cleistogamy**, **self-pollination**.)

Chirality – the property of a chemical, especially a crystal, of existing in left-handed and right-handed structural forms. (See also **tendril perversion**.)

Cleistogamy/cleistogamous – self-pollination in non-opening flowers: a well-known syndrome in many species of Violets. Among the weedy species Field Pansy (*Viola arvensis*) and in family Lamiaceae Henbit (*Lamium amplexicaule*). (See also **chasmogamous**, **chasmogamy**.)

Compositae – an older name for the Asteraceae, no longer accepted in modern plant systematics.

Compound – of an inflorescence comprising few to many smaller flowers; of leaves, comprising few to many smaller leaves/leaflets. (See also **simple flower**.)

Coprolites – phosphate-rich fossil dung of fish, reptiles and birds.

Corm – a short, swollen underground stem, that of the next year, arising at the top of the old one, and close to it; the protective brown scales surrounding the corm are the remains of the previous year's leaf bases. (See also **bulb**, **rhizome**.)

230

Corolla – the petals collectively. (See also **corolla tube**).

Corolla tube – a tube is formed when the margins of the individual petals are completely or partially fused. In some species the tube may be very long and/or very narrow, e.g. *Lamium amplexicaule*. (See also **corolla**.)

Cross-pollination – the transfer of pollen from the stamens of one individual to the pistil of another individual of the same species, to ensure outbreeding. This is achieved by intermediary agents, notably insects, wind, animals and, less commonly water.

Cruciferae – an older, now less frequently used name for the Brassicaceae (Cabbage family) and no longer accepted in modern plant systematics.

DEFRA – Department for Environment, Food & Rural Affairs – formed in June 2001 when the Ministry of Agriculture Fisheries and Food (MAFF) was merged with part of the Department of Environment, Transport and the Regions (DETR) and with a small part of the Home Office. (See also **ADAS**, **MAFF**.)

Dicotyledons/dicotyledonous – one of the two major groups of flowering plants, the other being Monocotyledons. The Dicotyledons are named because the germinating embryos (seeds) usually have two cotyledons. They may be either herbaceous, shrubby of trees. Other distinguishing characters include flower parts, usually in fours or fives, or multiples of, vascular bundles in a ring, and a primary root that develops into a tap root. (See also **monocotyledons**.)

Dioecious – with separate male and female plants. From the Greek, meaning living in separate houses. (See also **monoecious**).

Diploid – a nucleus or individual having two sets of chromosomes (twice the haploid number) in the nuclei of its somatic cells. (See also **haploid**, **gamete/gametophyte**, **meiosis**, **somatic**.)

Early land plants – single and multi-cellular green marine algae were the earliest forms of plant life to leave a watery environment and adapt to life on land. In the sea their cells were kept moist but on dry land they had to overcome a lack of constant moisture. An important advance in the conquest of land by plants was the evolution of vascular tissue which allowed water to be transported from ground level to tissue higher up the growing plant. The mosses (Bryophytes) are considered to be the most primitive of living plants – they lack a vascular system, which more evolved land plants possess, to transport water to their cells. Because of this they cannot gain height and must inhabit damp places.

Elaiosome – an oil-secreting structure, found on some fruits or seeds that attract ants as dispersal agents.

Electron microscopy – a parallel beam of electrons from an electron gun is used to illuminate the subject via a series of magnetic lenses. There are two types of electron microscope. The first is a scanning electron microscope – where electrons are bounced back off a thick section, or complete subject, and collected by an electron detector – of which there are various types, the most commonly used in biology being a secondary electron detector. The image produced is three-dimensional. In the other type of electron microscopy, 'transmission', the electrons penetrate through an ultrathin film (nanometres thick) of the subject. The resolving power of modern electron microscopes is in excess of 50,000 times higher than that of light transmitting microscopes. (See also **light microscope**.)

Endosperm – storage tissue in the seeds of most flowering plants, but not in any other seed plants. It is a compact triploid tissue without intercellular spaces; starch, hemicelluloses, proteins oils and fats are stored in endosperm.

Epicalyx – a calyx-like extra whorl of bracts positioned below the calyx. (See also **calyx**.)

Epidermis/epidermal – the outermost layer of cells.

Epiphyte – a plant growing on and attached to another plant without deriving nourishment from it.

Families of plants – plants, like other biological organisms, are grouped into taxonomic hierarchies based on the closeness of their genetic relationship to each other. For flowering plants the main groups are: angiosperm orders, followed by families, genera and species. (See also **taxonomy**.)

Filament – (in relation to stamen and anther) the stalk of a stamen bearing the anther at its apex. (See also **anther**, **stamen**.)

Floral symmetry – most flowers or compound flowers (e.g. daisies) have either bilateral or radial symmetry (see also **actinomorphic**, **zygomorphic**).

Flower – the reproductive unit of angiosperms consisting of stamens and carpels concentrated on a terminal axis of limited growth. The unit comprises a central axis (receptacle), and usually some non-essential floral parts (sepals, petals) surrounding the essential parts. (See also **carpels**, **petals**, **sepals**, **stamens**.)

Flower head – a general term often used loosely to describe an inflorescence. (See also **inflorescence**.)

Floral axis – the junction of the flower or inflorescence with the stem.

Fruit – the seed-bearing organ. It may have a single seed (e.g. daisies – achenes), or many seeds (e.g. poppies) and it may be fleshy (e.g. Wild Arum: one-seeded) or dry (e.g. the spurges: three-seeded).

Funiculus/funicle – the stalk attaching the ovule, and later the seed, to the placenta or ovary wall in angiosperms. It serves as an anchor and provides a vascular supply to the ovary and seed.

Galls – an abnormal localised swelling or outgrowth produced by a plant as a result of attack by a parasite. They may be caused by bacteria, fungi, nematodes, insects or mites.

Gamete/gametophyte – a cell or nucleus that may participate in sexual fusion to form a zygote. It is normally haploid and thus on fusion of two gametes a diploid zygote is formed. (See also **diploid**, **haploid**, **zygote**.)

Glume – the bracts, usually occurring in pairs, at the base of a grass or sedge spikelet. (See also **lemma**, **palea**, **spikelet**.)

Glyphosate – a non-selective organophosphate herbicide use to kill weeds in crops.

Gramineae – an older, now less frequently used name, for the Poaceae (Grass family), no longer accepted in modern plant systematics.

Gymnosperms – the other major group of seed plants, differing from angiosperms in having naked seeds with no carpellary structure and no double fertilisation event. Gymnosperms include araucarias, conifers, cycads, ephedras, gingkos, Gnetaceae and *Welwitschia*. (See also **angiosperms**.)

Gynodioecy/gynodioecious – having female and hermaphrodite flowers on separate plants. (See also **hermaphrodite**.)

Gynoecium – the female organs of a flower, comprising one or more pistils (stigma + style + ovary). Where there is only one pistil 'carpel', 'gynoecium' or 'syncarpous gynoecium' are synonymous.

Hair(s) – outgrowth(s) of the epidermis consisting of one or more elongated cells. (See also **epidermis**, **stinging hairs**.)

Haploid – a nucleus or individual with one set of chromosomes: i.e. only one representative of each chromosome of the chromosome complement. (See also **diploid**.)

Haploid/haplophytic generation – the gametophyte.

Herbarium – a collection of pressed and dried plants, labelled and systematically stored in a damp- and pest-free environment for scientific study. The Herbarium of the Royal Botanic Gardens, Kew, with at least eight million specimens, is not only the largest in the UK, but also one of the largest in the world.

Hermaphrodite – a flower (or animal) with both male and female organs. (See also **bisexual**, **perfect flower**.)

Heterogamous – with two kinds of flowers. Notably, in the Daisy family (Asteraceae/Compositae) the flower head is a mass of individual florets – the outer marginal 'ray florets' are usually unisexual or neuter, and the inner/central florets are usually bisexual/hermaphrodite. In some species of the Daisy family the flower heads do not have ray florets, or they are reduced, and un-showy.

Hilum – the scar left on a seed by the stalk of the ovule.

Hominid – man-like fossil, of the genus 'Homo' (man), an animal of the family Hominidae, comprising humans and their now extinct bi-pedal (two-footed) ancestors. More recently the family has been taken to include the four genera of great apes: Pongo, Gorilla, Pan and Bonobo.

Incompatibility – in flowering plants, failure to fertilise and subsequently set seed after pollination has occurred. (See also **pollination**.)

Indehiscent – (of fruits) not splitting open. (See also **fruit**.)

Inflorescence – a branching arrangement of (often small) flowers on the floral axis. The flowers may be highly condensed (e.g. daisies), or loosely grouped (e.g. lilac). (See also **compound**, **flower head**.)

Involucre – bracts, usually green, forming a more or less calyx-like structure around, and just below the base of a usually condensed inflorescence, notably in the Daisy family – Asteraceae. (See also **bract**, **calyx**, **epicalyx**.)

Labiatae – an older, now less frequently used name for the Lamiaceae (Dead-nettle family). No longer accepted in modern plant systematics.

Legume – a dry dehiscent fruit containing one or more seeds. It develops from a single carpel which, on ripening, splits along the ventral and dorsal sutures to form two valves, each bearing seeds alternately on the ventral margin. The ripe dry valves of the legume split open to release the seed. In some species the valves also twist during dehydration which dislodges any remaining seeds, for example, among the weedy species: Common Vetch (*Vicia sativa*) and Gorse (*Ulex europaea*). (See also **pod**, **silicula**, **siliqua**.)

Leguminosae - an older, now less frequently used name for the Fabaceae (Pea family). No longer accepted in modern plant systematics.

Lemma – the outermost of two bracts enclosing the grass flower. (See also **glume**, **palea**, **spikelet**.)

Liane(s) – the woody stem of a climber, notably in tropical forest habitat, that helps the plant to climb upwards to achieve greater access to light in the forest canopy. (See also **bine**.)

Light microscope – a microscope where the light is focused on the subject via a series of precision-ground glass lenses. The resolution is between 100 and 1500x. (See also **electron microscopy**.)

Locule – the cavity of the carpel in which the ovule or ovules are born. (See also **carpel**, **ovule**.)

231

MAFF – The Ministry of Agriculture, Fisheries & Food – a United Kingdom government department created by the Board of Agriculture Act 1889, and at that time called the *Board of Agriculture*. From 1903 it became the *Board of Agriculture and Fisheries*, and from 1919 the *Ministry of Agriculture and Fisheries*. It attained its final name in 1955 with the addition of responsibilities for the British food industry. This name lasted until the Ministry was dissolved in 2002, at which point its responsibilities had been merged into The Department for Environment, Food, and Rural Affairs. (See also **DEFRA**, **ADAS**.)

Micron/micrometer – a thousandth of a millimetre (abbreviation – µm). (See also **nanometre**.)

Meiosis – reduction division of the diploid cell to form four haploid cells. (See also **mitosis**, **zygote**.)

Mitosis – the process by which a cell divides to form two 'daughter' cells, each having a nucleus containing the same number of chromosomes with the same genetic composition as the original cell. (See also **meiosis**.)

Monocarpous – with a single carpel, for example in the pea family (Fabaceae) pea pods (although a pod may have one, or more ovules). (See also **apocarpous**, **ovules**, **pod**, **syncarpous**.)

Monocotyledons/monocotyledonous – one of the two major groups of flowering plants, the other being Dicotyledons. The Monocotyledons are named because the germinating embryos (seeds) usually have one cotyledon. Most are herbaceous, the stems lack secondary thickening and true trees do not occur, although some groups, such as the palms, have species with arborescent forms. Other distinguishing characters include flower parts usually in threes, or multiples of, scattered vascular bundles, and a fibrous root system. (See also **dicotyledons**.)

Monoecious – with separate male and female flowers on the same plant. From the Greek, meaning living in the same house. (See also **dioecious**.)

Morphology – the study of form, particularly of external structures. The introduction of the word is attributed to the poet Johann Wolfgang von Goethe (1749-1832), who also made very important contributions to botany and other branches of the natural sciences. (See **Bibliography**.)

Nanometer – a thousandth of a micron (a millionth of a millimetre).

Native species – plants already in the UK prior to human settlement.

Neophytes – plant species which have arrived and naturalised since 1500AD.

Nitrogen fixation – Legumes, in particular, contain symbiotic bacteria called rhizobia within nodules in their root systems, producing nitrogen compounds that help the plant to grow and compete with other plants. When the plant dies, the fixed nitrogen is released making it available to other plants and this helps to fertilise the soil. (See also **symbiotic**.)

Nut – a one-seeded indehiscent fruit with a hard, dry, pericarp – the shell, which is derived from a one-loculed ovary. (See also **locule**, **nutlet**, **ovary**, **pericarp**.)

Nutlet – a small nut. (See also **nut**.)

Ovary – the swollen basal region of a pistil (cf. carpel) containing one or more ovules. (See also **carpel**, **ovule**, **pistil**.)

Ovule – the female gamete structure of seed plants (angiosperms, gymnosperms) which develops into a seed after fertilisation of its egg cell. (See also **seed plant**.)

Palaeobotany – the study of fossil plants. (See also **palaeopalynology**.)

Palaeopalynology – strictly the study of fossil spores and pollen recovered from sedimentary rocks of all ages, but usually applied more broadly to include the study of a much wider range of fossilised, microscopic, acid-resistant organic bodies ranging in size from 5 to 500 microns. (See also **palaeobotany**, **pollen morphology**.)

Palea – the innermost of the two bracts enclosing the grass flower. (See also **glume**, **lemma**, **spikelet**.)

Palynology – the study of pollen and other acid-resistant biological micro-organisms. (See also **pollen morphology**.)

Pappus – a modified calyx, consisting of a ring of fine hairs, scales or teeth that persist after fertilisation and may aid wind-dispersal of the attached fruit (seed). In a hairy pappus the hairs may arise directly from the top of the seed or be on top of a slender 'beak/stalk' forming a parachute-like structure. Among the weedy species described in this book they are typical of many, but not all, members of the Daisy family (Asteraceae). A hairy pappus should not be confused with the feathery 'plumed' seeds that develop inside the elongate four-valved pods/capsules of willowherbs. (See also **beak**, **calyx**, **stalk**.)

Perennial – a plant that lives for more than two years, usually flowering every year. Herbaceous perennials survive winter in cold climates with underground storage: roots, bulbs, corms, rhizomes or tubers. Woody perennials are trees and shrubs with aerial stems that persist above ground; they may be deciduous or evergreen. (See also **annual**, **biennial**.)

Perfect flower – of an individual flower having both male and female organs. (See also **bisexual**, **hermaphrodite**.)

Pericarp – the wall of the ripened ovary, often divisible into epicarp (outermost layer), mesocarp (middle layer) and endocarp (innermost layer).

Petal – an individual unit of a corolla. (See also **corolla**, **sepal**, **tepal**.)

Petiole – a leaf stalk. (See also **stipule**.)

pH level – a number used to express the degree of alkalinity in solutions. Usually related by formula to a standard solution of potassium hydrogen phthalate which has a value of 4 at 15° C. The pH of pure water = 7 and represents neutrality on the pH scale. If acid is added, the hydrogen ion concentration will increase, and consequently its pH decreases according to degree of acidity: thus a pH level of less than 7 = low to high acidity, while pH levels of more than 7 = low to high alkalinity [p = potenz/power; H = the symbol for hydrogen].

Photoperiodism – the alternation of light and dark periods that affects the physiological activity of many plants as day length changes through the year. Various responses are shown by plants, depending

232

on whether they are 'long-day' or 'short day' plants. The length of the light period is more important than the intensity of the light.

Pistil – an individual carpel comprising an ovary, a style and a stigma. (See also **carpel, ovary, stigma, style**.)

Placenta – the part of an ovary wall on which the ovules are borne.

Pod – a general term for a dry dehiscent fruit with a firm outer layer enclosing a hollow centre with one or more seeds. (See also **legume, silicula, siliqua**.)

Pollen – collective term for pollen grains. (See also **pollen grains, pollen morphology**.)

Pollen grain – the male gametophytic multicellular structure containing a single set of chromosomes that produce the male sperm cells in flowering plants. (See also **gamete/gametophyte, pollen, pollen morphology**.)

Pollen morphology – the systematic study of family and species specific characteristics of pollen grains. (See also **pollen, systematics**.)

Pollination – transference of pollen grains from one seed plant to the stigma of another plant of the same species – usually this involves an external agent – animals, wind or water. (See also **self-pollination**.)

Raceme – a flowering inflorescence of indefinite growth, with florets on (usually) short flower stalks from the main stalk/axis, with youngest flowers developing from the tip of the raceme.

Radial symmetry – referring to flowers or flower heads that are arranged in a regular, usually, circular pattern from a central point when viewed from above, e.g. daisies, buttercups. (See also **actinomorphic, bilateral symmetry, zygomorphic**.)

Receptacle – the expanded region at the top of the main stem (*peduncle*) to which the floral parts are attached. It is usually convex but may become flattened or concave.

Rhizome – an underground stem lasting more than one growing season.

Runner – a creeping stem that develops from an axillary bud and runs along the ground giving rise to young plantlets at its nodes, e.g. strawberries, Creeping Buttercup, Creeping Cinquefoil. (See also **axillary, rhizome, stolon**.)

Saponin – a glycoside derived from various plants, e.g. Soapwort, that gives a soapy froth. See also Red or White Campions.

Seed – the structure that develops from the fertilised ovule in seed plants (angiosperms and gymnosperms), carrying all the genetic materials to form a new diploid plant. (See also **diploid**.)

Seed plants – seed producing plants – angiosperms and gymnosperms. (See also **angiosperms, gymnosperms**.)

Self-pollination – the ability of a plant to self-pollinate in the absence of insect visitors. (See also **chasmogamy, cleistogamy**.)

Sepal – individual unit of a calyx. (See also **calyx, petal, tepal**.)

Septum – the central, usually translucent frame, forming part of the silicule or silique of a pod-like fruit, typical of many members of family Brassicaceae. When ripe, the paired outer casings (valves) split off and the ripe seeds fall away from the septum. (See also **pod, silicle, silique**.)

Silicula (pl. siliculae) – a broad pod-like fruit divided into two cells by a thin central partition (septum), opening by two valves which fall away from the central, usually translucent, frame on which the seeds are borne; more than three times as long as wide. Particularly associated with family Brassicaceae (Cruciferae). Weedy examples include Shepherd's Purse (*Capsella bursa-pastoris*) and Penny Cress (*Thlaspi arvense*). (See also **pod, septum, siliqua**.)

Siliqua (pl. siliquae) – a long pod-like fruit divided into two cells by a usually thin, translucent, central partition (septum). The silique opens by two valves which fall away from the central frame on which the seeds are borne. It is defined as being more than three times as long as wide. Particularly associated with family Brassicaceae (Cruciferae). Weedy examples include Charlock (*Sinapis arvensis*) and Jack-by-the-hedge (*Alliaria petiolata*). (See also **pod, septum, silicula**.)

Spadix – a specialised inflorescence in which the flowers are sessile and borne on a large fleshy axis, often with a sterile part extending beyond the inflorescence.

Spathe – a large bract enclosing a spadix, notably among the weedy species Wild Arum. (See also **bract, spadix**.)

Spikelet – in grasses (Poaceae/Gramineae) and sedges (Cyperaceae), a structure comprising two basal sterile bracts (glumes) and a number of florets – each floret consisting of a lemma, palea and flower. (See also **glume, lemma, palea**.)

Stalk – any support of a plant organ that has some length. (See also **stem**.)

Stamen(s) – the male pollen producing reproductive organ of a flowering plant, collectively the androecium. (See also **androecium, anther, filament, pollen**.)

Stem – the main axis of a plant bearing roots, leaves and/or flowers. (See also **stalk**.)

Stigma – the receptive, often highly modified region at the top of the pistil (carpel) which receives the pollen. (See also **carpel, pistil**.)

Stinging hairs – a tubular hair filled with an irritant liquid, which, when broken, ejects the liquid, e.g. stinging nettles.

Stipule – leaf-like, spine-like or scale-like appendages of the leaf, usually in pairs at the base of the petiole. (See also **petiole**.)

Stolon – a long branch that is unable to support its own weight and consequently bends to the ground. When a node on the stolon touches the soil, a new plant may develop from the axillary bud, e.g. Blackberry. (See also **axillary, runner**.)

Style – the region of the pistil (carpel) between the stigma and the ovary. (See also **carpel, ovary, pistil, stigma**).

Symbiotic – an intimate relationship; in its narrow sense, of mutual benefit to both the organisms involved, however, in a wider sense it

233

also covers relationships which can be destructive to a participant, for example, parasitism, or only of beneficial gain to one participant (commensalism), e.g. epiphytic orchids.

Syncarpous – a fruit with united carpels, e.g. tulips. (See also **apocarpous**, **monocarpous**.)

Systematics – science of classification based on natural relationships, and study of the variation an evolution of taxa, a more specific term than taxonomy. (See also **taxa**, **taxon**, **taxonomy**.)

Tap root – a persistent tough primary root, often penetrating some depth below ground level. In some species this root has a specialised storage function, e.g. in Creeping Thistle (*Cirsium arvense*), Perennial Sow-thistle (*Sonchus arvensis*), Wild Carrot (*Daucus carota*) and Parsnip (*Pastinaca sativa*). The tap roots of the last two species have been domesticated to exploit this characteristic for human consumption.

Taxon/taxa/taxonomy – the study of the principles and practices of classification and naming. It is strictly applied to the study and description of variation in the natural world and the subsequent compilation of classifications. (See also **families of plants**.)

Tendril perversion – a geometric phenomenon found in helical structures such as plant tendrils, in which a helical structure is divided into two sections of opposite chirality, with a transition between the two in the middle, e.g. in White Bryony (*Bryonia dioica*). An amusing domestic example is telephone wire which, infuriatingly, has a tendency to do this, often more than once. (See also **chirality**.)

Tepal – a division of the perianth, i.e. a sepal or petal, used especially when it is unclear which is which – e.g. in stinging nettles. (See also **petal**, **sepal**.)

234

Triploid – having three sets of chromosomes. (See also **diploid**, **haploid**.)

Tuber – a swollen part of a stem or root, usually modified for storage, and lasting for one year only. A stem tuber can be distinguished by presence of buds (or eyes), for example the potato, while dahlias develop root tubers from adventitious roots. Tubers of the succeeding year do not arise, or bear a position relative to the old ones. (See also **adventitious**, **bulb**, **corm**.)

Tubercle – a small protuberance or growth, for example on the fruits of Docks and Sorrel (e.g. *Rumex crispus* or *R. acetosa*).

Umbel – a flowering stem on which is arranged a group of separate, usually quite small, flowers, each on its own slender stem. This arrangement, notably in the British species belonging to the Apiaceae, has the appearance of the spines of an open upside down umbrella. (See also **Umbelliferae**.)

Umbelliferae – an older, now less frequently used name for the Apiaceae. No longer accepted in modern plant systematics.

Unisexual – separate male flowers (with stamens), and female flowers (with pistils). (See also **bisexual**, **hermaphrodite**, **perfect flower**.)

Vegetative – non-flowering parts of a plant: roots, runners, stems, leaves etc.

Vitta/Vittae – aromatic oil tubes in the fruit of some Amaranthaceae and Apiaceae, see for example, among weedy plants, Hogweed (*Heracleum sphondylium*) and Giant Hogweed (*Heracleum mantegazzianum*).

Zygomorphic – flowers that have only one plane of symmetry, either side of an imaginary central line with bilateral symmetry, e.g. foxgloves, dead-nettles, Gorse and pansies. (See also **actinomorphic**, **bilateral**, **radial symmetry**.)

Zygote – the product of the fusion of two gametes before it has undergone mitosis or meiosis.

BIBLIOGRAPHY

20TH-21ST CENTURY IDENTIFICATION GUIDES TO BRITISH WEEDS *(in chronological order)*

Long, H.C. (1910) *Common Weeds of the Farm and Garden*. [Modern reprint from the unaltered edition published by Frederick A Stokes Company, New York.]

Brenchley, W.E. (1920) *Weeds of Farmland*. Longmans Green & Co, London [modern reprint by Kessinger Publishing].

Long, H.C. (1938) *Weeds of Grassland*. Bulletin No. 41, Ministry of Agriculture and Fisheries, HMSO, London.

Chancellor, R.J. (1966) *The Identification of Weed Seedlings of Farm and Garden*. Blackwell Scientific Publications, Oxford.

Allan, M. (1978) *The Gardener's Book of Weeds*. Macdonald & Janes, London [describes weeds of UK and USA].

Phillips, R. (1986) *Weeds*. Elm Tree Books/Hamish Hamilton, London.

Williams, J. & Morrison, J. (1987) *ADAS Colour Atlas of Weed Seedlings*. Wolfe Publishing, London [reprinted 2003 by Manson Publishing, London].

Roth, S. (2001) *Weeds: Friend or Foe*. Carroll & Brown, London [describes weeds of UK and USA].

Walker, J. (2003) *The Daily Telegraph Weeds*. Cassell Illustrated, London.

Hessayon, D.G. (2009) *The Pest & Weed Expert*. Third edition. Expert Books, London.

Thompson, K. (2009) *The Book of Weeds*. Dorling Kindersley, London.

Edmonds, W. (2013) *Weeds, Weeding (& Darwin). The Gardener's Guide*. Frances Lincoln, London.

OTHER BOOKS ON WEEDS *(in alphabetical order)*

Dewey, L.H. (1895) *Weeds and how to kill them*. U.S. Dept of Agriculture, No 28.

Heiser, C.B. (2003) *Weeds in my garden: observations on some misunderstood plants*. Timber Press, Portland, USA & Cambridge, UK [describes garden weeds of USA].

Hill, T.A. (1977) *The Biology of Weeds*. Studies in biology No. 79, Edward Arnold, London.

Mabey, R. (2010) *Weeds*. Profile Books, London.

Salisbury, E. (1961) *Weeds and Aliens*. New Naturalist series No. 43. Collins, London.

Sudell, R. (Ed.) (undated, between 1926-1935) *The New Illustrated Gardening Encyclopaedia*. Odhams Press, Long Acre, London [a fascinating, widely sold book of its time; included here for its advice on weeding, and garden chemicals commonly in use pre-WWII].

BRITISH WILD FLOWERS – Illustrated Guides or Accounts And Other Useful References *(in alphabetical order)*

Cannon, J. & Cannon, M. (1994) *Dye Plants and Dyeing*. The Herbert Press, Huntingdon, Cambridgeshire.

Chancellor, R. J. (1962) *The Identification of Common Water Weeds*. Bulletin No. 183, HMSO. Blackwell Scientific Publications, Oxford.

Clapham, A.R., Tutin, T.G., Warburg, E.F. (1973) *Excursion Flora of the British Isles*. Second edition. Cambridge University Press, Cambridge.

Cope, T. (2009) *The Wild Flora of Kew Gardens*. Kew Publishing, Surrey.

Cope, T. & Gray, A. (2009) *Grasses of the British Isles*. BSBI Handbook No. 13. Botanical Society of the British Isles, London.

Darwin, C. (1865) On the movements and habits of climbing plants. *Botanical Journal of the Linnean Society of London* (Botany), volume 9 pp. 1-118.

Darwin C. (1892) *The Effects of Cross and Self-Fertilization in the Vegetable Kingdom*. Appleton, New York.

Duvel J.W.T. (1902) Seeds buried in soil. *Science* No. 17, p. 872-873.

Flower, C. (2008) *Where Have all the Flowers Gone? Restoring Wildflowers to the Garden and Countryside*. Papadakis Publisher, London.

Gardener, M. & Roberts, C. (2010) *Guide to Common Meadow Grasses*. Field Studies Council Publications, Shrewsbury [A laminated fold-out guide].

Garrard, I. & Streeter, D. (1983) *The Wild Flowers of the British Isles*. [Re-published 1998 by Midsummer Books, London].

Gilmour, J. & Walters, M. (1954) *Wild Flowers*. New Naturalist Series No. 5. Collins, London.

Grigson, G. (1955) *The Englishman's Flora*. J.M. Dent & Sons, London & Melbourne.

Grigson, G. (1974) *A Dictionary of English Plant Names*. Allan Lane, London.

Johns, C.A. (1949) *Flowers of the Field*. Revised edition. Routledge & Kegan Paul, London.

Hubbard, C.E. (1968) *Grasses*. Second edition. Penguin Books Middlesex, UK & Maryland, USA.

Hutchinson, J. (1945; 1946) *Common Wild Flowers*. Revised edition. Penguin Books Middlesex UK & New York, USA.

Hutchinson, J. (1948) *More Common Wild Flowers*. Penguin Books Middlesex UK & New York, USA.

Hutchinson, J. (1950) *Uncommon Wild Flowers*. Penguin Books Middlesex UK & New York, USA.

Keble Martin, W. (1965) *The Concise British Flora in Colour*. Ebury Press and Michael Joseph, London.

Kesseler, R. & Harley, M. M. (2004) *Pollen: The Hidden Sexuality of Flowers*. Papadakis Publisher, London [fourth edition published 2014].

Mabey, R. (1996) *Flora Britannica*. Sinclair-Stevenson, London.

Mabberley, D.J. (2009) *Mabberley's Plant-Book: a portable dictionary of plants, their classification and uses*. Third edition, Cambridge University Press, Cambridge.

Nicholson, B.E., Ary, S., Gregory, M. (1973) *The Oxford Book of Wild Flowers*. Revised edition. Oxford University Press, Oxford [Re-issued as **Ary, S., Gregory, M., Nicolson, B.E. (1980)** *The Illustrated Book of Wild Flowers*. Peerage Books, London].

Phillips, R. (1980) *Grasses, Ferns, Mosses & Lichens of Great Britain and Ireland*. Ward Lock., London.

Phillips, R. (1977) *Wild Flowers of Great Britain*. Pan Books, London.

Proctor, M. & Yeo, P. (1973) *The Pollination of Flowers*. New Naturalist series No. 54. Collins, London.

Rose, F. (2006) *The Wild Flower Key. How to identify wild flowers trees and shrubs in Britain and Ireland*. Revised and updated by Clare O'Reilly. Warne, London.

Stace, C.A. (1997; 2010) *New Flora of the British Isles*. Third edition. Cambridge University Press, Cambridge.

Turrill, W.B. (1959) *British Plant Life*. The New Naturalist series No. 10. Collins, London.

Wilson, P. & King, M. (2003) *Arable Plants – A Field Guide*. Wild Guides, Basingstoke.

Woodward, M. (1964) *Gerard's Herball: the Essence thereof distilled from the First Edition of Th. Johnson, 1636*. Spring Books, London.

USEFUL WEBSITES

http://www.mobot.org/MOBOT/research/APweb/ Stevens, P.F. (since 2001). Angiosperm Phylogeny website. Version 12, 2012 [and more or less continuously updated since].

http://www.bsbi.org.uk The Botanical Society of Britain and Ireland (until 2013 the Botanical Society of the British Isles).

http://www.floralimages.co.uk Very useful for British flora – usually with a number of different images to show a range of characteristics for the species illustrated.

http://www.fwag.org.uk The national association represents local farming and wildlife advisory groups (FWAGS) across the UK. Established over 40 years ago, the local groups help British farmers by providing trusted independent environmental advice.

http://www.gardenorganic.co.uk Incorporates the Henry Doubleday Research Association (HDRA).

http://www.organicweeds.org.uk A weed dedicated website of 'Garden Organic'.

http://www.nonnativespecies.org Non-native Species Organisation. To check invasive status of imported plants.

https://www.rhs.org.uk Helpful advice on weed management for gardeners.

http://www.theseedsite.co.uk Very useful for seed characteristics.

http://www.soilassociation.org/farming

http://www.organicfarmers.org.uk

http://www.brc.ac.uk/plant atlas/ Online Atlas of the British and Irish Flora.

INDEX

ACKNOWLEDGEMENTS

I am indebted to two very special friends who have not only encouraged me in the preparation of this book, but been prepared to act as my mentors: Kathy Meek and Tim Rich. Kathy, with her excellent command of the English language, has steered me round or past much of the flotsam and jetsam that I am apt to swim into in my enthusiasm to commit my ideas to paper. While Tim, with his wide knowledge and understanding of the British flora, has not only answered my questions and queries and offered wise advice, but has read all the plant species descriptions, and pointed out inconsistencies and botanical errors that might otherwise have been missed. Any lack of clarity or ambiguity that still exists is of my making, in spite of their combined best efforts – thank you both so much.

I am especially appreciative of the help given to me by people at Wiltshire Wildlife Trust: notably Fiona Dunster who guided me to sites for Giant Hogweed and Japanese Knotweed, and to Ben Fitch for providing the image of Giant Hogweed flowers. Special thanks go to June and George Jeffreys for allowing me to disturb a peaceful summer afternoon so that I could photograph Giant Hogweed *in situ* (but too late for the flowers) in their beautiful estate. Local farmers have, probably unwittingly, provided invaluable support in their provision of footpaths, headlands and fields where I have wandered, seemingly endlessly, photographing and collecting weeds, especially the Pickford family in the village where I live. To my long term professional base – the Royal Botanic Gardens, Kew where, on various visits, I have photographed some of 'my' weeds. Some of my friends and relations encouraged me to weed their gardens, which gave me additional opportunities to take photographs of weeds, in what they considered to be, the less than perfect corners of their 'acres': thank you Pat and Hugh Bazley, Basil and Annette Harley, Annie House and Jill Cowley. To other friends who have helped with useful comments, or answered my questions – or simply by being genuinely interested in what I have been trying to achieve: John and Jatmi Dransfield, John and Ann Heritage, Ray Harley, Sanda and Keith Redfern, David and Andra Papworth, Terry Poole, Unsook Song, Sue Zmarzty, Roger and Diana Polhill and Tom Cope. To my family who have listened patiently to my verbal ramblings, even though wild flowers are not quite their thing, thank you Sam, and Ben and Jenny just for being there. Locally I have much appreciated the interest and encouragement shown by Bob and Janet Deacon, Dulcie Owens, Jean Farthing, David and Clare Evans and Madge Bell.

To the publication team my very special thanks to Aldo Sampieri for his beautifully designed layouts throughout the book; also to Caroline Kuhtz, the Production Co-ordinator, for her unwavering patience, understanding and support. Finally a very big thank you to my publisher, Alexandra Papadakis, who never quite gave up on the idea of publishing this book. To anyone else I have not mentioned by name who has encouraged me, perhaps unwittingly, to complete a dream which has, at times, made me think myself if not quite crazy, then at least sometimes rather pre-occupied and anti-social.